Western Medicine
in a Chinese Palace

To Aki

Western Medicine in a Chinese Palace

Peking Union Medical College, 1917-1951

JOHN Z. BOWERS, M.D.

The Josiah Macy, Jr. Foundation

Contents

Preface

The genesis of this book goes back two decades, when I first listened to Alan Gregg, Franklin C. McLean, and Harold H. Loucks talk about Peking Union Medical College (PUMC). In the ensuing years I became increasingly interested in the unique role of the college and the array of brilliant American doctors who had taught there.

Whenever possible I talked with people who knew about PUMC. Serious work on this book began in the summer of 1969 with the support of Joseph C. Hinsey, then chairman of the China Medical Board. Mary Ferguson, who was working on her book, *China Medical Board and Peking Union Medical College*, generously turned over to me her documentary history of the institution. It was an invaluable resource during a month of preparatory study that I spent as a guest of the Rockefeller Foundation at Villa Serbelloni. Throughout the preparation of this manuscript Mary Ferguson and Harold Loucks have been invaluable sources of guidance and encouragement.

Whereas Miss Ferguson's excellent book focuses primarily on administrative history, I have turned to the people and the programs. I have had the pleasant and rewarding experience of talking to a number of men and women who were associated with PUMC:

Marshall C. Balfour

Brown Chang

Stephen Chang

K. K. Chen

Francis R. Dieuaide

Ernest C. Faust

Marian Feng

Claude E. Forkner

L. Carrington Goodrich

John B. Grant

Alan Gregg

A. Baird Hastings

Victor G. Heiser

Paul C. Hodges

Alice Hsu

Chester S. Keefer

Gordon King

Khaw Oo-kek

Lim Kha-t'i (Lin Chiao-chih)

Morgan Liu

Loo Chih-teh

John L. McKelvey

Charles F. McKhann

Franklin C. McLean

Helen V. McLean

Alfred E. Mirsky

Eugene L. Opie

P'eng Tah-mou

Katherine E. Read

Carl F. Schmidt

Aura E. Severinghaus

Hans Smetana

Harry B. Van Dyke   A. Ashley Weech
Donald D. Van Slyke   James Yen
Wang Shih-chun   Yu Tao-chen
Jerome P. Webster   Yu Ts'ai fan

Helen Choat and Phyllis Brachman collected information from those who had been associated with the School of Nursing:

Gertrude E. Hodgman
Anne H. McCabe
Gertrude Ai-ching Pao Sing
Florence Tsun-chun Chaing Szutu
Margaret P'ing Chang Tseng
Mamie Huan-wei Kuo Wang
Daisy Tsai-Yun Yen Wu
Yu Tao-chen
Ruth V. M. Zia

Others who supplied me with material were John A. Anderson, George Packer Berry, Jean A. Curran, John F. Enders, Thomas B. Fitzpatrick, Sir Theodore Fox, Sidney D. Gamble, Oliver R. McCoy, Atsumi Minami, Peter D. Olch, Willard C. Rappleye, J. B. de C. M. Saunders, Wilbur H. Sawyer, Virgil C. Scott, John C. Snyder, and Robert B. Watson.

All or parts of this manuscript were read by Roger Crane, L. Carrington Goodrich, Virgil Scott, and Robert Watson.

Phyllis Brachman spent many hours working with me on earlier drafts, and she also compiled the bibliography.

The final manuscript benefitted immeasurably from the skillful and constructive editorial work of my colleague, Elizabeth Purcell.

My wife, Akiko, has been a constant source of encouragement—and has tolerated many hours when my pen and my thoughts were in far-off Peking.

JOHN Z. BOWERS

CHAPTER ONE

Western Medicine in Old Peking

The most beautiful medical school in the world is the Capital Hospital in Peking, China. It occupies a block of graceful buildings with curved jade green glazed tile roofs that glitter in the bright sunshine of north China. The buildings were erected by the China Medical Board (CMB) of the Rockefeller Foundation and dedicated ceremonially on September 19, 1921, as the Peking Union Medical College (PUMC). The faculty was drawn principally from the United States and the United Kingdom. Until its seizure by the Japanese on December 8, 1941, PUMC was not only the leading medical center in Asia but one of the world's outstanding medical schools. Closed during World War II, the school was formally reopened on October 27, 1947; it was nationalized by the Communist Chinese government on January 20, 1951.

Today the former PUMC is the leading medical center in China, but by decree it now teaches and practices Chinese traditional medicine as well as Western medicine. Pessimists would say that the great aspirations that were voiced in the formative years have been dashed. More sanguine analysts could say that by educating many of the medical scientists, administrators, and practitioners who placed Western medicine on a firm base in China, the college and its associated programs paid a handsome dividend for the 45 million American dollars invested in them.

The leaders in the development of the school were some of America's most distinguished citizens and scholars—John D. Rockefeller and his son, John D., Jr.; their advisor, Frederick T. Gates, who was the earliest proponent of a China program; Charles W. Eliot, president of Harvard University; Henry Pratt Judson, president of the University of Chicago; and John R. Mott, director of the International YMCA, who was in 1946 to be Nobel Laureate

1

for International Peace. Also in this select group were two leaders of American medicine, William H. Welch, dean of the Johns Hopkins School of Medicine, the leading medical educator and statesman in the United States, if not in the world, and Simon Flexner, director of the Rockefeller Institute.

Committed from the beginning to excellence, the school attracted a brilliant young faculty deeply dedicated to the advancement of Western medicine in China. They were lured in part by the sensuous appeals of the mysterious East: China was the last great country to "open" to the world; some were moved by a missionary zeal to save the heathen; others were drawn by a sense of high adventure; but all were tempted by the realization that diseases that were unknown or had largely disappeared in the West still flourished in China.

The opportunities for medical research in well-equipped laboratories and clinics were limitless. Men such as Welch and Flexner, who stood at the summit of American medical science, backed the program wholeheartedly, and with their support the young college could tap the reservoirs of brilliant young medical talent that were largely concentrated at the two institutions they headed. As PUMC flourished, it, in turn, became a reservoir of bright young American medical scientists who were later called back to assume professorships in medical schools in the United States. A vigorous program of visiting professorships attracted distinguished medical scientists who brought with them scientific inspiration as well as reports of the latest advances in Western scientific research. For the young scientists and the visiting professors it was an intellectual paradise of medical science set in the middle of one of the world's most beautiful cities in one of the world's most fascinating countries.

THE CITY

Peking was the historic, cultural, and political capital of China. Although centuries earlier a splendid city had developed on the site under varying names, its official founder was the famed Kublai Khan, who mounted the throne in 1260. His successors—both Chinese and foreign invaders—added to the magnificence of the Summer Palace, the Forbidden City, the Sea Palaces, and the innumerable temples and exquisite pagodas, thus creating a city whose beauty was almost unrivalled.

The Chinese have always been artists in their use of color, and the tinted mortar that forms some of the walls of Peking gives the city the appearance of a magnificent tapestry: the soft pink walls of the Imperial City, the violet-tinted walls of the Forbidden City, the glazed jade green roofs that contrast dazzlingly with the imperial yellow tiles of the palace roofs create an unforgettable image.

Actually, Peking is several cities in one. There are two walled cities, the Inner City, often referred to by Western writers as the "Tartar City," and the Outer or "Chinese City."

When people speak of the City of Peking they refer to the Inner City where government offices, legations, banks, hospitals, and the homes of prosperous families are located. The city is in the form of a square, with walls fifty feet high and more than fifteen feet wide at the top. The south wall is pierced by three gates; the other walls each have two gates; roads leading from them cut through the city.

The Outer City is sometimes referred to as "Cap City" since it fits around the Inner City much like a cap fits the head. This area too is protected by great walls, though not as high as those of the Inner City. The Outer City adjoins the main railway terminal and enjoys a bustling trade, with many small hotels, the entertainment areas, old temples, secondhand bookstalls, small stores, and, formerly, the brothels.

Within the Inner City are two other walled cities: the Imperial City in the northern section and the Forbidden City. In the Imperial City is a landmark all visitors are anxious to see: a huge, artificial, tree-covered mound rising 210 feet into the air, known as Ching-shan (Prospect Hill). It is unexpected in its enormity and in its unbroken greenness—even the palace at its summit is entirely green, inside and out.

Legend gives many reasons for the erection of this enormous hillock: to ward off evil influences that by tradition were always thought to come from the north; to be used as a watch tower; to serve as a source of fuel in case of siege, since it was declared to be made of coal; to indulge an imperial whim. But whatever the reason, Cathcrine the Second of Russia was so impressed by the descriptions of this man-made mountain that she commanded that one be built on her palace grounds.

The Forbidden City had almost every facility that a sovereign might desire: theaters, a library, temples, shops, streets of state apartments, and quarters for women.

The visitor to Peking is always struck by the feeling of immensity, of unlimited space. Hatamen Boulevard, where PUMC was located, runs north and south in an unswerving line for about three miles and is at least seventy feet wide; Tienanmen Boulevard, which runs east and west in front of the Forbidden City, is approximately 150 feet wide.

The Great Wall, some thirty-five miles north of Peking, was begun before the time of Shih Huang Ti, who unified China and became its first emperor. One of his earliest decrees, in about 221 B.C., was that the northern part of the country be fortified by completion of the Great Wall.

THE ORIGINS OF PEKING UNION MEDICAL COLLEGE

The first Western doctor to reach Peking was William Lockhart, who became senior physician to the British Legation in September 1861. Lockhart, who had "walked the wards at Guys," was no stranger to China. In 1839 he had joined the staff of the Canton Ophthalmic Hospital, but as the Anglo-Chinese War advanced he was evacuated to Java where he studied Chinese. He later returned to Canton and shortly thereafter was assigned to Chusan as part of the occupation force. During the year he spent in Chusan, Lockhart established a small hospital, and in a period of six months treated some 4,000 patients. He then moved to Macao, but when the Treaty of Nanking was signed in 1842 he went to Hong Kong, where he stayed for one year. With characteristic enterprise, he founded a hospital in the beautiful seaport, sponsored by the London Missionary Society. (It was the forerunner of today's well-known Nethersole Hospital.)

But again Lockhart moved on, returning for another year in Chusan. He then settled in the newly opened seaport of Shanghai where he founded another landmark hospital, known as the Chinese Hospital, situated at the North Gate on Shantung Road. (Almost a century later, in 1926, it was endowed by a wealthy British broker, Henry Lester, and became the Lester Chinese Hospital, to which was later added the Henry Lester Institute of Medical Research.) Lockhart remained in Shanghai throughout the Tai Ping Rebellion, from 1835 to 1854, including the siege and capture of the city, and hundreds of soldiers and civilians who were wounded in the conflicts came under his care.

In 1857 Lockhart went on a four-year furlough to London where he earned a fellowship in the Royal College of Surgeons and wrote *Medical Missionary in China: A Narrative of Twenty Years' Experience*.[1] The book presents a documentation of the advance of Western medicine in China during the first half of the nineteenth century. In regard to the role of the missionary, he expressed strong opposition to the common practice of combining training in evangelism with medicine:

> I have seen this in Protestant and in Romish Missions; a man attempts to follow two professions, and always fails signally in one, sometimes in both, and thus loses rather than gains influence for power and good.[2]

When Lockhart received word that Peking had been opened to foreigners he left for China immediately, reaching the capital city on September 13, 1861. A month later, on October 23, he opened his fourth hospital in China. It was known as the Peking Hospital of the London Missionary Society (also the London Missionary Society's Chinese Hospital in Peking) and was located in a dwelling that adjoined the British Legation.

The hospital was an immediate success—in the first year Lockhart treated a total of 22,144 patients, or more than sixty a day. He was impressed with the wide range of their backgrounds:

> Persons of all classes, officers of every rank and degree, came and sent their wives, mothers, children and other relatives. Merchants and shop-keepers, working people and villagers, together with numerous beggars, assembled at the hospital. Ladies and respectable women also were present in large numbers, and it was

surprising to see the readiness with which they both came for relief and brought their children who were suffering from various diseases.[3]

After three years this indefatigable medical pioneer, who had practiced in six Chinese cities, returned to London. His extensive library of Chinese documents was presented to the London Missionary Society where it is available today as the Lockhart Collection. He lived to the age of eighty-five and died in 1896, revered by his colleagues at the missionary society.

Lockhart was succeeded in Peking by John Dudgeon, an Edinburgh graduate. Dudgeon was interested in everything, and his diaries contain observations ranging from medical care, climatic conditions in north China, and opium, to an account of a Chinese coroner's inquest on the tradition of binding feet.

In his first annual report to London, Dudgeon included a brief description of what was generally referred to as a hospital in China:

> The word "hospital" conveys to European minds no notion of the Peking one. It is composed of about twenty rooms or wards, each room having a *kang* [sic], or large brick and earth platform, covered with matting, on which the patients sleep. In winter these are heated with balls, made of coal dust and mud, and the *kang* having flues arranged regularly under it is kept very warm. . . . Each *kang* may accommodate from 12 to 14 persons according to its size.[4]

Dudgeon shared Lockhart's surprise at the apparent popularity of Western medicine among the Chinese:

> When the dispensary was first opened, multitudes came, principally with eye diseases, whose cases were beyond all remedial measures. . . . They dread nothing in the foreign practice; if there be any fault, it is in their placing too much faith in our skill.[5]

It was not long after Dudgeon's arrival in Peking that the British Legation, because of its expanding staff, found it necessary to take possession of his temporary hospital. Determined to continue his work, Dudgeon decided that the permanent site should be on Hatamen Boulevard, the main thoroughfare of the Tartar City section of Peking. The building he selected was a Buddhist temple and when it had been acquired there were unique problems for the priest who was charged with dismantling it:

> The chief obstacle was the removal of the gods, incense burners and other idolatrous articles. The priest could hardly venture to undertake this work, perhaps from a secret fear of the divinities or of public censure. He also feared outraging the public feeling of the neighborhood, and drawing down upon himself the notice and the ire of the officials, who would make any pretext to extort money from him. Night was chosen as the time for the removal of the larger gods. The work was safely accomplished as far as regards the priest. The gods, however, suffered rather severely from the removal. The neighbors expected that the priest would be suddenly seized from a severe malady, as a just retribution for this insult

to the deities. But apparently this sudden change of fortune called forth no practical proof of their power, for the priest is still well and in possession of a small temple in an adjoining lane.[6]

The temple compound was converted into a singularly ornate, spacious, and reasonably functional hospital:

> The premises consist of five courts, with large, high, commodious and well-ventilated rooms. It opens directly on the great street by a large gateway. On the street and in front of the building are two flagstaffs, each seventy feet high.* In the first court are waiting rooms for female patients and the higher class of Chinese society. The large hall stands on the east side of this court, facing the street.
> It is perhaps the finest and handsomest native building used for such purposes in East Asia. The roof is high and beautifully painted and decorated. The large stone pedestal upon which sat the god of fire serves for a platform or table. In this court is a stone tablet upon which it is intended to inscribe the date of the foundation of the hospital, and the introduction of Protestant Christianity into Peking. A small room and court to the south of the chapel is set apart for beggars who may be under treatment in the hospital. They are locked up at night and released in the morning to prevent thefts and for greater security. . . . In the court immediately behind the hall is a building of three apartments devoted to wards. On the north side of this court is the dispensary, and in a small court to the west of the dispensary are the hospital kitchen, and assistants' quarters; on the east side are two other courts with extensive accommodation for patients. The hospital is beautifully painted according to the original elegant and ornamental style. The style of the temple architecture gives ample scope and effect to the pencil and the brush.[7]

Despite an overwhelming load of work, Dudgeon found time to write a simple anatomical atlas in Chinese, as well as papers on such subjects as diseases of the eye, inoculation, and the circulation of the blood. He was critical of the gluttony of the European community: "Many of my countrymen here in Peking, they eat and they drink and they drink and they eat."[8] But they blamed their sins on China: ". . . when they die they write home to say the climate had killed them."[9]

John Dudgeon also taught medicine at the Imperial College, T'ung Wen Kuan, in Peking, which had been established primarily to train men for the diplomatic service. In 1884, twenty years after he had replaced Lockhart as director, his relationship with the Peking Hospital of the London Missionary Society was terminated because he was overly committed to the private practice of medicine. He embarked for Britain but after a year returned to Peking where he resumed a busy practice until his death on February 23, 1901.

---

* When the two seventy-foot flagstaffs were toppled by a gale in 1914, the Chinese, in accord with their traditions, accepted it as a harbinger of impending change. They were quite correct, for just one year later the Union Medical College which now occupied these premises became the property of the Rockefeller Foundation and a program was launched that was to bring striking changes to medicine in China.

S. W. Bushell, physician to the British Legation, served as temporary director of the hospital from 1884 until the arrival of Dudgeon's successor, E. T. Pritchard, in 1886. Heretofore most of the hospital's activities had been centered in the outpatient clinics, but Pritchard emphasized the care of the inpatient. Medical students from the nearby Imperial College came to the outpatient clinic at weekly intervals and Pritchard encouraged them to follow their patients after they were admitted to the wards.

Pritchard trained two Chinese auxiliaries. Li Hsiao-ch'uan and Liu Pao-ch'ing, to give first aid, to prepare and dispense simple medicines, and to apply dressings. When ill health forced Pritchard to leave China in 1893, Li and Liu carried on the medical work of the hospital and continued to be the backbone of medical care for the next seven years, because Eliot Curwen, who had succeeded Pritchard, found it necessary to leave China on two occasions, also because of ill health.

In 1891 an additional plot of land was acquired, new buildings were erected, and the existing facilities modernized. But the London Mission Compound, including the Peking Hospital, was destroyed during the savage Boxer Rebellion in the summer of 1900 and the missionaries, along with British diplomats and their staff, were besieged in the British Legation. The relief of Peking was achieved on August 14, but the destruction of the hospital facilities and the disruption of its programs were so complete that it was not until five months later that Li Hsiao-ch'uan could open a makeshift dispensary in an abandoned shop adjoining the legation. Male patients requiring hospitalization were transferred to a German field medical unit, and females to temporary British hospitals supervised by Lillie E. V. Saville in the western and eastern sections of the city.

The rebellion, in which more than 100 Protestant missionaries were slain, focused the attention of the missionaries on Peking, the center of the uprising, as the city in which medical and evangelistic programs were most urgently needed. It also became clear to them that their efforts in medical care and education were far too splintered; the limited financial resources of a single missionary society were inadequate for such massive needs—united efforts were essential. The first of the union efforts was organized around the London Missionary Society, the largest and the most powerful in the field. The American Presbyterian Mission and the American Board of Commissioners for Foreign Missions joined the London society to establish the North China Educational Union, and Peking was selected as the site of the first union medical school.

Thomas Cochrane, a Scot who had studied medicine at Glasgow, was the founder of the new Union Medical College (UMC), which later became PUMC. Cochrane's portrait shows a man with a stern, square face, dominated by a strong chin and steely eyes that hold one under withering scrutiny. He had first served in Chaoyang in Manchuria from May 19, 1897, to the spring of

1900, using a three-room clinic for inpatients and for surgery. There were usually more than 100 outpatients a day, and his only assistant was a farmer's son who wished to become a doctor.

At the time of the Boxer Rebellion grateful patients and a loyal houseboy saved Cochrane's life. The patients informed him of the impending arrival of the Boxers, who were ruthlessly killing all foreigners in his area. Cochrane, dressed in Chinese robes, mounted a bicycle and fled, with his houseboy in hot pursuit calling on him to stop. In his hand the houseboy carried a Chinese cap with an artificial queue that he handed to Cochrane pointing to his head. Cochrane snatched off the derby he had grabbed in his hasty departure, stuffed it under his robe, replaced it with the cap and queue, and escaped to safety.* Cochrane was subsequently invalided home with malaria, complicated by exhaustion from the strains and stresses of the insurgency.

Cochrane's organizational ability and surgical skill had come to the attention of the elders of the London Missionary Society, and he was sent back to China to assume the leadership of the union school at Peking. When he reached the city on November 20, 1901, he first viewed the charred wreckage of the Peking Hospital. Shaken, but with indomitable determination, he opened a dispensary in the only available space, a tumbledown grain shop. A wooden board served as his operating table and a stable as a hospital ward:

> Soon after my arrival I was doing all kinds of major operations with marvelously good results. My in-patients were housed in what had formerly been the stable from which the mules were turned out and the walls whitewashed.[10]

Cochrane was fortunate in establishing a well-deserved and rewarding professional relationship with the Imperial Court of the dying Manchu dynasty. The power was still held by the now aged Empress Dowager, Tz'u-hsi, known as "Old Buddha," who ruled in splendor amidst ladies-in-waiting and eunuchs. Her nephew, Kuang Hsü, was the titular emperor, and Cochrane was called in to care for him and his son. Another high-ranking person of the court, the Dutchess Te, a lady-in-waiting who was married to a nephew of the empress dowager, also sought Cochrane's services, but under a peculiar arrangement:

> She was anxious for me to perform a delicate and difficult operation but she feared that, when she went back to court, she would get into trouble for having allowed a man to operate on her . . . she went through a ceremony whereby I became her brother-in-law and then it was considered proper for me to operate.[11]

Another patient from the Imperial Court was the head eunuch, Li Lien-ying who was required to be constantly at the beck and call of the empress. On one occasion he hurried into Cochrane's clinic and said breathlessly: "I am in a great hurry. I can only get out to attend to my own affairs when the Old Buddha is asleep."[12]

---

* Katherine E. Read 1971: Personal communication.

It was Li who, at Cochrane's suggestion, persuaded the "Old Buddha" of the importance of the projected medical school and hospital, and she contributed the equivalent of £1,400. A document in the files of the London Missionary Society reads:

> The Empress Dowager has shown her interest in the Union Medical College at Peking by a munificent donation of Taels 10,000 to its funds. . . . Dr. Cochrane was recently summoned to the palace to treat the chief eunuch Li in a difficult illness. His success has no doubt afforded to her Imperial Majesty a valuable object lesson in the efficacy of foreign medical skills.[13]

The gentry of the court in turn added £1,600 as a second gift for the medical school.

The dedicatory ceremonies in 1906 were described in a letter to London by the society's secretary in Peking:

> The Medical College was opened on Monday and Tuesday last, February 12 and 13. The former day was for the dedication of the building. A religious service was held in which all denominations took part. It was restricted to missionaries and native workers. The room available for the service could accommodate about 200, and the Christians generally were not asked. The result was that in point of numbers it was hardly a success. Still we had the people we wanted. Addresses were given in English by Bishop Scott and by Dr. Wherry of the American Presbyterian Mission. . . . The two English addresses were exceedingly good. The Bishop displayed a very fine spirit, and expressed wishes for a measure of union far in advance of anything we have seen.
> The second day's proceedings created by far the greater interest. Invitations had been sent out to all the high officials of Peking and to the members of all foreign legations. The President of the Foreign Office, Na T'ang, represented the Empress Dowager and presented her good wishes . . . the Russian Minister being the only important absentee. He excused himself on account of ill health.[14]

The foreign dignitaries at the dedication included the British minister, Sir Ernest Swatow; the American envoy, W. W. Rockhill; and the most influential Westerner in China, Sir Robert Hart, who had served for forty years as inspector-general of the Imperial Chinese Customs Service. Hart paid tribute to Lockhart's pioneering role in Peking and then ventured to peer into the future with striking intuitive cognition:

> Just as this pioneering man has been followed by a succession of devoted descendants, so too will not fail this pioneer College to be productive. If it does not itself develop into the Imperial College of Surgeons of China, it will prepare the way and produce such a College, and will yet see other offspring, other medical schools and colleges, seats of the truest learning, and the broadest culture in every quarter of this deathless empire.[15]

The first building, Lockhart Hall, named for the medical pioneer of Peking, housed classrooms, laboratories, and about thirty beds. One year later, in 1907, a dormitory was opened as the gift of Oliver W. Jones of Liverpool and was named for its benefactor.

Forty students were enrolled in the study of medicine in the first year. As in the other missionary medical schools, Chinese was the language of instruction but the students were also required to learn English. The curriculum was five years in duration: the first two years in the basic medical sciences and the remaining three in clinical subjects. Most of the original faculty of nine members had British qualifications.

An early honor in the summer of 1906 was the Empress Dowager's bestowal of official sanction on degrees granted by the school. She instructed her Board of Education to conduct examinations in each subject and to issue appropriate diplomas to the successful candidates.

There was also an International Examining Board composed of physicians attached to the British, German, Italian, Japanese, and American legations; the board expressed satisfaction with the students' knowledge of the basic sciences after their first examination in January 1909.

On April 7, 1911, the first sixteen graduates received their diplomas, stamped with the purple seal of the Board of Education, from the grand counselor of China. In the same year a total of 104 students was enrolled. A one-year premedical course was opened, as well as a postgraduate program leading to a higher qualification.

In 1912 Cochrane transferred from foreign missions to the headquarters of the London Missionary Society.

The successful development of the UMC may be said to represent the highwater mark of the first century of the missionary effort in medicine. For in the same year that the first class graduated, a few men with vision in the United States—led by John D. Rockefeller's advisor, Frederick Gates—were conceptualizing a program to establish the supremacy of Western medicine in China. Through private philanthropy they could muster far greater resources, both intellectual and financial, than could the missionaries. A new era was about to dawn in the rise of Western medicine in China.

NOTES TO CHAPTER ONE

1. William Lockhart, *Medical Missionary in China: A Narrative of Twenty Years' Experience* (London: Hurst and Blackett, 1861).

2. *Ibid.*, p. vi.

3. *Ibid.*, p. 59.

4. *PUMC Weekly Calendar*, 11 December 1940, pp. 86–7.

5. *Ibid.*, p. 87.

6. *Ibid.*, p. 87–8.

7. *Ibid.*, p. 88.

8. *Ibid.*, p. 88.

9. *Ibid.*, p. 88.

10. Francesca French, *Thomas Cochrane: Pioneer and Missionary Statesman*, p. 59.

11. *Ibid.*, p. 66.

12. *Ibid.*, p. 65.

13. Thomas Cochrane, 27 August 1904, Eastern No. 3349, Arrival No. 5557, Archives of the London Missionary Society.

14. S. E. Meech, 16 February 1906, Archives of the London Missionary Society.

15. K. Chimin Wong and Lien-teh Wu, *History of Chinese Medicine*, p. 387.

CHAPTER TWO

Missionary Medicine

We have examined developments in Peking because it was the seat of this history. When the China Medical Board of the Rockefeller Foundation made the decision to purchase the Union Medical College of Peking, rather than to start a new college, they did so because "the creditable beginnings made by the missionary societies" should not be discarded.[1] It had been a long road toward these "creditable beginnings," one that spanned just over a century of struggle and sacrifice and of devotion to a cause—better health for the Chinese people. Being aware of the history we can more fully appreciate the situation the foundation faced when it took over this missionary medical school.

Let us now look at the broader events in the rise of Western medicine in China before returning to Peking and the founding of PUMC.

The missionary era began with the Jesuits whose principal scientific interests were in astronomy, mathematics, and cartography. Little attention was paid to medicine in their training, and at times they were specifically forbidden to care for the sick. Despite this negative attitude, the first European to prepare a treatise in Chinese on the structure of the human body was a young Swiss Jesuit, Father Jean Terrenz (Terrentius), who had arrived in Macao in 1621. A Polish Jesuit, Father Michael Boym, 1612–1659, published the first European work on Chinese botany with descriptions of plants of medicinal value: *Flora Sinensis, ou Traité des fleurs, des fruits, des plantes et des animaux particuliers de la Chine*.[2] The volume contains sketches of twenty-three varieties of flora and fauna. In another manuscript, *Clavis medica ad Chinarum doctrinam de pulsibus*, Father Boym prepared the first descriptions for the West of some of the practices of Chinese traditional medicine. One year before Boym's death the manuscript was sent to Batavia for dispatch to Europe, where Father Ph. Couplet was to supervise its publication, but it fell into the hands of a German surgeon, Andreas Cleyer, serving with the United East India Company in Batavia, who plagiarized the manuscript and published it.[3] The manuscript included four treatises on the pulse by a famous practitioner, Wang Shu-hua; a description of the appearance of the tongue in different diseases; and an exposition on simple drugs that had been prepared by the missionaries at the direction of Chinese herbalists. An edition giving the name of the correct author was published in 1686.

CHINESE TRADITIONAL MEDICINE

The traditional system of medicine, *Chung-i*, on which Boym's *Clavis Medica* was based, has a historic, detailed, and fascinating philosophy, but since it has been fully described by a number of Western scholars, we will summarize only its essential features.

In brief, each person is considered a microcosm constantly interacting with the surrounding universe. Health is dependent upon the maintenance of harmony with the universe, and this is achieved through a series of extensive and intricate relationships. *Tao* is the central "way," and two opposing forces, *yin* and *yang*, are everywhere, including the human body. *Yin* is feminine—cold, moist, dark, the shady side of the hill; *yang* is masculine—warm, dry, bright, the sunny side of the hill. In the human body *yin* and *yang* must be maintained in perfect balance; otherwise disease will supervene. All natural phenomena are divided into five extensive series of relationships based on the five Chinese "elements": wood, earth, fire, metal, and water. As an example, some of the relationships for fire are joy, summer, south, heat, bitter, red, ripening, heart, ears, small intestine, and arteries. Man must adjust his mood and conduct to five seasonal cycles each dominated by its element. If he does not, disease will appear, and it will be caused primarily by a malfunction relating to a lack of harmony with the existing cycle of correspondences.

The diagnosis of disease is also based in part on the division of the organs into *yin* and *yang* groups: the heart, liver, kidney, spleen, and lung are *yin* organs, while the stomach, gall bladder, small intestine, large intestine, and urinary bladder are *yang* organs. If the individual has a "*yang*" temperament one or more of the organs in that group is the seat of his disease; if he has a "*yin*" temperament the organs in that group are suspected. Volatile, talkative, extroverted individuals are classified as *yang*, while reticent, quiet introverts belong to *yin*.

Within the body there are six major channels, or meridians, of *yin* and six of *yang* from which emerge numerous minor channels leading to the viscera. This network connects hundreds of points on the skin with the internal organs and is the basis for the two therapeutic techniques: acupuncture and moxibustion.

Acupuncture is unique to Chinese traditional medicine, and its most popular procedure. It is based on the belief that each of the skin points just mentioned relates to a particular organ of the body. To cure an illness, slender needles are inserted into the site or sites on the surface of the body that relate to the malfunctioning organ. Twelve hypothetical and undissectable channels course to the organs.

In moxibustion, small cones from the mugwort, *Artemisia vulgaris*, are burned at the same points in the skin as in acupuncture.

The cardinal procedure in diagnosis is meticulous palpation of the pulse; for a female the right pulse is palpated first, for a male the left pulse. If the rate is above seventy per minute the disease is *yang* in origin; if the rate is below seventy, the origin of the disease is *yin*. A strong pulse indicates a *yang* disease while a weak one indicates a *yin* disease. If the "direction" of the pulse beat is thought to be "external," toward the skin or the outside of the body, the disease is caused by external forces; if it is "internal," toward the radius, the disease is caused by internal forces. The pulse at each wrist is divided into seven superficial, or *piao*, segments and eight deep, *li*, segments, each of which represents an internal organ. The segments are palpated meticulously to determine the state of the organ they represent.

A second procedure is a detailed inspection of the tongue for color, moisture, and furring. If the tongue is furred, the thickness and direction of the furring are studied. Changes in appearance in the middle of the tongue are attributed to disorders in the stomach; on the root, in the kidneys; on the sides, in the liver; and on the tip, in the heart.

The Chinese place great emphasis on psychosomatic origins of disease and the practitioner therefore observes the patient at length to determine his "mood." In taking the history, the family also is interrogated as to possible psychosomatic factors.

There is a truly massive materia medica that has made important contributions to Western medicine. Arsenic, calomel, alum, camphor, talcum, cinnabar, seaweed (for goiter), opiates, and ephedrine are among the drugs that were first used in China.

The two most popular medicines in the Chinese formulary, ginseng and powdered horn, have dominated the pharmacopeia for centuries—far longer than all other medicines, Eastern and Western. Their popularity is undiminished today.

Ginseng, *Panax ginseng*, is a forked root, resembling mandrake, usually about four inches in length. A medicine to prolong life or bring about immortality was sought by all Chinese, who for centuries believed that ginseng held these magical powers, in part because it resembled a human figure. They also used it for many other purposes: as a cure for nausea, as a sedative, as a stimulant, and as an aphrodisiac.

Powdered horn was highly regarded as a potent tonic and also as an aphrodisiac. "Unicorn" horns were believed to have special powers. They were usually imported by foreign traders and were either the tusks of the pachyderms of East Africa or the single horn of the narwhal, *Monodon monoceros*, of the Arctic seas. The popularity of calcified materials extended to "dragon's teeth," which were usually dentition from fossil remains in the Gobi Desert or simply human molars.

Dissection of the human body, or removal of any of its parts during life, was for many centuries forbidden in China due to both religious and nonreligious cultural attitudes. The human body was considered to be a personal treasure and it was essential that it be kept intact for the hereafter. Two dissections are, however, recorded in the dynastic histories of 16 A.D. and 1106 A.D. Ancient anatomical charts also suggest that there had been dismemberments for the study of the human body before the advent of Buddhism in the second century. Subsequently, dissections were performed rarely and then only on the bodies of beheaded criminals. Thus it is not surprising that there were major errors in the Chinese anatomical treatises and charts. For example, the Chinese believed that the liver had seven lobes, and that a structure called the "Gate of Life" was located between the kidneys. There were three "warmers" or "burning spaces," one for the heart, one for the upper abdomen, and one for the lower abdomen.

Backward as their medical practices may have seemed to Western eyes, the Chinese made efforts to inoculate against smallpox as early as 1000 A.D. One of their techniques was the insertion of powdered scabs, taken from patients recuperating from the disease, into the nostril with the quill of a goose feather —into the right nostril for a boy and the left for a girl. Another method entailed putting fluid from vesicles on a plug and inserting it in a similar manner. A third and even less attractive procedure was to wear the foul undergarments of a person suffering from the disease, preferably those of a child. Although these methods attracted attention in Britain there is no evidence that they were successful.

THE ADVENT OF WESTERN MEDICAL PROCEDURES

Edward Jenner's epochal studies on vaccination with cowpox were published in 1798,[4] and five years later, in 1803, an attempt was made to introduce his method to Hong Kong; it failed because the virus had lost its effectiveness on the long passage from Bombay. In 1805, however, Alexander Pearson, a surgeon with the East India Company, was successful in introducing vaccination to China. Pearson was one of the British surgeons who at the beginning of the nineteenth century gave medical care to the coolies in the employ of the company.

As trade with Britain, the United States, and other Western powers grew in importance, medical and evangelistic missionaries, principally from Scotland, England, and the United States, followed in its wake.

It was the power and prestige of the traditional system of medicine that posed a major problem for the medical missionaries in their efforts to introduce Western medicine. A second problem was the ban against dissection, which balked efforts to perform autopsies and to teach anatomy as well as to perform surgery. The missionaries struggled unsuccessfully against the age-old Chinese superstition that the human body was a sacred treasure that must remain unmarred for this life and for the spiritual hereafter. When now and again procedures were agreed upon, it was with the stipulation that if any part of the body, such as an eye or an extremity, was removed, it would be presented to the patient so that he would be intact when he journeyed to the hereafter. A third problem was the low status of traditional medicine in a society dominated by an abstract Confucian philosophy.

A fourth obstacle was China's historic rejection of intercourse with the West. As the all-powerful "Middle Kingdom," for centuries she had scornfully rejected every approach made by Western nations, her bitterness based on such wanton acts as the Opium Wars of 1839–42; the Anglo-French seizure of Canton, which resulted in the Treaties of Tientsin in 1858; the Anglo-French occupation of Peking and the destruction of the Imperial Summer Palace in 1860; and the vengeance of the Western powers after the Boxer Rebellion in 1900. These pillages justifiably heightened the xenophobia of the Chinese. Rumors were rife that the missionaries performed barbaric acts, such as cutting out the eyes of children for use in compounding medicines. Even climatic aberrations were attributed to the presence of the missionaries. In a letter to London at the time of the Boxer Rebellion, a missionary complained that even "the want of rain is being put down to the Christians."[5]

Beyond her conflicts with foreign powers, China was in almost constant turmoil: there was continual agrarian unrest due to absentee landlordism, official levies, and natural disasters, all of which resulted in armed banditry and rebel groups who not only harassed but physically attacked the missionaries.

Here it is appropriate to ask, why then did the Westerners go? What was the lure of China? One reason was that China was the last great country to be opened to the West. Beginning with the Portuguese in 1520, the Spanish, the Dutch, the British, and the French were all rebuffed until the middle of the nineteenth century, except for their use of Canton as an entepôt. For the missionaries, foreign traders, and adventurers, China presented the last great golden opportunity.

At the end of the nineteenth century the eyes of Americans were turning toward the Far East. American clipper ships were returning from Canton with silks, porcelain, screens, paintings, and other prized Chinese art forms for museums and the mansions of the wealthy. The admission of Washington and other western territories to statehood heightened our expansionism in the Pacific. We acquired our first and only oriental colony in the Philippine Islands.

Another factor was the deep religious awakening that was sweeping the United States, including the campuses of our colleges and universities. We were especially concerned with the salvation of the heathen who "bows down to wood and stone."

For physicians China offered limitless opportunities to apply their skills in the conquest of disease: smallpox, tuberculosis, parasitic diseases, and essentially every form of malnutrition abounded.

A final and enduring reason was the sensuous lure of the mysterious East. Despite the many obstacles that faced them, the medical missionaries committed their lives to China.

The first Protestant missionary to reach China was Robert Morrison of the London Missionary Society, who had completed a special combined theological-medical course at St. Bartholomew's Hospital Medical School. Arriving in Canton on September 4, 1807, he put the emphasis on religion rather than medicine. His principal contribution was as official translator for the East India Company in which capacity he completed translations of the Holy Bible and other religious texts and compiled a dictionary of six quarto volumes that was published in 1823.

When John Livingston, a surgeon, opened a dispensary at Macao in 1829, he became the first fully-qualified doctor to practice Western medicine in China. Livingston developed a deep interest in Chinese traditional medicine and collected over 800 volumes on the Chinese materia medica. As his interest grew he employed in his clinic a practitioner of acupuncture and an herbalist.

The high prevalence of eye diseases and blindness made a lasting impression on the pioneer Western doctors in China. Trachoma, ophthalmia, xerophthalmia, opacities from smallpox, keratitis, and cataract were widely disseminated. It was a common and touching sight to encounter a scrawny child leading a half-blind adult to the shady side of a street, with the child shading his eyes because of early trachoma.

In 1828 Thomas R. Colledge, a surgeon with the East India Company, at his own expense opened a clinic in Macao primarily for eye diseases. One year later he moved to Canton where he opened a second clinic.

Peter Parker, the first American medical missionary and a legendary figure in the annals of Western medicine in China, arrived in Canton on September 18, 1834. A favorite subject of current historical studies, Parker had considered enrolling at Harvard but had been advised that "Harvard was not the place of young men with pious intentions . . . Yale was a truer school of the prophets."[6] He studied medicine and attended lectures in theology at Yale where he was awarded the M.D. degree in 1834 and soon after sailed for the East. Parker first went to Singapore and then to Macao where he worked in mission hospitals and studied Chinese for a year. He then went on to Canton where on November 4, 1835 he opened the Canton Ophthalmic Hospital at 7 Green Pea Street in the Fung Tae Hong district. For the patients and their families who sat in the street all night to be assured of admission to the clinic, the vigil was enlivened by the streams of sailors and whores pouring in and out of the brothels, saloons, and opium dens that lined Green Pea Street, which was known to sailors around the world as "Hog Lane." Assisted by Chinese whom he had trained, Parker moved from chair to chair practicing the ancient technique of "couching" to dislocate the opaque lens in patients with cataract. Parker was the first surgeon in China to perform mastectomies, lithotomies, and hysterectomies, and, in 1847, the first operation under a general anesthetic, sulfuric ether.

One of the unheralded incidents in Parker's complicated life was a voyage to Japan. On July 3, 1837, he sailed from Macao on the *Morison* with a group of American missionaries whose purpose was to repatriate a group of Japanese castaways. Parker was invited to join the mission because of the high regard the Japanese were known to hold for Western medicine and surgery. In addition to a stock of medicines, Parker carried a supply of virus for smallpox vaccinations and a Chinese translation of a treatise on vaccination written by Alexander Pearson. They sailed with all guns discarded in order to demonstrate the completely peaceful nature of their mission.

During a visit to the Loochow (Ryukyu) Islands en route, Parker introduced smallpox vaccination to the inhabitants. The fact that the ship was unarmed did not mollify the xenophobic Japanese, who fired on it at both Edo (Tokyo) and Kagoshima. The Japanese repatriates were so distressed by the belligerence of their countrymen that they shaved their heads to show the missionaries that they had abdicated from the empire forever. The mission finally returned to China with the castaways still aboard.

In 1836 Colledge and Parker prepared a preliminary statement: "Original Suggestions for the Formation of a Medical Missionary Society in China." Two years later the Canton Medical Missionary Society came into being at a public meeting on February 21, 1838. The society set lofty aims:

> 1—To encourage Western medicine amongst the Chinese. 2—To extend to the Chinese people the benefits of the West. 3—To cultivate confidence and friendship and thus introduce the Gospel of Christ in place of heathenism. 4—To educate Chinese youths in Western medicine.[7]

Colledge was elected president of the society, and Parker one of the vice presidents. William Jardine, a founder of the great Jardine Matheson Trading Company and Parker's most intimate and loyal friend, became another vice president. Private merchants led by Jardine contributed to the treasury and the first two grants went to Colledge and to Parker.

Parker returned to the United States on furlough in 1841, at the point of mental and physical exhaustion, and received the accolades he so richly deserved; it was the apogee of his career. He was lionized as a hero, received by President Martin van Buren, and invited to address the Congress. Only a physician-clergyman in the mold of Albert Schweitzer could have received comparable honors.

Returning to China, Parker subsequently became enmeshed in diplomatic and political activities in which he was largely ineffectual. He was appointed to the United States Mission in China but became increasingly disillusioned with the hostile attitude of the Chinese toward the foreign communities. His sentiments were expressed with such mounting and open belligerence that in 1857 President Franklin Pierce had no choice but to recall him to the United States. He lived for thirty more years, essentially in retirement, a frustrated and broken figure.

SOME EARLY MEDICAL SCHOOLS

Parker's successor in Canton, John Glasgow Kerr, a graduate of Jefferson Medical College, and Wong Fun, the first Chinese to receive a medical degree from a foreign faculty, Edinburgh, took steps to expand the apprenticeship program established by Parker.

In 1866 they enrolled seven apprentices in a three-year program of instruction in anatomy, physiology, medicine, surgery, and materia medica, combined with the principles of Chinese traditional medicine. The barriers against dissection posed a major problem in anatomy, but occasionally the extremities of the body of a patient unclaimed by friends or relatives were superficially dissected. By 1871 Kerr could report that more than twelve students had spent at least three years in the study of medicine and were now in practice, primarily in smaller towns. The first two women, with their feet bound in the traditional manner, were admitted from the adjoining True Light Seminary in 1879.

In 1897 the curriculum was extended from three to four years, and in 1904 the school, now designated the South China Medical College, moved into new quarters. Meanwhile the first medical college for women in China was opened in Canton in 1901 as the Hackett Medical College for Women under the direction of Mary Fulton.

Although the Canton Hospital continued to flourish, the South China Medical College was unable to retain an adequate faculty. It closed in 1911, having educated more than 200 young men and women in medicine. In 1935 the school was reopened as the Sun Yat-sen Medical College in honor of its most illustrious student, who had been an apprentice there in 1886 before moving to Hong Kong to complete his studies.

The first medical school in China was established in the north China seaport of Tientsin in 1881 by a Scottish physician, John Kenneth MacKenzie. Funds for the school became available because of the enduring debt many Chinese patients felt for the ministrations of their physicians and their need to demonstrate this gratitude by making substantial gifts. The wife of Viceroy Li Hung-chang had been cured by MacKenzie of a long and seemingly fatal illness that had not responded to treatment by a series of practitioners of indigenous medicine. When MacKenzie's desire to establish a medical school became known, Li Hung-chang and his retainers contributed the necessary funds. The school subsequently became the Navy Medical College.

The educational program consisted of a three-year curriculum, and the students were largely drawn from a group that had been sent to colleges in the United States and who had been recalled because of serious unrest at home.

The Hong Kong College of Medicine for Chinese was opened in the British Crown Colony on October 1, 1887. It was based in a hospital that had been built by Ho Kai, a Chinese who had qualified in both medicine and law in Great Britain; the hospital was a memorial to his English wife, Alice. Ho gave it over to the control of the London Missionary Society with the stipulation that a clinical school of Western medicine should be attached to it. There were two students in the first class, one of whom was Sun Yat-sen. The first dean was the Scottish father of tropical medicine, Sir Patrick Manson, who later founded the precursor of the London School of Hygiene and Tropical Medicine. The Hong Kong College of Medicine did not expand appreciably and by 1910 a total of only 100 students had been enrolled. Upon graduation most of them moved to the mainland to establish their medical careers. In 1912 the school was merged with the newly opened University of Hong Kong and became its Faculty of Medicine.

Since instruction in the missionary medical schools was in Chinese, translations of Western medical texts were a principal need. The pioneer translator was Benjamin Hobson, an 1839 graduate of the University College Hospital Medical School in London, who served with the London Missionary Society in Canton and Hong Kong. In 1851 Hobson completed an anatomico-physiological text in Chinese; subsequent volumes covered general physics; astronomy and natural history; principles and practices of surgery; midwifery and diseases of children; the practice of medicine; materia medica; and a medical English-Chinese syllabary. The publications were so popular that the viceroy of Canton had them reprinted, complete with illustrations, in the classical style of the Chinese scroll. Foreign merchants in Shanghai contributed £2,000 for a larger edition, which also became popular in Japan. In ensuing years the need for more complete texts became evident and books were published in a number of medical fields. John Glasgow Kerr was also a prolific author and translator with over fifteen texts and treatises to his credit.

Two medical schools with very different origins developed in Manchuria. One was founded by Dugald Christie, a Scottish Presbyterian and the pioneer British medical missionary in Manchuria, who came to Moukden in 1882. Christie's earliest efforts were devoted to training auxiliaries, whom he described as "medical evangelists,"[8] but his dream of a full-fledged medical school was not realized until March 1912, when the Moukden Medical College opened. The curriculum was of five years' duration, and although instruction was in Chinese the students were required to study English. The program developed to a standard that was recognized by the University of Edinburgh for graduates of the college seeking postgraduate training.

The second medical school in Moukden was the South Manchuria Medical College founded in 1911. A Japanese school, it was sponsored by the South Manchuria Railway, which also operated schools, mines, factories, and hospitals in Manchuria. The faculty was exclusively Japanese, as were the students. Because of its excellent research facilities the college attracted some of Japan's leading medical scientists.

Other foreign medical schools in China included the French-Jesuit Aurora University. Founded in Shanghai in March 1903, Aurora also had faculties of law, science, arts, and civil engineering. A medical school was established in Shanghai by a German, E. H. Paulun, which in 1909 was named for its founder. Another German program was established in Tsingtao, and a Franco-Chinese school in Canton.

AMERICAN-AFFILIATED MEDICAL SCHOOLS

As part of the intense religious revival that swept the campuses of the United States early in the twentieth century, three universities established programs in medical education in China: Pennsylvania in Canton and later in Shanghai; Harvard in Shanghai; and Yale in Changsha in Hunan Province.

Of the three the most renowned was Yale-in-China, whose history has been described in such detail elsewhere that we need only summarize it here. Hunan, a large interior province remote from the great coastal areas, represented a new field for missionaries. It was especially challenging because of the local population's deep hostility to foreigners. The establishment of the Yale Foreign Missionary Society in 1902 was soon followed by an invitation from Christian missionaries in Hunan for Yale to assume responsibility for developing programs in higher education, including liberal arts, the sciences, and medicine.

In 1905 Edward H. Hume, who graduated from Yale in 1897 and from the Johns Hopkins School of Medicine in 1901, came from missionary work in India to establish a medical school for Yale-in-China. He was a keen, sensitive, dedicated scholar whose later writings on Chinese medicine and on his career in China stand today as excellent resources for students of Chinese medicine.[9] A class of two students was enrolled at Changsha in 1908; the training of nurses began the following year.

In 1911, on furlough to the United States, Hume obtained a gift of $150,000 gold from Edward S. Harkness, his classmate at Yale and an associate of John D. Rockefeller, for the construction of a 400-bed teaching hospital at Changsha. In a letter stating the terms of the gift, Harkness followed the pattern he had used in December 1910, when he endowed the Presbyterian Hospital in New York City as a teaching facility:

> The hospital is to be a center of medical education, for my primary concern is not for medical practice alone. . . . It is to be a center the people of Changsha will regard as their own, to manage and support.[10]

A bright future seemed assured when a cooperative agreement was reached with the Hunan government, the essentials of which were that Yale would build the hospital and supply a Western staff while Hunan would finance the facilities for the medical school; the two participating parties would have equal representation on the governing board. As a symbol of Chinese and American solidarity, Hsiang-ya was adopted as the name for the medical center: *Hsiang*, the literary name for Hunan Province, and *ya* for Yale or *Yali*, as it was termed by the Chinese.

The dreams of a bright future were short-lived, however. Starting in 1916, independent, aggressive, xenophobic warlords split asunder a number of provinces, including Hunan; hostility toward foreigners mounted steadily after World War I, with the loss of Shantung to Japan as a result of the Treaty of Versailles. Hume left Hsiang-ya in June 1926 because of increasing unrest among the students and faculty. He is remembered as an effective pioneer of medical education in China.

Meanwhile, Chiang Kai-shek and his army were advancing northward and, as a stronghold of the opposition, Hunan became engulfed in conflict. The student's hostility was fanned to new heights and the faculty voted to close the school in January 1927. This was summarily accomplished when the American consulate required all Americans to evacuate Hunan.

Four years after the opening of Yale-in-China, the missionary zeal of a small group of Harvard medical students was responsible for the opening in Shanghai of the Harvard Medical School of China in March 1912.

The school was to be a five-year experiment; its Board of Trustees included Harvard's president emeritus, Charles W. Eliot, as chairman, and three distinguished Harvard professors: Dean Henry A. Christian, Walter Bradford Cannon, and William T. Councilman. There were, however, no formal ties with Harvard and the school had no affiliation with any missionary society.

Shanghai was chosen as the site for the school because of its importance as a port city and because it afforded the opportunity to work with two American Episcopal institutions, St. John's University and St. Luke's Hospital. The university had been founded in 1879 as St. John's College, and a medical department was opened a year later under the direction of Henry W. Boone; St. Luke's was its teaching hospital.

Financial support for the medical school came from Harvard alumni, Chinese sources, and private philanthropy. Three unusual sources of funds were the legislatures of California, Oregon, and Washington, which felt that by improving public health in Shanghai, where their lively Oriental trade was based, the threat of the spread of plague and cholera to the West Coast of the United States would be lessened. There had been 113 deaths from plague in San Francisco between 1900 and 1904, and a second outbreak between 1907 and 1909 took seventy-eight lives.

Several members of the Harvard faculty were later to play important roles in the rise of Western medicine in China; Henry S. Houghton, Harvey J. Howard, Paul C. Hodges, J. Heng Liu, and Andrew H. Woods later joined the faculty of PUMC.

The Harvard Medical School in Shanghai set a high academic standard—far too high for the students, who were inadequately prepared and relied exclusively on learning by rote. As a result the attrition rate was too great for an effective program: the first freshman class was reduced from twenty-one to nine at the end of the first term.

As the financial situation grew increasingly bleak, Eliot requested support from the newly established Rockefeller Foundation on two occasions; in the second appeal he urged that the foundation take over complete control of the school and hospital. Consideration was given to terminating the undergraduate course and developing a graduate program, but this did not eventuate. The Harvard Medical School of China closed its doors in 1917.

The third American medical school effort was that of the Christian Association of the University of Pennsylvania, which in 1907 sent a team led by Josiah C. McCracken to join the medical department of the Canton Christian College. There they affiliated with the Canton Hospital and its excellent staff, which included Harvey Howard in ophthalmology and Andrew Woods, chief of the medical staff, in neurology. McCracken later moved to the Pennsylvania Medical College of St. John's University, while Howard and Woods joined the Harvard faculty.

Following the establishment of the UMC in Peking in 1906, other union schools developed in Tsinan, Moukden, Hankow, Nanking, Hangchow, Foochow, Canton, and Chengtu. The West China Union University College of Medicine in Chengtu was the principal medical center in western China. It was founded by another distinguished medical pioneer and anthropologist, William Reginald Morse, who after graduation from McGill University in Montreal had done postgraduate work at Harvard, Hopkins, and University College in London. Reaching China in 1909 Morse went to the College of Medicine in Chengtu in 1914, and was elected dean in 1919, a position he held for nineteen years. An excellent anatomist and anthropologist, Morse performed the first dissection to be made west of Hankow.

At the biennial conference of the China Medical Missionary Association in 1913 a resolution was adopted urging that no further union medical schools be established until the eight colleges then in existence were on a firmer footing. In the words of one of the missionary leaders, Harold Balme: "It soon became evident that even that number was far beyond the power of the missions to render effective."[11] In 1913 there were about 500 students studying medicine in China.

PLAGUE

A devastating epidemic of pneumonic plague in Manchuria in 1911 was a crucial factor in the rise of Western medicine in China. The outbreak began in Manchouli on October 13, 1910, reached Peking three months later, and finally subsided in March 1911, leaving 60,000 people dead. Two students from the senior class of the UMC who volunteered to serve in the anti-plague medical forces were among the fatalities. There was a 50 per cent mortality rate among Chinese practitioners, who were lacking in knowledge concerning either protection or sanitation; among practitioners of scientific medicine the rate was only 2 per cent. Wu Lien-teh, the key Chinese physician who fought the epidemic, emphasized that the plague

> definitely laid the foundation for systematic public health work in China. Those in authority from the Emperor downwards, who had formerly pledged their faith to old-fashioned medicine, now acknowledged that its methods were powerless against such severe outbreaks. They were thus compelled to entrust the work to modern-trained physicians and to give their consent to drastic measures, such as compulsory house-to-house visitation, segregation of contacts in camps or wagons, and cremation of thousands of corpses which had accumulated at Harbin and elsewhere."[12]

To gather information on the plague and to plan the control of possible future outbreaks, Wu convened the first international medical conference in Chinese history in Moukden on April 3 to 28, 1911, with representation from Russia, Austria-Hungary, the Netherlands, Italy, Mexico, France, Germany, Japan, Britain, and the United States.

In his opening address the viceroy of Manchuria, Hsi Liang, acknowledged the superiority of Western medicine:

> We Chinese have believed in an ancient system of medical practice, which the experience of centuries has found to be serviceable for many ailments, but the lessons taught by this epidemic, which until practically three or four months ago had been unknown in China, have been great, and have compelled several of us to revise our ideas of this valuable branch of knowledge. . . . We feel . . . that if railways, telegraphs, electric light and other modern inventions are indispensable to the material welfare of this country, we should also make use of the wonderful resources of Western medicine for the benefit of our people.[13]

One of the principal recommendations to come out of the conference resulted in the establishment of the Manchurian Plague Prevention Service under the direction of Wu Lien-teh.

A major development occurred in early November 1913, when a decree was issued that legalized and established regulations for the dissection of human bodies. The decree required that physicians must first obtain the consent of the relatives. Because of the bitter cultural opposition to any violation of the human body, however, the lack of cadavers continued to be a major obstacle for the medical schools. Under the new law, one of the earliest dissections was made on the body of an executed criminal on November 13, 1913. Sixty-five persons were in attendance, pictures were taken of the corpse and the assemblage, and a pamphlet was published that claimed that this was the first dissection in China in 4,000 years. (On the assumption that the earlier dismemberments were not technically dissections.) In the following April the regulations were expanded giving all medical schools and hospitals the right to perform dissections.

It was now more than eight decades since Colledge had opened the first hospital to offer Western medicine to the Chinese people. Although the missionaries' aspirations in medical care were admirable, the most populous country in the world still had the poorest medical care. A comprehensive approach to scientific medicine at the highest standard, with the backing of the central government, was essential.

Meanwhile, medicine in the United States was moving away from its low state, dominated by proprietory medical schools. President Eliot had instigated the first reforms at Harvard Medical School in 1869, and the reform movement culminated in the founding of the Johns Hopkins School of Medicine in 1893. A far-sighted multimillionaire, John D. Rockefeller, had in 1901 richly endowed the Rockefeller Institute in New York City as a center for medical research.

The United States was affluent, and its religious fervor to save the heathen continued at a high pitch. China was the country that held the strongest appeal for American citizens dedicated to foreign programs. The greatest need in China was for an academic medical center, based on excellence, to which the Chinese could turn for leadership. At the time the viceroy of Manchuria was acknowledging the supremacy of Western medicine, discussions were already being held informally in New York on the means by which such a center might be established.

NOTES TO CHAPTER TWO

1. China Medical Commission of the Rockefeller Foundation, *Medicine in China*, p. 45.

2. Michael Boym, S.J., *Flora Sinensis, ou Traité des fleurs, des fruits, des plantes et des animaux particuliers de la Chine* (Vienna: 1656).

3. Andreas Cleyer, *Specimen Medicinae Sinicae Nive Opuscula Medica ad Mentem Sinensium Continens: (I–De Pulsibus Libros quatuor e sinico translatos, II–Tractatus de*

Pulsibus ad eruditio Europaeo collectos, III–Fragmentum Operis Medici ibidem ab eruditio Europaeo conscripti, IV–Excerpta Literis eruditi Europaei in China, V–Schematia ad meliorem praecedentium Intelligentiam, VI–De Indiciis Morborum ex Linguae colorbus & affectionibus) (Frankfurt: Johannes Petrus, 1682).

4. Edward Jenner, *An Inquiry into the Causes and Effects of the Variolae Vaccinae* (London: publisher unknown, 1798).

5. G. P. Smith, 1900, North China Folder, 1895–1945, Archives of the London Missionary Society.

6. Charles Snyder, "7 Green Pea Street," p. 887.

7. Harold Balme, *China and Modern Medicine*, p. 42.

8. Dugald Christie, *Thirty Years in Moukden, 1883–1913*, p. 82.

9. Edward H. Hume, *The Chinese Way in Medicine*, and *Doctors East, Doctors West*.

10. William Reeves, Jr., "Sino-American Cooperation in Medicine," p. 152.

11. Harold Balme, *China and Modern Medicine*, p. 116.

12. K. Chimin Wong and Lien-teh Wu, *History of Chinese Medicine*, p. 431.

13. Carl F. Nathan, *Plague Prevention and Politics in Manchuria, 1910–1931*, p. 10.

CHAPTER THREE

The First China Medical Commission

The years between the opening of the twentieth century and the outbreak of World War I saw the final disintegration of Imperial China. The central government was severely impeded by a lack of funds and an inefficient and demoralized civil service. The foreign powers, including Japan, had compelled China to grant them special concessions on trade and investments, as well as jurisdiction over their citizens residing in Chinese territory.

The position of China was the cumulative result of a series of defeats and failures in armed conflicts with foreign powers, led by Britain and Japan. The terms imposed by the Japanese as the victors in the Sino-Japanese War included cession of Formosa and renunciation of Chinese suzerainty over Korea.

After the Boxer Rebellion in 1900 there was increasing mutual suspicion between the foreign powers, especially Japan, Britain, and Russia. At the Portsmouth, New Hampshire, Peace Conference to end the Russo-Japanese War in August and September 1905, Japan was given the Russian leaseholds, including the railway in Southern Manchuria, thus establishing Japan as a power with extensive interests in China.

China continued to be an agricultural nation, and 90 per cent of her people relied on occupations related to agriculture for their inadequate livelihoods. Foreign exports were dominated by tea, raw silk, and silk products.

In the early part of the twentieth century American fervor to "save" China continued to mount. The establishment of a republic by Sun Yat-sen in 1912, after the overthrow of the Manchu dynasty, was a development that had great appeal for the freedom-loving citizens of the United States. There were attractive and intelligent Chinese students attending a number of American universities and colleges, and missionaries were returning to preach and to teach of the fascinations of China and the admirable characteristics of the Chinese people —their industry, integrity, and respectful friendliness. In addition the United States government was concerned about the rapidly rising power and militancy of Japan and wished to support China as a counterbalance.

THE ORIENTAL EDUCATION COMMISSION

But let us go back to 1892—two decades before the Rockefeller Foundation was chartered—when John D. Rockefeller invited a former Baptist minister, Frederick T. Gates, to become his principal advisor on finance and philanthropy. From that year until his resignation in 1923, Frederick Gates was the linchpin in philanthropic programs sponsored by the Rockefellers.*

With his combined dedication to missions and to medicine, the Orient attracted Gates, and Rockefeller agreed with his proposal to finance an Oriental Education Commission for the purpose of investigating conditions in the Far East. The two members of the commission, Ernest De Witt Burton, professor of theology, and Thomas Crowder Chamberlin, professor of geology, were both from Rockefeller's favorite institution, the University of Chicago. In 1909 the commission spent six months in Japan, India, and their principal target country, China. The fifth volume of their report contained a wide range of information on China, and included descriptions of existing programs as well as of opportunities in higher education.

In medical education they found that only three schools had been established by the Chinese; two were Army medical schools, in Canton and in Tientsin, that were well-organized and efficiently operated—perhaps an example of the deep concern of the Chinese about military aggression from without.

The report of the commission also mentioned missionary medical schools in Canton, Hangchow, and Shanghai, but the most impressive was the Union Medical College in Peking. The intake of students in the missionary schools remained at a low level, however, and Burton and Chamberlin estimated that there were fewer than 200 students in all of the missionary establishments. Another depressing estimate was that no more than that same number were enrolled in the medical schools operated by the government and the University of Hong Kong. Thus for a country of 400 million people suffering from widespread endemic and epidemic diseases and from malnutrition, where medical care was largely in the hands of an indigenous, nonscientific system of medicine, fewer than 400 students were studying Western medicine—one student for 1 million people.

The commission emphasized the urgency of the situation in medicine:

As soon as practicable there should be built up, at least in Canton, in the region of Shanghai, in Hankow, and in Chengtu, well organized and thoroughly equipped

---

* As a vacation diversion in the summer of 1897 Gates had read Osler's *The Principles and Practice of Medicine*,[1] which brought to his attention the gaps in medical knowledge, and spurred his determination to see Rockefeller's fortunes turned towards medicine. In 1901 he sparked the establishment of the Rockefeller Institute for Medical Research.

medical schools. Even these would be a meager supply for a population of 400 million people.[2]

The commission reviewed China's disappointing experience in educational relations with Japan. After opening her doors to other nations, China had turned first to the Island Empire because she was impressed by Japan's accomplishments. Between 1902 and 1910, 13,000 Chinese youths had gone to Japan to study, many at government expense, and hundreds of teachers had been imported from Japan to teach in Chinese schools. The results of both programs had been far below expectations, and in a reasoned but unfortunate decision the government had decided to hold dependence on foreign aid to a minimum. Burton and Chamberlin anticipated that this attitude would ease, but in the interim patience was necessary: "The Chinese government will *in time* not resent offers of cooperation in their educational work coming from friendly nations."[3] The government was manifestly suspicious of missionaries, and the vice president of the Imperial Board of Education in Peking, H. E. Yen Hsu, spoke to the commission in a derogatory manner about the educational programs of the missionary schools.

The report emphasized the importance of the "union" approach in the work of the missionaries and stated that the only institution in which this had been successfully achieved was at the UMC in Peking.

Gates had hoped that the commission's report would give him the necessary ammunition to recommend that a part of the Rockefeller fortunes be used to finance the development of a first-rate university in China. But in 1911 he reluctantly decided that the time was not propitious. His judgment was based in part on the anxieties of missionary bodies about the loss of status of and support for their programs from church sources. Another major barrier was the insistence of the Chinese government that the school must be controlled and directed by individuals whom it alone would select and appoint. Gates and others foresaw a morass of inefficiency, possibly aggravated by corruption. Despite these problems China continued to hold first place in Gates's priorities for Rockefeller-supported programs.

THE ROCKEFELLER FOUNDATION

With the establishment of the Rockefeller Foundation in the spring of 1913, Gates again focused on the possibility of a foundation program to bring Western medicine to China. He was stimulated in part by the striking success that the Rockefeller-sponsored International Health Commission was achieving in its fight against hookworm disease in the southern United States.*

---

* The Rockefeller Sanitary Commission began the fight against hookworm in the South in 1909. It was merged with the Rockefeller Foundation in 1913 and designated the International Health Commission, which in turn became the International Health Board in 1916, and the International Health Division in 1927.

Another early advocate of such a program was Jerome D. Greene, formerly secretary to President Eliot at Harvard and now the first secretary of the Rockefeller Foundation. His interest in advancing Western medicine in China had been strengthened through his association with Eliot and the Harvard Medical School of China. Gates and Greene were a formidable team in pressing for China and medicine.

The first aim of the trustees of the new foundation was to explore possible programs that might be established in the United States and abroad. They studied requests for a wide range of programs—from colleges, universities, medical schools, governments, and religious missions. At one of their frequent meetings, on October 22, 1913, Greene reopened the question of China in a memorandum entitled "Educational and Other Needs in the Far East," in which he suggested that the foundation appoint a commission to conduct a survey in the Orient and recommend feasible developments in medicine. Although no formal action was taken there was general support for the proposal. Greene also presented a request for financial support from the Executive Committee of Harvard Medical School of China, but it was tabled.

At another meeting of the trustees one month later, Greene urged that discussions be held promptly with individuals who were familiar with the problems and possibilities of educational and medical programs in China. He expressed the hope that such discussions would lead to the appointment of a three-man commission to survey educational and medical needs in China. Such a survey in his opinion would result in recommendations for specific programs.

THE CONFERENCE ON CHINA

The trustees met again in December and decided to implement Greene's suggestion for a conference on China. At the same meeting they received another request from the Harvard Medical School of China, this time for endowment that would allow the faculty in the clinical departments to become full-time. Still uncertain as to their future course in China, and with the conference to consider China imminent, the trustees again took no action on this request.

Participants in the conference included leaders of the principal missionary boards represented in China and several distinguished educators: President Emeritus Eliot of Harvard; Professor Paul Monroe of Columbia, a leading scholar on China; Henry Pratt Judson, president of the University of Chicago; Professor Burton who had led the 1909 mission; Simon Flexner, director of the Rockefeller Institute, and John R. Mott. Representatives of the General Education Board and the staff of the Rockefeller Foundation included Gates, Greene, Abraham Flexner, Wallace Buttrick, and Wickliffe Rose.

Buttrick, who was soon to become the first director of the China Medical Board, was president and secretary of the General Education Board. He was subsequently described by Raymond Fosdick as "one of the great educational statesmen of his generation."[4] As a Baptist minister, Buttrick had come to know Gates through their work on the Executive Board of the American Baptist Education Society. His clerical background, added to his personal warmth, understanding, and tact, made him especially effective in working with the missionary groups concerned with the UMC.

John Mott, another important voice at the conference, was described as "one of the greatest religious leaders and organizers that Protestantism has produced."[5] As a representative of the International YMCA, Mott had made frequent visits to China.

Wickliffe Rose, formerly a professor of philosophy at Peabody College in Nashville, was director of the International Health Commission.

At this point we should emphasize the major role that Charles Eliot played in the decision to establish a medical program in China. Eliot came to the conference with outstanding credentials, having made a study of China in 1912 for the Carnegie Endowment for International Peace. In his report, "Some Roads Toward Peace," Eliot gave the introduction of Western medicine into China the highest priority, not only because of the appalling health problems but because it could be the medium to introduce inductive reasoning. He noted the striking difference between East and West:

> Since the Oriental, except recently in Japan, has been a student of the abstract he has never practiced inductive philosophy to which the West owes its remarkable progress in the last 400 years—the inductive method of ascertaining truth. In contrast the Oriental has proceeded by intuition and meditation and has accepted his philosophy and religion largely from authorities.[6]

The wretched state of Chinese medicine made a deep impression on Eliot:

> They have no knowledge of the practice of scientific medicine and no knowledge of the practice of surgery in the modern sense. The Chinese physician uses various drugs and medicaments compounded of strange materials, employs charms and incantations, and claims occult powers, and he is always willing to puncture any gathering on the body which seems capable of yielding a liquid to the hollow needle;* but of scientific diagnosis, major surgery, anesthesia and asepsis he knows nothing . . . he possesses none of the modern chemical and bacteriological means of diagnosis . . . the treatment of disease in the mass of the Chinese population is ignorant, superstitious and almost completely ineffectual.[7]

He identified Western medicine as the vehicle to bring inductive reasoning to China:

> We find the gift of Western medicine and surgery to the Oriental populations to be one of the most precious things that Western civilization can do for the East. . . . There is no better subject than medicine in which to teach the universal inductive method.[8]

---

* Eliot had not been told that acupuncture needles are not hollow and do not withdraw fluid.

Eliot put his finger directly on the deepest flaw in Chinese education when he made the point that the existing system did nothing to stimulate creativity:

> The nature or quality of education in China has remained unchanged for more than 2,000 years; it has always been an education exclusively literary, with some small additions of a historical and metaphysical nature. . . . The ultimate object in view was the passing of the state examinations which admitted the student to the official class; and the passing of these examinations was chiefly a feat of memory.[9]

Beyond his knowledge of the Orient, Eliot brought another contribution to the discussions on China: he was one of the few American university presidents who understood the means of achieving excellence in medical education and the avenues through which it could be done. It was Eliot who was primarily responsible for elevating the Harvard Medical School from an essentially proprietary college to the world-renowned institution that it is today. In his reply to a letter of congratulations from Edward Everett Hale, at the time of his retirement in 1909, Eliot listed the accomplishments that he considered to be the "best fruits" of his forty years of service at Harvard; the first of these was "the re-organization and ample endowment of the Medical School."[10]

At the China Conference, as it was subsequently referred to, on January 10 and 11, 1914, after his introductory remarks cautioning the participants that the Rockefeller Foundation was still young and inexperienced, Rockefeller turned to the heart of the matter: he stated that the changes taking place in China might offer an opportunity for the foundation, but that no decision had been reached on a program. Jerome Greene then brought a clear focus to the conference through presentations on education, and medical education and public health.

President Eliot was asked to open the discussions and he presented the keynote address in which he set himself squarely behind a program in medicine:

> It does not take many days in China for any person accustomed to educational organization and to organizations for medical teaching through hospitals and dispensaries to see that the need in China is of the utmost urgency. I have never seen such a need anywhere in the world, so vast and so immediate—so pressing— there is no clearer opportunity anywhere in the world, and this touches . . . most of all, medical education and the public health. . . . The moment is now.[11]

He restated the value of medicine as the medium for bringing the inductive method of reasoning to China and in this was warmly supported by Paul Monroe. John Mott stated that the unsettled conditions in China should only spur a decision to initiate a program there as soon as possible.

After discussing education in general, the conference moved on to a consideration of medical education and public health and then focused on the desirable language of instruction. The representatives of the missionary medical schools, where all teaching was in Chinese, were on the defensive when English was recommended as the language of instruction. Eliot, however, cited the experience of Harvard of China, which had found it impossible to assemble a qualified staff to teach in Chinese. Another participant pointed out the scarcity of Western medical texts in Chinese. No decision on the question of language was reached. There was general agreement that the critical need was to educate Chinese to serve as future teachers and practitioners of modern medicine.

The conference then turned to premedical education, and at this point Abraham Flexner entered into the discussion. He expressed concern that the standards for admission to a new medical school in China might be too high. To fortify this position he described the low state of premedical education in the average American college:

> You must remember that it is only recently in this country that . . . biology, chemistry and physics . . . were introduced to most of the medical schools. . . . They are still a part of the medical curriculum, so far as they are studied at all. Many of the students entering today have no training in biology and never had any. . . . They are quite innocent of any direct knowledge of biological and physical phenomena, except so far as it relates to physiology, and their knowledge of chemistry is limited. . . . I should like to have the scheme of medical instruction conceived at a greatly lower level, not alone in the foreign schools, but in our own schools.[12]

Flexner went on to note that the study of chemistry and physics could be deferred—the training of the hand and ear were more important than the teaching of biology:

> An immense amount of medical treatment can be practiced with a very limited knowledge—or perhaps no knowledge in a wide sense—of chemistry, physics or biology—it is not very essential to put much emphasis on these subjects.[13]

Flexner also suggested that it would be a great waste of time to teach the students English when the need for doctors was so pressing. In this he was supported, not surprisingly, by a medical missionary.

Eliot took an entirely different tack and soon won Flexner to his side. He restated his theme that medicine based on a scientific background in biology, chemistry, physics, and mathematics was the essential medium for the inductive process. Flexner then supported Eliot and recommended that to assure a strong background in the sciences a new medical school in China ought to establish its own premedical school until other institutions could prepare students at a satisfactory educational standard.

On the second day of this historic meeting each participant was asked to express his opinion on what the Rockefeller Foundation might do in China and in which Chinese institutions it ought to begin. The suggestions ranged from the improvement of medical education and medical services—including, at the urging of the missionaries, support of existing hospitals and medical schools—the fostering of medical research, and the strengthening of public health by working through government channels, to such activities as improving agriculture and developing normal schools. A tally would have shown that medicine and public health were clearly the most popular fields.

In the course of the discussions someone remarked that to his knowledge there were no more than 500 Western physicians working in mission hospitals in China, and that many with little experience were serving on the faculties of missionary medical schools. Immediately extrapolating from this figure, Gates mused:

> Five hundred men inadequately supplied for the work they are sent to do. How can we help and enlarge the usefulness and power of these 500 men, and help them to a thoroughly good medical education? At $2,000 a year per man [the average annual missionary salary] you could double the number for $1 million which is no more than one institution of learning would cost in China.[14]

The substance of the China Conference was reported at a meeting of the Board of Trustees of the foundation on January 24, 1914, when several historic decisions were reached: First, any program undertaken in China should be in medicine; second, such work should be based in existing agencies, whether missionary or governmental. They also agreed "to establish a commission to study and report on conditions of public health and medicine in China."[15]

In recognition of his important contributions to the conference, Eliot was elected a trustee of the Rockefeller Foundation at the same meeting.

Following the conference, Gates, with his dedication to the improvement of medicine in China now near fruition, returned to his desk to crystallize a plan for action in a staff paper: "The Gradual and Orderly Development of a Comprehensive and Efficient System of Medicine in China." He recommended a sequence of programs: (1) The collection of all existing data on China in the United States, England, and Europe, and a survey in China of programs in medical education and medicine; (2) after the survey, the identification of a medical school associated with a good hospital that offered the best opportunities for development; (3) the assurance of adequate medical care programs in the selected area, including physicians and hospitals, and the upgrading of the medical school to the highest possible standard; a program of visiting professors from abroad; continuing education courses of three months' duration for all foreign physicians in the area; and the establishment of training schools for male and female nurses; and (4) the logical expansion of the program to other centers when it could be accomplished efficiently. Gates's paper served as the working document for future actions on China.

The chairman of the First China Medical Commission delegated to report on health conditions in China was Henry Pratt Judson. Francis Weld Peabody, a professor of medicine at Harvard and a brilliant figure in American medicine, was the second member of the commission; the third was the American consul general in Hankow, Roger Sherman Greene, the brother of Jerome Greene. The secretary was George Baldwin McKibben.

Roger Greene, aged thirty-two, was a graduate of Harvard and had served as consul in Harbin, Manchuria. He was described by Wu Lien-teh, who led the fight against pneumonic plague in Manchuria, as the only friendly foreign consul he had met in plague-ridden Harbin in December 1910. Wu remembered Greene as "a tall, lanky man with a prominent forehead, deep-sunken eyes, and a slight mustache; kindly, well-educated, and full of human sympathy."[16] Soon after this encounter Greene was promoted to consul general in Hankow. On March 27, 1914, Roger Greene accepted an invitation to join the staff of the foundation and for the next twenty-one years he was a leading figure in the activities of PUMC. Greene was a man of broad intelligence with unyielding devotion to his responsibilities.

Before setting out for Peking, Henry Judson visited the White House where President Wilson expressed his full support of the mission, as did Secretary of State William Jennings Bryan.

THE COMMISSION SETS OUT

The commission arrived in Peking on April 18, 1914, and during the next four months visited seventeen medical schools that were considered to be representative of the state of medical education in China. At that time the central government maintained two medical schools, Peking Medical Special College and Peiyang Military Medical College in Tientsin, as well as three provincial schools in Kiangsu, Chekiang, and Tientsin. The commission concluded that the best of the governmental institutions was the Peiyang medical school.

The China Medical Missionary Association had approved the programs of the nine missionary schools located in Moukden, Peking, Tsinan, Chengtu, Hankow, Nanking, Hangchow, Foochow, and Canton, but the Rockefeller commission felt that the schools in Shanghai and Changsha also had merit, as did German-supported medical schools in Tsingtao and Shanghai; a French school in Shanghai; and the Japanese South Manchuria Medical School in Moukden. In addition there were three medical colleges for women.

A group of second-rate "medical special colleges" also existed that corresponded to the *semmon gakko* in Japan, into which students without any premedical education were admitted directly from middle school into a four-year curriculum. Since practically all of the Chinese who studied medicine in Japan entered a *semmon gakko*, they naturally carried this pattern back home. Some of the medical special schools were supported by provincial treasuries, others were private institutions.

The report of the First China Medical Commission described in detail each of the medical schools visited, the most important of which was the UMC in Peking. The college was housed in five buildings: Lockhart Hall; a men's hospital of sixty beds; a women's hospital of thirty beds; an outpatient department; and a dormitory—Oliver Jones Hall. The staff consisted of fourteen foreign doctors for a total of ninety-five medical students in a five-year curriculum, and forty-three students in a preparatory department with a one-year program. The commission gave the school high rank:

> The Union Medical College at Peking, while its organization is not wholly satisfactory, appears to be more firmly established and better supported than any other missionary institution in the country.[17]

The commission's general impression of the state of medical education in China was mixed:

> There is no medical school now in China which is adequately equipped and no school which is adequately manned. Some of the schools, however, have really high standards and sound ideas and the advanced men on other faculties have the right policies in mind.[18]

The commission identified 244 so-called mission hospitals in China, staffed by a total of 446 Western doctors—fewer than two doctors for each hospital. One-quarter of the missionary hospitals were exclusively for women and were staffed by female physicians who, incidentally, represented one-quarter of all of the missionary doctors. It was noted that Chinese men were finally beginning to submit to the ministrations of female physicians.

The improved quality of medical care by the missionaries was cited:

> As in any large group of men, one finds almost every type among the medical missionaries in China. On the whole, the standard both of medical and of general efficiency is high, and not a few would have made their mark professionally anywhere in the world. The day of the half-trained medical missionary is rapidly drawing to a close.[19]

Because of the wide range of demands for his services, they suggested that every doctor who went to China should have at least two years of postgraduate training, preferably in a specialty.

Beyond his varied professional responsibilities the missionary doctor had a number of other roles: he had to be business and financial manager of the hospital, architect, builder, and handyman—and, usually, evangelist.

There was no uniform pattern of operation in the missionary hospitals. Many were based in old native dwellings with small, dark, poorly-ventilated rooms and the barest bathing and toilet facilities. Central heating was nonexistent and there was no running water. In the older hospitals in the north, for warmth, patients still lay on a *k'ang*, a brick platform built over a fireplace. The commission suggested that the filthy bedding and clothing of the patients contributed to the prevalence of typhus fever among foreign doctors. Some hospital staffs did not try to bathe new patients for fear that they would then refuse medical care. For the same reason they permitted patients' relatives and friends to come and go freely, and as a result the wards were heavily contaminated. Because of overwhelming pressures for patient care there was little clinical laboratory diagnosis, save in the largest cities. Similarly, in many hospitals the doctor did not have time to work up his cases: "Time is one of the things that the doctor does not have, so he is forced to take a hasty look, guess, and trust that he is prescribing correctly."[20] The bad impression created by such "hasty looks," the commission thought, might be the reason the Chinese preferred their indigenous medicine to that of the West; the traditional practitioner took a leisurely approach to his patients. On the other hand, the Chinese welcomed Western surgery, to such a degree that the missionary doctors had little time for internal medicine.

The commission was not enthusiastic about the training of medical auxiliaries: "The great difficulty is that there is no means of controlling the type of work that they will do, and they are almost sure to deteriorate as soon as they leave the hospital."[21]

The major disease problems were syphilis, hookworm, and tuberculosis, especially tuberculosis of the bone. Smallpox was regarded by the people as "a matter of course;"[22] and outbreaks of cholera were at times severe in the south.

A principal question facing the commission was to identify the cities and the institutions where programs should be established. They chose Peking as by all odds the best place for a strong and influential medical school, basing their decision on a number of factors: Peking would probably continue to serve as the capital, as it had for three dynasties; it was the educational center of the country—students came to Peking from all parts of China; it was easily accessible by rail or by sea; and the Peking dialect had been that of the ruling classes for many centuries.

As for the UMC, the school had an excellent site and several of its buildings would unquestionably be useful for many years. The commission was also impressed by the fact that it was the only missionary school recognized by the Chinese government:

> For all these reasons the commission feels that it is most important that a strong medical school should be maintained at Peking, and that, if possible, the very creditable beginning made by the missionary societies, and their experience, should be utilized by assisting their institution instead of founding a new one.[23]

On the other hand, the commission concluded that a second program in medical education should be initiated through a fresh start in a new medical school. It would represent a merger of the resources of all programs in medical education in the Yangtze region. In their opinion there was no medical school in Shanghai that was established on a truly permanent and satisfactory basis. While the commission maintained a completely objective position toward the Harvard Medical School of China, they were concerned about its lack of a physical plant and financial base:

> The school has, however, as already noted, no buildings of its own, the funds for its maintenance come mainly from subscriptions pledged for a short period which is about to expire. Its financial position is therefore not entirely secure. While the

attitude of the school toward the missionary movement is sympathetic, it has the great advantage of being entirely free from religious restrictions. Most of the staff have now a good grasp of the medical educational situation in China and with their local experience are well qualified to become the nucleus of a strong medical faculty.[24]

Since Canton was the seat of Western medical influence, going back to Peter Parker, it was not surprising that more students were studying medicine in Canton than in any other city and that the profession of medicine was highly esteemed. The long-standing reputation of the Canton Hospital and the remarkable clinical material available at that institution were important assets. So the commission recommended that support should go to Canton Christian College for a joint program in medical education with the Canton Hospital.

A major question that faced the commission was the setting of standards for the new programs in medical education. Recognizing the pressing need for doctors in China, should the emphasis be on quality or quantity? The commission's recommendation was clearly for quality:

Medical instruction in which the foundation is concerned should be on the highest practicable standard. Such standard at the present time seems to include as a requirement for admission to a medical school the training of a middle school (roughly equivalent to an American high school), supplemented by two years of premedical work devoted to instruction primarily in English, Chinese, physics, chemistry and biology.[25]

The inadequacies of the mission hospitals were of special concern to the commission. Its recommendations included an expansion of staff, an increase in salary for Chinese doctors and foreign nurses, and more and better equipment. The administrative burden on the missionary doctors could be alleviated by the appointment of nonmedical business managers, while the medical care programs would be strengthened by the development of clinical diagnostic laboratories. Several medical reference library centers should be established that would offer easy access to current advances in medical sciences. The training of nurses, which was woefully inadequate, should be encouraged.

Other recommendations included aid to Yale-in-China; the establishment of two model tuberculosis hospitals; six annual fellowships for Chinese to study abroad; scholarships for needy medical students; ten annual postgraduate fellowships for missionaries; and special instruction for Chinese graduates in residency programs at Rockefeller Foundation-sponsored medical schools.

THE CHINA MEDICAL BOARD

These recommendations were adopted by the trustees of the foundation as a working basis for a future program in China, and on November 30, 1914, they voted to establish the China Medical Board (CMB) of the Rockefeller Foundation to implement the program in medicine in China.

Wallace Buttrick was appointed as the first director of the CMB; other members included John Mott, Wickliffe Rose, Frank Goodnow, president of the Johns Hopkins University, who had served as advisor to the Chinese government on constitutional and administrative law, William H. Welch, and Starr J. Murphy, Rockefeller's legal counsel.

Rockcfeller was the first chairman of the CMB, and E. C. Gage its first secretary. Buttrick, Gates, Greene, Murphy, Peabody, and Rockefeller constituted the Executive Committee.

The first meeting of the CMB was held in New York City on December 11, 1914. The major actions taken were the establishment of fellowships for recent Chinese medical graduates, and of scholarships for the handful of female Chinese nurses to study in the United States. Buttrick was asked to work out a basis for cooperation between the board and the various missionary societies.

The CMB approved the purchase of the beautiful old Chinese palace of Prince Yü that adjoined the UMC, thus giving the Peking Union Medical College its colloquial name—"Yu Wang Fu" (Prince Yu's Palace). For those familiar with the source of Rockefeller's great wealth there was an amusing pun on the prince's name: by changing it to *Yü* instead of *Yu*, the name of the building became the "Oil King's Palace," and that is how it became known to the Chinese, just as the institution was usually referred to as the Rockefeller Hospital.[26] Often the college was referred to simply as "the Fu," or "the palace."*

On March 15, 1915, Rockefeller wrote a letter to all American and British missionary bodies working in China advising them of the proposed programs of the CMB and assuring them of the good intentions of the Rockefeller Foundation. In his letter Rockefeller first reviewed the proposed programs in China and emphasized the CMB's wish for cooperative efforts with the missions. He then made a key statement: the foundation agreed "to select only persons of sound sense and high character, who were sympathetic with the missionary spirit and motive."[27] On the other hand, he held the reservation that the foundation could not "properly impose tests of a denominational or doctrinal nature, such as were deemed desirable by missionary boards for their own medical missionaries or agents."[28]

PURCHASE OF UMC

On March 20, 1915, Buttrick sailed for England to enlist the full support of the British missionary societies and to establish terms for the final purchase of UMC. No man was better suited for the mission:

> The great China Medical School, which has set up a high standard for medical education throughout the Orient, was the result not only of the professional knowledge of the physicians I have mentioned, but of Dr. Buttrick's superb

---

* Mary E. Ferguson 1972: Personal communication.

diplomacy, which completely disarmed the missionaries and the societies supporting them and brought about co-operation in the achievement of an educational
project detached from religious activity.[29]

The minutes of the London Missionary Society give the details of the sale: On
April 27, 1915, the Eastern Committee of the society received a report from F. H.
Hawkins, foreign secretary of the society, reminding it of earlier proposals for
broadening the financial base of UMC, and noting that the proposals had been
received sympathetically by the American societies that belonged to the union.
Hawkins was proud to report that the commission had described UMC as the
"most efficient" medical school in China and had recommended that the first
work of the Rockefeller Foundation in China should be undertaken there.[30]
As a statement of reassurance to the committee, Hawkins drew attention to
Rockefeller's pledge of allegiance to missionary institutions.

Hawkins reported that Buttrick was about to join the discussions with a
proposal that the Rockefeller Foundation purchase the UMC for £25,000–
30,000. When Buttrick, who had been waiting in the corridor, entered the meeting he "gave the strongest assurance that if the transfer was carried out, the
work of the College would be continued on its present lines as a Christian Missionary College."[31] After citing Mott as the type of man associated with the
enterprise, Buttrick retired from the meeting.

The founder of UMC, Thomas Cochrane, now director of medical missions
for the London Missionary Society, threw his prestige and experience completely behind the transfer when he stated that:

> The proposals afforded a great opportunity for continuing the work of the Col-
> lege and the hospitals on a scale far beyond anything possible by the unaided
> efforts of the societies interested, and would, in his judgment, greatly further the
> prospects of successful evangelistic work amongst the medical students in the
> hospitals, and that the money received would enable the Society very greatly to
> strengthen its evangelistic, educational, medical and other work in China.[32]

The Eastern Committee approved Buttrick's proposals in principle but was
apprehensive over a possible diminution in the Christian character of the
institution:

> Its chief concern is that, if the transfer is made, the missionary side of the work of
> the College should be maintained and increased.[33]

At the same time there was no concern about the level of the academic
program:

> The Committee notes with interest that it is proposed to carry on the work in the
> future as in the past on the lines of a first-rate British medical school.[34]

The committee endorsed the transfer of the property and of other holdings to
be accomplished by the directors of the society.

A subcommittee of the Eastern Committee held two meetings with Buttrick
to discuss what they considered to be the critical question—the constitution of

the governing body. The directors of the London Missionary Society suggested that it should consist of a representative of each of the six missionary societies, matched by six representatives of the CMB. They asked assurance that the society would be

> at liberty to do all in their power to maintain the religious tone and work in the College and Hospitals, and [that] the Church Building and the building used as a street Chapel in connection with the dispensary work should continue, and in complete union with other Missionary Societies. In any reconstruction of the buildings, accommodations for these two activities should be provided and at least one of the houses on the present L.M.S. Compound should be reserved for a man in charge of the religious work. It would be well to have, in addition to the dispensary chapel, referred to, further accommodation for any patients who may not wish to wait in the chapel, e.g., a reading or other rest room.[35]

The subcommittee also asked that the salaries of staff in the new enterprise be kept close to the low levels of other missionaries in north China and that the present staff at UMC be continued, especially George G. Wilson, the business manager, and Bernard Read, the chemist.

The directors' last action was to express their deep gratitude to Cochrane for his invaluable services, first in creating and developing the UMC and now in effecting its transfer to the Rockefeller Foundation. They appreciated his sacrifice in giving up a mission to study programs in the territories of Papua and New Guinea in order to handle the transfer. A final minute noted that the directors would present an enlarged portrait of Cochrane to the medical college in Peking.

PUMC IS CREATED

To complete the sale, Cochrane came to New York and attended the meeting of the CMB on May 25, 1915. With Buttrick and Gates he presented a formal proposal that summarized the plans for the future: the incorporation of a Board of Trustees under the laws of the state of New York for an institution to be called the *Peking Union Medical College;* arrangements to enable the CMB to hold property in China on the same basis as "other missionary boards"; the deeding of the properties of the London Missionary Society to the CMB for US $200,000; and the leasing of this property to PUMC. A memorandum of agreement providing for the sale was executed on June 2, 1915, and on July 1 the CMB assumed full support of the college.

Since it had become obvious that PUMC would require considerably more property than the nine-and-one-third acres acquired from the London Missionary Society and the Presbyterian Board, the CMB appropriated funds for the purchase of an adjoining one-acre parcel of property from the Belgian Legation and a one-and-one-half acre plot just behind the hospital.

At the same time the CMB was implementing other recommendations of the China Medical Commission. The first fellowship for a missionary physician went to Adrian S. Taylor of the Southern Baptist Mission in Yangchow, who, after studies at Harvard and Hopkins, was appointed the first professor of surgery at

PUMC. The Yale Foreign Missionary Society was notified that the CMB was prepared to make a five-year grant of $16,200 a year for the combined salaries of up to six faculty members at the Yale-in-China Medical School in Changsha. Under the program to strengthen clinical laboratories the first grant of $1,000 went to the Kuling Medical Missionary Association.

The first grant to medical education in Shanghai was an appropriation of $15,000 for general support of the Harvard Medical School of China. In making this grant the board affirmed that it was not expedient at that time to consider founding a new medical school in Shanghai and expressed the hope that a co-operative program would be developed by the medical schools in the Shanghai area. Grants also went to the American Board of Commissioners of Foreign Missions, the Presbyterian Board, and the Christian Missionary Society, all aimed at elevating the level of medical practice in China.

The mission boards had agreed that the work of the PUMC should be carried on with a Board of Trustees consisting of thirteen members, seven to be appointed by the CMB and one to be appointed by each of the six missionary organizations that had previously maintained the college. Subsequently the following men were appointed as the first trustees of PUMC: Buttrick, Simon Flexner, Gates, Mott, Rockefeller, Rose, and Welch representing the CMB; and from the participating missionary societies: Hawkins (London Missionary Society); Arthur Wenham (Medical Missionary Association of London); J. Auriol Armitage (Society for the Propogation of the Gospel in Foreign Parts); Frank Mason North (Board of Foreign Missions of the Methodist Episcopal Church); Arthur J. Brown (Board of Foreign Missions of the Presbyterian Church); and James L. Barton (American Board of Commissioners for Foreign Missions).

NOTES TO CHAPTER THREE

1. Sir William Osler, *The Principles and Practice of Medicine* (New York: D. Appleton and Co., 1892).

2. China Medical Commission of The Rockefeller Foundation, *Medicine in China*, p. 287.

3. *Ibid.*, p. 110.

4. Raymond B. Fosdick, *The Story of The Rockefeller Foundation*, p. 12.

5. K. S. Latourette, *A History of Christian Missions in China*, p. 404.

6. Charles W. Eliot, *Some Roads Towards Peace*, p. 1.

7. *Ibid.*, p. 21.

8. *Ibid.*, p. 26.

9. *Ibid.*, p. 25.

10. Henry James, *Charles W. Eliot, President of Harvard University, 1869–1909*, vol. 2, p. 170.

11. Mary E. Ferguson, Documents.

12. *Ibid.*

13. *Ibid.*

14. *Ibid.*

15. China Medical Commission of The Rockefeller Foundation, *Medicine in China*, p. v.

16. Lien-teh Wu, *Plague Fighter*, p. 15.

17. China Medical Commission of The Rockefeller Foundation, *Medicine in China*, p. 44.

18. *Ibid.*, p. 33.

19. *Ibid.*, p. 65.

20. *Ibid.*, p. 64.

21. *Ibid.*, p. 69.

22. *Ibid.*, p. 3.

23. *Ibid.*, p. 45.

24. *Ibid.*, p. 51.

25. *Ibid.*, p. 91.

26. Mary E. Ferguson, *China Medical Board and Peking Union Medical College*, p. 28.

27. *Ibid.*, p. 22.

28. *Ibid.*, p. 23.

29. Abraham Flexner, *I Remember*, pp. 224–5.

30. Director's Minute Book, 1914–1918, Archives of the London Missionary Society, p. 162.

31. *Ibid.*, p. 162.

32. *Ibid.*, p. 162.

33. *Ibid.*, p. 163.

34. *Ibid.*, p. 163.

35. *Ibid.*, p. 164.

CHAPTER FOUR

The Second China Medical Commission

The challenges that Wallace Buttrick faced in his new position as director of the China Medical Board were staggering. He had need of all those characteristics Raymond Fosdick ascribed to him: massive common sense, a love of people, the ability to absorb ideas from contacts rather than from books, and above all "a solid kind of wisdom."[1] Abraham Flexner, who worked closely with Buttrick and who was his great admirer as well as his friend, cited other strengths: "[he was] shrewd, canny, diplomatic, humorous, and gifted with a remarkable instinct for biding his time."[2]

Flexner recalled Buttrick remonstrating with Frederick Gates on the ground that he, Buttrick, was unfit for the position for two reasons: he knew little about either medical education or China. To this Gates responded instantly, "But you know missionaries, and no one alive can prepare the ground as you can."[3]

Gates knew that relations between the CMB and the missionaries and their societies had to be handled delicately; the majority of the missionaries were on the defensive—suspicious but not openly hostile. Communication was another major difficulty, for New York was more than 9,000 miles from Peking and the journey by land and sea took about a month. Buttrick now faced a heavy responsibility in medical education for the first time. Soon the eyes of medical educators everywhere would be watching Peking and the CMB of the Rockefeller Foundation.

It was clear to Buttrick that he needed the wisdom as well as the complete support of the leaders of American medicine. So he turned to two men who were at its summit, William Welch and Simon Flexner, both of whom were closely identified with Rockefeller programs. Welch, the acknowledged leader of medical education in the United States, had served for thirteen years as president of the board of the Rockefeller Institute and was esteemed by both John D. Rockefeller and Gates. It was he who had recommended that Simon Flexner, his former student, be the first director of the institute.

Buttrick made his first approach to Welch and Flexner just a month after assuming his new responsibilities, when he joined them at the residence of a mutual friend in Dixville Notch, New Hampshire, during a Christmas weekend. As they re-examined the recommendations of the First China Medical Commission they mulled over the most crucial statement in the report: "That medical instruction in which the foundation is concerned should be of the highest practicable standard."[4] Since Welch and Flexner were totally committed to carrying American medical education to such a standard, they could hardly reconcile themselves to anything less, even in distant Peking.

As directors of the two institutions that were the major sources of medical scientists, they could play invaluable roles in the recruitment of a faculty. Thus if Buttrick could lure them into joining him on a mission to China the program would take a long step forward.

The report of the first commission had laid out a truly massive development. Now the CMB must turn to hard facts—what were the priorities and how could they be implemented; how high a standard could be envisaged in the recruitment of faculty; how ought PUMC relate to the missionary medical schools; should the language of instruction be Mandarin, following the practice of the missionaries, or English? Flexner suggested that the whole question be studied from a different point of view than that of the report. Although the records give no specific indication of his thoughts he was probably concerned with focusing on the establishment of one or two centers of excellence, setting priorities, and resolving the thorny question of the language of instruction. Flexner urged Buttrick to make a study along those lines, but the latter countered with the proposal that Welch and Flexner should join him on a second medical mission to China. Later Buttrick recalled his seeming boldness in making such a proposal:

> I know they smiled at my presumption, and so did Mr. Rockefeller when I told him about it. I imagine he wondered why I didn't ask the President of the United States and the Secretary of State to go out to China.[5]

Welch and Flexner, as befitted their roles of leadership, not only carried heavy responsibilities at their own institutions but were also involved in a variety of national programs: the long journey to China seemed out of the question for them. But Buttrick proved himself a master strategist. Over a period of several months he emphasized repeatedly his reliance on their counsel, and this heightened their strong sense of duty and their patriotic allegiance in this great overseas adventure; Welch and Flexner agreed to be members of the Second China Medical Commission.

At a meeting of the CMB on May 25, 1915, invitations to Welch and Flexner became official; they were asked "to advise the Board in regard to the measures to be taken for the promotion of public health and medical education in the Republic of China."[6]

The appointment of Welch and Flexner represented a personal triumph for Wallace Buttrick. Whereas Rockefeller had merely smiled when Buttrick told him several months earlier of his efforts to enlist their support, he now expressed his gratitude and the importance that he attached to their presence on the mission in a heart-warming letter that Welch and Flexner received shortly before they sailed:

> Probably you, Dr. Welch and Dr. Flexner, with your charming modesty, realize less than anyone else, how significant to this medical movement, both in China and in America, is your relation to the expedition. Not only will your going to China indicate, as nothing else would, the high ideals upon which the work of the China Medical Board is founded, but it will win for the enterprise the confidence and respect of the leading medical men, officials and citizens. . . . It dignifies the medical cause in China and creates as nothing else could do, a powerful incentive to the ablest and most promising young American medical men to serve in that new field. . . . You are rendering a very great service to the cause of medicine in China; such a service as no other two men in the country could render.[7]

THE COMMISSION EMBARKS

Buttrick served as chairman of the mission to China and Frederick L. Gates of the Rockefeller Institute, a son of Frederick T. Gates, joined as secretary. The party sailed for Yokohama from San Francisco on the *Tenyo Maru* on August 7, 1915, with the exception of Welch who had gone ahead to visit Hawaii.

During their three weeks in Japan they appraised the programs of the medical schools at the imperial universities in Tokyo and in Kyoto. In Tokyo, they also visited the institute named for Shibasaburo Kitasato who in 1894 had been the first scientist to identify the plague bacillus. St. Luke's Hospital in Tokyo, founded in 1900 by a medical missionary, Rudolf B. Teusler, representing the Protestant Episcopal Church in America, was also included in their schedule. Throughout the visit they were repeatedly impressed by how completely the Japanese had adopted Western medicine.

The commission sailed from Japan to Korea where they visited Severance Union Medical College and hospital in Seoul, which had been established in 1899 by O. R. Avison with a gift from L. H. Severance of Cleveland, and with the support of the American Methodist and Presbyterian missionary boards. From there they went by train to Moukden where they were joined by Roger Greene and Charles W. Young, dean of the Union Medical College in Peking.

Greene outlined the plight of the missionary medical schools; he emphasized the pressures under which all the medical missionaries were working and discussed at length the state of UMC: the faculty had been reduced to only three foreign physicians and very little effort was being made to fill the ranks; there were only two cadavers available for study for the entire student body; and there was not a single piece of equipment for the physics laboratory. Morale was at its lowest ebb, as all the staff were anxious about their future. Second-hand reports and a stream of rumors concerning the new program of the Rockefeller Foundation had been the major factors occasioning their distress.

Greene's concern about the loss of staff was shared in London, and at a meeting of the Examination Committee of the missionary society the following resolution was referred to the Joint Governing Board:

> That the attention of the Directors of the London Missionary Society be called to the serious depletion of the staff of the Union Medical College, Peking, and that they be earnestly requested to use every endeavour to fill the vacancies on the Society's staff at the College at the earliest possible moment.[8]

During the commission's stay in Moukden the members visited the Moukden Medical College and were deeply impressed by Dugald Christie, whom Welch described as

> a remarkable man, evidently of great force, perhaps fifty-five years old, a Scot, who has been here since 1883. . . . Christie has been eminently successful in establishing cordial, even intimate relations with Viceroys, Governor Generals, guilds, and the Chinese community generally, and during his thirty years here has done a really great work.[9]

The hospital had 140 beds; there was an X-ray department, and "a good operating room with evidences of antiseptic technique."[10]

The other institution visited in Moukden was the medical school sponsored by the South Manchuria Railway, where there were ninety-seven Japanese and thirty-seven Chinese students enrolled. As a lifelong pathologist, Welch was interested in the excellent specimens from the pneumonic plague epidemic in the pathology museum.

Welch and Flexner served both as investigators and diplomats. They wished to assess the state of medical education in China, as well as to explore the attitudes of the medical missionaries toward the proposed program in Peking on such issues as the acceptance of new programs and the language of instruction. A principal need was to lay the groundwork so that the standard of excellence that was proposed for Peking would be accepted by the missionaries. It could be a bitter pill, for they had labored against almost overwhelming odds, with totally inadequate facilities, and at great personal sacrifice. There was also the need to allay the concerns of the missionaries about the religious attitudes and character of the men who would staff the new school.

After spending three weeks in Peking the commission followed the itinerary of the First China Medical Commission, with visits to Tientsin, Tsinan, Hankow, Wuchang, Changsha, Nanking, Shanghai, Soochow, Canton, and Hong Kong. Welch was responsible for institutions in north China, Flexner for east, central, and south China, and Gates for the central region. Their days were filled with conferences, inspections of facilities, and discussions that frequently continued well into the night. But at noon and at dusk they enjoyed the world's finest cuisine. This was especially pleasing to Welch, a renowned gourmet.

While Gates was being entertained in Changsha, the home of Yale-in-China, he saw a large banner at one end of the hall, the calligraphy on which read: "Your philanthropy is a model to the world. The Republic grips your hands in welcome."[11]

As an 1870 graduate of Yale College and a member of the secret and prestigious Skull and Bones, Welch made a special visit to the Chinese institution that bore the name of his alma mater. On October 17, 1915, he addressed the students at Yale-in-China during the Sunday morning chapel service. His principal message was the transcending importance and appeal of medical work in China —a message that he pledged to carry back to the students and staff at Johns Hopkins.

> Why do so many eke out their lives amidst the unsatisfactory environment and the meager opportunities that come to most of them? If they have intellectual curiosity, something of the spirit of adventure, desire to advance medical knowledge, desire for beneficent service, where can any opportunity make a stronger appeal than that here in China today, especially in the development of modern medical science and practice in China?[12]

FLEXNER'S FINDINGS

Flexner's comments were always detailed, penetrating, and completely candid. Concerning the relationship between St. John's University and the University of Pennsylvania mission in Shanghai, he was critical and sarcastic: "The University of Pennsylvania has probably nothing but good will to contribute."[13] In the same vein he felt that St. Luke's Hospital, which was controlled by St. John's, "would be an embarrassment as a teaching hospital."[14]

The Harvard Medical School of China was naturally Flexner's principal interest in Shanghai. He found the teaching "perhaps better done than anywhere else in China." (A footnote in longhand adds: "except the German school at Shanghai.")[15] Students at Harvard came from Nanking, Foochow, Soochow, and from as far south as Canton, as well as from Shanghai. Flexner felt that the buildings and equipment of the school were valuable, but that its location in the residential section of the international concession was not the most desirable for a hospital and a medical school. Because of the large foreign population and its role as a great seaport, the opportunities for autopsies were far better in Shanghai than in other cities; autopsies were performed on 50 per cent of the patients who died at the Red Cross Hospital. Henry S. Houghton, then head of the school, told Flexner that he was able to obtain all the cadavers that were required for the dissecting room and for surgical anatomy.

Flexner also assessed the caliber of the staff and concluded that Houghton and Albert M. Dunlap in otorhinolaryngology would be qualified for appointments in the projected new school in Shanghai. He felt that Houghton should be the dean but held some reservations; his "temperament is that of the executive, and not of the investigator and leader of men. He lacks power to give original impulse and direction to teaching or investigation."[16] At the same time Flexner acknowledged that Houghton's understanding of high quality medical education as well as his experience with the Chinese and the missionaries would be valuable assets for the dean of the new school. Finally, he noted that Harvard had established a program to train Eurasian women in Shanghai as nurses.

Canton was a disappointment to Flexner. He found the famed Canton Hospital to be deteriorating with "a depressing, rather than an elevating influence at the moment on the educational affairs of the city,"[17] and that the level of medical instruction was especially low. At the Hackett College for Women, middle-aged multipara were permitted to enroll, although it was recognized that they would "practice medicine as an aside to their usual domestic duties."[18]

He was impressed with the University of Hong Kong, where he found excellent opportunities for Chinese students to study medicine.

Flexner summarized his findings: "The present standard of medical education maintained by the colleges under missionary and other auspices is with inconsiderable exceptions, low."[19] He attributed this to poor preliminary education, limitations imposed by the use of Chinese as the language of instruction, lack of facilities, and faculties that were not only insufficient in numbers but in most instances simply not prepared to teach. He concluded that it would not be possible to upgrade existing schools to a suitable standard, and that it would be necessary to make two completely fresh starts—one in the north and a second in the south. Aware that women were already working actively in medicine, he recommended that they should be admitted to premedical training on the same basis as men.

WELCH'S FINDINGS

Welch judged that Western medicine was less advanced in north China than in the central and southern regions of the country. Yet he felt that the best opportunities lay in the north where the relatively tall, sturdy, vigorous noodle-eaters offered potentially the best brains for Chinese medicine. His primary concern was of course the UMC in Peking, and he stressed the need to recruit new faculty who were well grounded in the medical sciences:

> Nothing is so important for the success of the undertaking to which the China Medical Board is committed as to secure as soon as possible at least one man and, if such can be found, more men of the character indicated who shall proceed to Peking at as early a date as practicable.[20]

In regard to students he felt that they should be enrolled from across the country and that a special premedical department should be established at PUMC:

> For the present at least it will be well for the Board to furnish opportunities in connection with its school and for the prosecution of studies in English, Chinese, physics, chemistry and biology.[21]

Welch did not approve of the divided administrative responsibilities at UMC which, in the British pattern, included both a principal and a dean. He recommended the abolition of the position of principal.

The sad state of higher education was brought home to them by Chang Po-ling, superintendent of the middle school at Tientsin, who had been described to them by Eliot as the most interesting and admirable person he had met in China. Chang expressed to the commission his deep regret that there was not a single university, college, or professional school in China in which his students who were especially fluent in English had any desire to enroll after graduation.

In their approaches to the missionaries, Flexner and Welch were a study in contrasts. Flexner was inclined to be more direct, more critical, and more provocative. He emphasized the urgent need to elevate their educational programs to a higher standard. Welch, on the other hand, was more tactful and preferred to introduce his comments on inadequacies by first recognizing the contributions of the missionaries; he sought to assuage rather than provoke. They made a perfect team.

The question of the language of instruction was raised repeatedly. When it was broached to the faculty of UMC, only Dean Young favored instruction in English. Flexner stated that his views had changed since his arrival in China and that he was now persuaded that English must be the language:

> As a historical point, you might be interested to know that I first supposed that of course teaching would be in Chinese. It is since I have come over here and have seen the attempts and their results, and have faced the problem from the point of view of education in general, that my view has changed radically.[22]

As the time for departure approached, Flexner was even more firm in his statements. He presented the aims of the CMB to the Executive Committee of the China Medical Missionary Association at a meeting in Shanghai and made the point that they could not be accomplished if teaching was in Chinese:

> The opportunity for the China Medical Board is to set up one or two modern establishments and to bring to them trained, gifted, inspiring leaders and teachers. That kind of knowledge and inspiration cannot be delivered at present in Chinese.[23]

He went on to point out that

> the aim was to develop a body of Chinese medical men and women, who themselves, as producers and teachers, would be able to establish modern medicine and surgery in China on a permanent basis.[24]

Welch spoke of the language problem in what might be described as a more placatory manner:

> We have found that a burning question everywhere. We cannot see that this problem is so intense and important. The essential thing is to raise the Chinese to be first-class medical men, and every proposition must be considered from that point of view. . . . Now as to the language question: dictionary makers have little influence on language, which is determined by custom.[25]

MISSIONARY DISTRESS

The missionaries frequently raised questions about the Christian nature of the new medical college. In reply, the members of the commission referred to Rockefeller's letter of March 15, 1915, in which he had stated that the faculty would be selected from among persons "who were sympathetic with the missionary spirit and motive."[26]

Welch was especially sensitive to the anxieties of the missionaries. In an address before the Saturday Club of Shanghai on October 30, 1915, he paid eloquent tribute to their contributions:

> The work that these men have done is beyond all praise. . . . They came primarily not for medical teaching, but as the work grew they felt the need of training men to help them. So the medical schools as they now exist have gradually grown up to supply this need. Considering the inefficient staffs and meager equipment it is wonderful what they have done.
>
> But these men would be the first to realize that they are merely meeting the immediate needs of the day. They would be the first to welcome the coming of others to build on the foundations they have laid. . . . It is the purpose of Mr. Rockefeller and the Foundation to connect this work of the China Medical Board with the missionary effort. I doubt that a similar opportunity has ever come to the missions before.[27]

On one occasion Flexner went directly to the heart of the problems in the missionary schools:

> The essential is this: that you must have equipment for modern medicine and convey modern medical knowledge to such men as are especially prepared. The fault of the missionary schools is that they have not been able to get the equipment or the men to handle the problem. The great men of the world are those who have been nurtured and not allowed to escape from their educational environment until they are well prepared. That feature of education has been lacking here, for you have not had expert teachers. The men who have come out as teachers were not teachers and were not trained for the work.[28]

He then challenged the missionaries concerning their participation in advancing Western medicine:

> Our problem is strictly the educational one, in cooperation with the missions. If you want to keep on creating inferior men, I shall not be the one to hinder you, but those countries which have not followed that method have fared the best. The responsibility lies in your hands. If we do less than the very best we can do, I shall be sorry that I ever came to China. . . . I have seen zeal and complacency but not much efficiency in China.[29]

After listening to such comments a number of the missionary teachers became even more concerned about their future. Harold Balme, dean of the medical college at Tsinan, expressed the opinion of his fellow missionaries when he said that it appeared to him that the CMB was determined to press for the withdrawal of all missionaries from the medical faculties. It was necessary for Roger Greene to spend many hours in placatory meetings, especially with the already distressed handful of staff at the UMC.

Looking back six years later Balme summarized the reactions of the missionaries:

> In the first place they had to face the fact that the best standards were now to be introduced into China, and there was a risk that it might possibly be said of the missionary schools that they were offering to the Chinese a type of medical education that was of a lower standard.[30]

Some of the missionaries felt that they should continue to foster a number of low-grade medical schools, while others insisted that they should concentrate only on that number of schools that they could make

> absolutely efficient. To retire at so promising a state was unthinkable for that would mean the surrender of a wonderful opportunity of infusing medical instruction with Christian ideals and principles, and of winning a large number of future leaders of the medical profession for the service of Jesus Christ.[31]

The missionaries were also concerned that since PUMC proposed to teach in English, their efforts toward the creation of a medical terminology in Chinese and the translation of medical texts would fall into abeyance. They felt that it was important to continue to develop a Chinese terminology, as well as the translations, since sooner or later all teaching ought to be in Chinese.

While Welch, Flexner, and Gates were busy visiting medical schools and hospitals, Buttrick put his clerical background to good use in numerous discussions with representatives of missionary societies and addresses to missionary groups and to branches of the YMCA in Peking and Shanghai. He stressed the high objectives of the board, the integrity of its members, and the commitment to work with the missionaries.

REPORT OF THE COMMISSION

On January 28, 1916, the report of the second commission was presented to the CMB. A major recommendation was that a new leader should be appointed to PUMC as no one on the existing faculty was deemed suitable. The 128 students currently enrolled at the UMC were not qualified for the new program, and it was therefore proposed that admissions under existing standards be closed and that the first- and second-year students be transferred to other schools teaching in Mandarin, particularly the Shantung Christian University at Tsinan. The third-, fourth-, and fifth-year students would be allowed to graduate from the UMC.

Admissions standards for the new program should as nearly as feasible follow those adopted by the leading medical schools in the United States. After completion of high school every student would be required to spend two years in a premedical curriculum that would include biology, chemistry, physics, and mathematics, and courses in English and Chinese. The commission also recommended a long-range approach to upgrading premedical education throughout China:

> A greater and much needed service would be rendered to the broad educational work of the college and the cause of higher medical education in China by aiding certain colleges to supply the required training in the fundamental sciences.[32]

The commission restated its attitude toward the language question:

> We have had impressed upon us the importance of continued study of their own language by Chinese students, and are convinced that this should not be neglected in the medical schools, although we are equally convinced that it is impossible to train students properly in modern medicine through the medium of this tongue.[33]

They echoed the perceptive words of President Eliot:

> Everything should be done to develop the spirit of scientific inquiry which is probably only latent and not really absent, for China stands today where Western nations stood before the introduction of the experimental method into science at the beginning of the 17th century, which marked the entrance of those nations upon that path of material progress which has enabled them to outstrip so far the Oriental races.[34]

The commission also recommended the establishment of a nurses' training school for both female and male students.

The new Peking school, they suggested, should follow a step-like development, adding a year each year, rather than defer the admission of students until a full-fledged, five-year medical school could be opened.

It was essential that new faculty should henceforth have proven ability in scientific research, since such men would not only generally be the best teachers but would also exert a stimulating effect on their colleagues and on the students. It would not be possible to attract such a faculty with the low salaries paid to the medical missionaries.

The commission concluded by expressing satisfaction with the site of the school and with the steps being taken to acquire adjacent properties.

One of the more important results of the Second China Medical Commission was the impact on Welch and Flexner of their months in China. They returned with an even deeper determination to assure the development of an outstanding institution in Peking.

PUMC TRUSTEES ARE APPOINTED

The trustees of PUMC held their first meeting in New York City on January 24, 1916, and Welch read that part of the report of the second commission relating to UMC. Welch and Flexner were appointed to the new, vitally important Standing Committee on the Recruitment and Appointment of Faculty.

The trustees' meeting ended with the election of the following officers: chairman, John Mott; vice chairman, James L. Barton; secretary, Wallace Buttrick. The Executive Committee consisted of Frederick T. Gates as chairman, with Arthur J. Brown, Buttrick, Simon Flexner, and Frank Mason North.

The question of the development of a school in Shanghai was raised through a communication to the CMB from Charles W. Eliot and E. B. Drew, representing the board of the Harvard Medical School of China which was now in dire financial straits. The Harvard board did not wish to operate a second-rate program, and it stated that:

> The Executive Committee would be glad to have its entire work taken over at once and carried on by your Board, until such time as the new proposed medical school for Shanghai is opened and is ready to merge our school in its larger project.[35]

In response to this appeal, the board approved the purchase of the property in Shanghai and made funds available for the students who were enrolled to complete their medical education elsewhere. A fellowship for study in the United States was awarded to Albert Dunlap, and responsibility was assumed for the modest endowment funds. Houghton joined the staff of the CMB and was assigned as director of the Red Cross Hospital, looking toward the day when he might head the new medical school in Shanghai. A final resolution stated that the board would establish a medical school in Shanghai at a capital cost not to exceed $1 million and with annual expenditures of $250,000.

SELECTING A LEADER

As the spring of 1916 approached, attention turned to the appointment of an academic leader for PUMC. The choice lay between a man of proven ability in medical education and a young, relatively unproven man of outstanding promise. In the former category there were only a few choices. A majority of American medical schools were proprietary, and leadership lay in the hands of practitioners of medicine who had little if any understanding of or interest in medical science. A young man of great promise was therefore the logical choice.* Simon Flexner was aware of the high regard that Rufus Cole, director of the hospital at the Rockefeller Institute had expressed for his young assistant resident physician, Franklin C. McLean. Buttrick reported the board's sentiments in a communication to Roger Greene:

> From the beginning of our negotiations, Dr. Flexner has felt that probably McLean was the best man we could select. We are now convinced of that fact.[37]

FRANKLIN C. MCLEAN

On June 20, 1916, the Executive Committee of PUMC endorsed the unanimous recommendation of the Standing Committee on Faculty, and appointed as head of PUMC Franklin C. McLean, aged twenty-eight, professor of internal medicine.

---

* In his autobiography, G. Canby Robinson records that in April 1916, at the request of Simon Flexner, he discussed the new school in Peking with him and Buttrick. He was offered the position of medical director but declined because he had a new-born son and was too involved with developments at Washington University.[36]

Franklin McLean was a "boy wonder" whose first love was scientific scholarship; his happiest hunting ground was the research laboratory. After graduating from the University of Chicago at the age of nineteen, with a Phi Beta Kappa key, he completed his medical studies at Rush Medical College in 1910. He became one of the youngest professors in the country when he was appointed professor of pharmacology and materia medica at the University of Oregon Medical School immediately after completing his internship. From 1911 to 1914 he taught pharmacology and established himself in research through his studies on chlorides in the urine and the pharmacology of organic iodine compounds. During this period he developed the first clinical method for the determination of blood sugar. Deciding that he needed further experience in a strong research environment, McLean accepted an appointment that proved to be the turning point in his life—a residency at the hospital of the Rockefeller Institute. Here he was tapped for Peking.

Before McLean left New York in June 1916, Rufus Cole gathered a group of more than twenty guests at the Century Association for a farewell party. There were brief toasts by Cole, by Oswald Avery, a bacteriologist at the institute, and by Christen Lundsgaard, later a distinguished professor of medicine at Copenhagen, who was then working with Donald Van Slyke at the institute. All predicted a great future for McLean in his new career in China.

Franklin McLean's first visit to China was packed with discussions at medical schools and hospitals, both missionary and governmental, numerous conferences, and many hours with Roger Greene assessing every aspect of the existing program. A delicate question was the evaluation of the qualifications to be applied in the choice of teachers for the new faculty. There was also a series of discussions regarding the design and development of the physical plant. In addition there was the central question of how to move ahead with the steplike development recommended by Welch and Flexner. In implementing this policy it was decided that the premedical department should be established at the earliest possible date.

SHOCKING SHORTAGE OF NURSES

In their visits to hospitals and in the ensuing conferences, the shocking shortage of nurses was repeatedly brought to the attention of McLean and Greene. Despite the work of the missionaries over many decades there continued to be a widespread feeling that women should not care for male patients. At the Union Medical College Hospital, which was exclusively for men, and at other hospitals they found only male nurses whose training had been totally inadequate. When they visited the missionary hospitals for women they found little to hearten them. A handful of Chinese girls with little preliminary education functioned as low-level nurses' aides performing the most menial chores.

Their discussions with Houghton in Shanghai were heartening, however. Houghton was an eloquent advocate of nursing as an honorable profession for women, who should be trained to care for both male and female patients. He strongly believed that nursing should be established at a standard that would attract intelligent young women with a good basic education. McLean and Greene agreed with him wholeheartedly and determined that the development of a nursing school at a standard equal to that envisaged for the medical school should be placed near the top of the list. By the time he was ready to leave China, McLean had visited all of the significant medical programs in the north and central regions.

DEVELOPING A PROGRAM

Together McLean and Greene prepared a report for the CMB entitled "Present Conditions at the Union Medical College in Peking with Suggested Plans for Development." It contained an extensive section on the development of a premedical program, and a lengthy commentary on the proposed physical plant: the teaching facilities for the medical school; patient-care units and supportive units for the staff; an administration building with a library; and, in conformity with the agreement reached with the London Missionary Society, a separate building for religious programs.

In early 1917 George E. Vincent, former president of the University of Minnesota, succeeded Rockefeller as president of the Rockefeller Foundation and chairman of the CMB. Vincent was a brilliant, highly articulate man whose insistence on high standards made him an ideal leader for the new program in Peking. From the beginning he took a deep personal interest in the program, which the leaders of the faculty understood—and cherished.

THE PHYSICAL PLANT

An appropriation of $1 million for land, buildings, and equipment for PUMC was made by the Rockefeller Foundation on April 11, 1916. The following month a Boston architect, Charles A. Coolidge, was commissioned as "consulting architect," on the recommendation of Simon Flexner; they had worked together in a most satisfactory manner on the design and construction of the Rockefeller Institute. Coolidge had an added qualification: he was architect of the new buildings on the quadrangle of Harvard Medical School. The Chicago firm of Shattuck and Hussey was subsequently given full responsibility for the architectural program and for construction.

The soaring costs of the physical plant have been recounted in detail by Mary Ferguson.[38] It is sufficient to say here that inefficient administrative arrangements, the CMB's lack of experience in construction in China, and shipping problems occasioned by World War I brought the final cost to $7,552,836 gold, against an estimate in April 1916 of $1.5 million.

It was in the summer of 1919 that the great American philosopher and educator John Dewey went to Peking. He was struck by the true beauty of the buildings that were rising beside Prince Yü's Palace, and on July 8 he wrote to his daughter:

The Rockefeller buildings are lovely samples of what money can do. In the midst of this worn and weak city they stand out like illuminating monuments of the splendor of the past in proper combination with the modern idea. They are in the finest old style of Chinese architecture; green roofs instead of yellow, with three stories instead of one.[39]

Bertrand Russell visited Peking a year later and recognized the beauty of the plant:

The Rockefeller Hospital is a large conspicuous building, representing an interesting attempt to combine something of Chinese beauty with European utilitarian requirements. The green roofs are quite Chinese, but the walls and windows are European. The attempt is praiseworthy, though perhaps not wholly successful. The hospital has all the most modern scientific apparatus but, with the monopolistic tendency of the Standard Oil Co., it refuses to let its apparatus be of use to anyone not connected with the hospital. . . . The Peking Union Medical College teaches many things beside medicine—English literature, for example—and apparently teaches them very well. They are necessary in order to produce Chinese physicians and surgeons who will reach the European level, because a good knowledge of some European language is necessary for medicine as for other kinds of European learning.[40]

But Russell was definitely uncharitable in discussing his view of American aims in China:

Although the educational work of the Americans in China is on the whole admirable, nothing directed by foreigners can adequately satisfy the needs of the country. . . . Americans . . . always remain missionaries . . . not of Christianity, though they often think that is what they are preaching, but of Americanism. What is Americanism? "Clean living, clean thinking, and pep," I think an American would reply. This means in practice, the substitution of tidiness for art, cleanliness for beauty, moralizing for philosophy, prostitutes for concubines (as being easier to conceal), and a general air of being fearfully busy. . . . If the American influence prevailed it would no doubt by means of hygiene save the lives of many Chinese, but would at the same time make them not worth saving.[41]

During his visit to Peking, Russell developed pneumonia and years later reluctantly recorded his debt to PUMC:

I probably owe my life to the Rockefeller Institute in Peking which provided a serum that killed the *pneumococci*. I owe them the more gratitude on this point, as both before and after I was strongly opposed to them politically and they regarded me with as much horror as was felt by my nurse.[42]

NOTES TO CHAPTER FOUR

1. Raymond B. Fosdick, *The Story of The Rockefeller Foundation*, p. 13.

2. Abraham Flexner, *I Remember*, p. 205.

3. *Ibid.*, p. 224.

4. China Medical Commission of The Rockefeller Foundation, *Medicine in China*, p. 109.

5. Mary E. Ferguson, Documents.

6. *Ibid.*

7. *Ibid.*

8. Records of the Examination Committee, 1915. Archives of the London Missionary Society.

9. Simon Flexner and James T. Flexner, *William Henry Welch and the Heroic Age of American Medicine*, pp. 401–2.

10. *Ibid.*, p. 402.

11. Simon Flexner, "Report of the Second China Medical Commission."

12. William Henry Welch, *Papers and Addresses by William Henry Welch*, vol. 3, p. 175.

13. Simon Flexner, "Second China Medical Commission."

14. *Ibid.*

15. *Ibid.*, p. 24.

16. *Ibid.*, p. 30.

17. *Ibid.*, p. 38.

18. *Ibid.*, p. 4.

19. *Ibid.*, p. 3.

20. *Ibid.*, p. 6.

21. *Ibid.*, p. 14.

22. Mary E. Ferguson, Documents.

23. Simon Flexner, "Second China Medical Commission."

24. *Ibid.*

25. Mary E. Ferguson, Documents.

26. *Ibid.*

27. William Henry Welch, *Papers and Addresses*, p. 172.

28. Mary E. Ferguson, Documents.

29. *Ibid.*

30. Harold Balme, *China and Modern Medicine*, pp. 122–3.

31. *Ibid.*, p. 123.

32. Mary E. Ferguson, *China Medical Board and Peking Union Medical College*.

33. Simon Flexner, "Second China Medical Commission."

34. *Ibid.*

35. Mary E. Ferguson, Documents.

36. G. Canby Robinson, *Adventures in Medical Education*, p. 235.

37. Mary E. Ferguson, Documents.

38. Mary E. Ferguson, *China Medical Board*, pp. 30–4.

39. John Dewey and Alice Chipman Dewey, *Letters from China and Japan*, p. 273.

40. Bertrand Russell, *The Problem of China*, p. 231.

41. *Ibid.*, p. 233–4.

42. Bertrand Russell, *The Autobiography of Bertrand Russell, 1914–1944*, p. 189.

CHAPTER FIVE

Opening the Premedical School

It was decided that the admissions standards for Peking Union Medical College should follow those adopted by the twenty or so better medical schools in the United States which required at least two years of college level premedical education. In the other American schools, standards were inadequate: one group required only a high school graduation certificate for entry, while a third —though dwindling—group had no standards, save the tuition fee.

On December 20, 1916, the Executive Committee of the trustees of PUMC approved Franklin McLean's recommendation that the school should establish a preparatory (premedical) school as its first program. Admission would be based on a stiff entrance examination that students could register for after one year's study in an approved college. Students with higher qualifications would be considered for admission to advanced standing. The first proposal was for a two-year program, but before the Premedical School opened it was decided to extend it to three years. The subjects of instruction would include biology, chemistry, mathematics, physics, Chinese, English, and modern European languages.

The China Medical Board also implemented the recommendations of William Welch and Simon Flexner to strengthen premedical education in selected colleges and universities in China, looking toward the day when they would produce qualified applicants and the PUMC Premedical School could be closed. The grants included funds for faculty salaries, for fellowships for existing faculty, for equipment, and for the expansion of facilities. The first grant was approved on December 19, 1917, and went to St. John's University in Shanghai.

Other mission schools that received support were Ginling College—a woman's school in Nanking—Nanking University, Soochow University, Yale-Hunan, and Yenching University. Two medical schools operated by the Chinese government were also awarded grants: Southeastern University in Nanking, with its brilliant president, P. W. Kuo, and Tsinghua College, whose president, Y. T. Tsur, later became chairman of the trustees of PUMC. Other grants went to a private Chinese university, Nankai.

Meanwhile, September 11, 1917, was set as the date for opening the Premedical School, which would be located in Lockhart Hall, the main building of the old Union Medical College. Early in April, as the representative of the CMB, Roger Greene sent bulletins to the leading colleges and middle schools in China announcing the schedule of entrance examinations. The bulletin also included a statement that, although the college was not now prepared to accept female students because adequate dormitory accommodations were not available, it would do so in due course. Even before the dormitory was ready, however, a few female students were housed in the nurses' dormitory.

While announcements had been made concerning the opening of the Premedical School, a faculty still had not been assembled. Time was short, but McLean was a superb recruiter. His attributes included intellectual brilliance, great personal charm, and a total dedication to his job; the three assets combined made him highly persuasive. Then of course as additional ammunition he had the vigorous support of Flexner and Welch, and the attraction of the already prestigious Rockefeller Foundation. In concert with the CMB he assembled an excellent faculty for the Premedical School and had already begun to recruit outstanding young scientists for the medical college, which would open in two years.

THE TEACHING STAFF

One of McLean's first selections for the staff of the Premedical School was the dean and professor of physics, William Warren Stifler, who had been instructor in physics at Columbia. Stanley D. Wilson, who had a Ph.D. in chemistry from the University of Chicago, was appointed to lead the chemistry program. For biology the choice was Charles R. Packard, who had earned a Ph.D. at Columbia in the laboratories of Edmund B. Wilson and Thomas Hunt Morgan; he reached Peking in 1918. Two years later he was joined by Aura E. Severinghaus, also from Wilson's laboratory. Leslie R. Severinghaus, his brother, was appointed to the staff in 1922 to teach modern European languages.

What later proved to be perhaps the most notable appointment was that of L. Carrington Goodrich as a teacher of English. The son of a Congregational missionary in China, Goodrich had graduated from Williams College in 1917 and had recently returned to China. He was teaching English in a higher school when he was appointed to the Premedical School. Goodrich had a remarkable facility in Chinese and became the semiofficial interpreter for PUMC. Unfortunately, after only a year he decided to return to the United States to go into the army. In 1921, however, he was designated assistant director of the CMB, a post he held in Peking until 1925 when he once more returned to the

United States, this time to launch a distinguished career as a scholar on China at Columbia University. He is the author of the classic *A Short History of the Chinese People*, in which he demonstrated his unique ability to merge historical development and cultural change.[1]

In line with the trustees' declared wish to hire Chinese personnel whenever possible, several Chinese were also engaged for the premedical faculty: Ma Kiam, to teach Chinese; Y. Tong, physics; and C. T. Feng, chemistry.

When McLean was searching for a teacher of Chinese, Greene suggested that he seek out Hu Shih, a promising young Chinese graduate student at Cornell. Early in 1910 Hu had been awarded a Boxer Indemnity Scholarship for study in the United States. At Cornell University he studied agriculture, graduating in 1914 with a Phi Beta Kappa key.

Hu's studies aroused in him a deep concern about the cultural problems of modernizing the agriculture-based economy of China. After a year of graduate studies in agriculture, however, Hu changed direction by a good 180 degrees and became a student of philosophy under John Dewey at Columbia. He was studying at Morningside Heights when he declined the instructorship in Chinese that McLean offered him. The post eventually went to Ma Kiam, who later headed the Department of Chinese at neighboring Yenching University.*

In the meantime, Hu Shih went on to an illustrious career. He returned to China in 1917 and was appointed professor of philosophy at the National Peking University. As the father of the Chinese renaissance, Hu Shih led the movement to establish the Chinese vernacular as the language of the people. As a further step toward the modernization of China he became the chief advocate of "subjecting to a scientific scrutiny all of China's historical personages, classics, and doctrines."[3] In 1929 Hu Shih was appointed a trustee of PUMC.†

LAYING THE CORNERSTONE

On September 11, 1917, eight students were enrolled in the Premedical School. Thirteen days later the cornerstone for the first new structure for PUMC—the anatomy building—was laid with proper ceremony by the Honorable Fan Yuan-lien, the minister of education. Frank S. Billings, dean and professor of medicine at Rush Medical College and a leading figure in American medical education, now in the uniform of a lieutenant colonel of the U. S. Army Medical Corps, spoke briefly. The American Minister, Paul S. Reinsch, also spoke, and the Right Reverand F. L. Norris, Anglican bishop of north China, pronounced the benediction.

Franklin McLean reaffirmed the purpose of the trustees of PUMC: "It is the best of our modern medicine that we desire to give to China, that China may take advantage of our own recent progress."[4]

---

* A complete list of the staff of the Premedical School is in Appendix B of Mary Fergusons's book.[2]

† It was Hu Shih who described PUMC as an airplane institution in a wheelbarrow country.

McLean returned to New York soon after the ceremony, and on October 23, 1917, presented an encouraging progress report to the trustees of PUMC: the spirits of the staff were high, adverse criticism from Chinese and foreign groups was lessening, and the Ministry of Education had assumed a cooperative attitude.* The trustees now gave McLean the formal title of director of PUMC.

McLean Accepts a Military Commission

McLean had earlier been offered a commission in the Medical Corps of the U. S. Army, which he had declined. Now, with his deep sense of patriotism and his affection for variety and adventure, which he never lost, McLean sought a leave of absence from Wallace Buttrick to accept a commission. He felt that the PUMC program was launched and that for an interval it would continue to develop satisfactorily under the leadership of others. His request was granted with reluctance and in mid-December 1917 he received orders to active duty.

There was an informal and, in retrospect, perhaps an unwise understanding between McLean and the boards of the CMB and PUMC that he would continue to serve as director of PUMC while in uniform. For the six months that he was stationed in the United States, McLean made every effort to remain deeply involved in all aspects of the program at Peking. In mid-July of 1918, however, he was sent overseas where he served as deputy to Brigadier General William (Billy) S. Thayer, a leader of the Department of Medicine at Hopkins. McLean was kept informed on all major developments at PUMC, including faculty appointments, but the program was moving too rapidly for a director *in absentia.*

---

* Jerome Webster of the Department of Surgery states that the jealousy of some of the Americans in China was epitomized in their transliteration of PUMC to PUNK.

NOTES TO CHAPTER FIVE

1. L. Carrington Goodrich, *A Short History of the Chinese People*, 3rd ed. (New York and Evanston: Harper Torchbook, Harper & Row, 1963).

2. Mary E. Ferguson, *China Medical Board and Peking Union Medical College*, p. 243.

3. Shou-yi Ch'en, "Hu-Shih (1891–1962)," p. 134.

4. Mary E. Ferguson, *China Medical Board*, p. 40.

CHAPTER SIX

Opening the Medical College

Franklin McLean's first love was the research bench; after he was released from active military service in 1919 he spent several months in the laboratories of Lawrence J. Henderson at Harvard working on the acidity of hemoglobin and the influence of oxygen on the distribution of chlorides between the corpuscles and plasma of the blood.

In early April 1920 he was invited to attend one of the periodic Rockefeller Foundation "strategy" meetings at which trustees and foundation officers met informally to explore major issues before they were placed on the docket for the full meeting of the trustees. The participants in this particular discussion at Gedney Farms, New York, included President George Vincent, William Welch, Abraham Flexner, Henry Judson, Frederick T. Gates, Roger Greene, and a newcomer to the staff of the foundation, Richard Pearce.

The topic was Peking Union Medical College: Was the objective of education at the "highest level" realistic for China? Should the school educate a small group of excellent teachers of medicine or train a larger group of well-qualified practitioners? Could a faculty of adequate quality be recruited and retained? What should be the proper balance between teaching and research? And, finally, was the "highest level" realistic for the Rockefeller Foundation in a financial sense or would the school become a millstone around its neck. The staggering increase in the cost of the physical plant had given the trustees special concern about the administration of a developing medical school 9,000 miles from New York.

When McLean was asked his opinion about the future in Peking he had no hesitation in putting himself squarely on the side of a center of academic excellence for a talented few who would become the future leaders of medicine in

China. His ideas were expressed with such clarity and conviction that he was asked to embody them in a written statement:

> Within the limits of the resources made available, the scientific aims of the Peking Union Medical College are:
>
> 1. Primarily to give a medical education comparable with that provided by the best medical schools of the United States and Europe, through:
>   a) an undergraduate medical curriculum;
>   b) graduate training for laboratory workers, teachers, and clinical specialists; and
>   c) short courses for physicians.
> 2. To afford opportunities for research, especially with reference to problems peculiar to the Far East.
> 3. Incidentally to extend a popular knowledge of modern medicine and public health.[1]

With a few additions and modifications the statement was endorsed by the meeting and on April 14, 1920, adopted by the trustees of PUMC as the basis for future plans. So, restated once more, the program of PUMC was to be aimed at excellence—equal to the best that the world offered and with a strong emphasis on research.

The frequent interruption of his research at Harvard, occasioned by his continuing administrative relationship with PUMC, was one factor in McLean's decision to relinquish the directorship. Another was his increasing awareness of the fact that it was becoming a full-time job and that he would have to leave the laboratory. Perhaps at this time, also, he began to appraise his own future in research. His fundamental investigations on fluid and electrolytes, and his clinical studies on the new technique of electrocardiography, did not fit in with his statement that research at PUMC should emphasize "problems peculiar to the Far East." On April 6, 1920, he submitted his resignation as director to concentrate on building a strong department of medicine at PUMC.

RICHARD PEARCE

Under the leadership of Wallace Buttrick and Abraham Flexner, a principal purpose of the General Education Board was the strengthening of selected medical schools in the United States. While the trustees bore in mind the charge laid down by Rockefeller "to promote the welfare of mankind throughout the world," by charter, the board's activities were restricted to national programs. In 1919, therefore, the foundation had established a Division of Medical Education to advance medical education on a truly global basis. Richard Pearce, Musser Professor of Research Medicine at the University of Pennsylvania, and former associate in pathology with Simon Flexner, was appointed director of this new division. One of his two lieutenants was Alan Gregg, who in subsequent years was to have perhaps as great an impact on medical education on a world-wide basis as any man in history.

Pearce had had only a year to settle into his new position at the foundation when it was suggested that he spend a year at PUMC. There was a strong feeling that an experienced medical educator who understood the roles, responsibilities, and relationships of administration and faculty in a first-rate American medical school should bring his experience to bear on the developing program at Peking. It is probable also that the foundation trustees wanted assurance on the future stability of the program from an educator who was one of their family. With McLean's resignation, and the new medical school and teaching hospital nearing completion, there was a strategic opportunity for someone who had no vested interest in the origins of the school to take stock and establish a sound organizational pattern. Further, since Pearce was leading a new program to advance medical education internationally, a first-hand experience with medical education in the Orient would be salutary.

Pearce had strong qualifications for the task of making PUMC a truly academic institution; he knew the world of academe intimately. Raymond Fosdick described him as "a man of uncomprising thoroughness, deeply concerned with education."[2] A modest man, Pearce was always direct and candid in expressing his opinions, and had absolutely no desire for self-aggrandizement. Carrington Goodrich, who served as his interpreter and guide on tours of Chinese institutions, was deeply impressed with Pearce's wisdom, perception, and academic strengths. In one year Pearce left an indelible stamp on PUMC—he set the school on a firm academic basis. Henceforth it was no longer a missionary institution but an academic medical center.

Pearce and his family arrived in Peking on October 23, 1920, and he immediately opened a series of conferences with Henry Houghton, Greene, and members of the faculty to gain a detailed appraisal of every aspect of PUMC.

Administering PUMC

The administrative relationships at PUMC were complex and continued to be a problem throughout the life of the school. On paper it had two governing bodies, the CMB and the college's Board of Trustees, but principal policy matters were the responsibility of a third group, the trustees of the Rockefeller Foundation. All three bodies were located in New York, and their decisions were based on the printed word. In Peking there was a resident director representing the CMB and a director of the medical school; the two worked side by side. In addition, there were the missionaries with their abiding concern over the Christian character and motives of the school, which led at times to conflicts between the deeply religious missionary doctors and the "new breed" of faculty who regarded medical science and medical education as their pole stars.

The budget for 1921–22 was to receive special scrutiny in New York and Vincent had asked Houghton to return with a proposed budget, explain the programs, and defend the requests. After three weeks of discussions with

Pearce, Houghton left for the United States with the budget and several important administrative recommendations.

An Administrative Board carried not only the administrative but all academic responsibilities for the medical college and the hospital. With the faculty now numbering close to fifty there was a clear need to delineate academic and administrative channels. The recommendation to New York, therefore, was that the Administrative Board be abolished. Responsibility for all academic matters —curriculum, appointments, promotions, and admissions—would be vested in a medical faculty; all administrative and fiscal matters—nonprofessional personnel, budgetary allocations, and hospital operations—would be the responsibility of a new administrative council.

In Houghton's absence in New York Pearce agreed to the Administrative Board's request that he serve as acting director until Houghton's return, and asked the board to recommend a permanent director. Their choice was prompt and unanimous—Henry S. Houghton. The recommendation was subsequently approved by the PUMC trustees to become effective on January 1, 1921.

Pearce soon recognized the difficulties inherent in the New York–Peking relationship which to him was completely anomalous. A lack of continuity in academic leadership in Peking was an additional factor that had contributed to the undue concentration of decision-making in New York. McLean had been in and out of Peking—mostly out—during the four years he had held the title of director, and, as acting director, Houghton had been hesitant to take a strong rein. Further, he had never held academic rank in a major medical school, where he would have learned how administrative and academic relationships and responsibilities developed.

Pearce in the meantime had learned that there were no uniform or rational budgetary procedures. Without prior administrative approval, department heads took their requests directly to Greene who in turn, if persuaded, endorsed their requests and sent them directly to New York. Pearce also foresaw that the cost of operating the teaching hospital could dwarf other aspects of the program. But he was now fully convinced of the existing obligations and future opportunities at Peking, and he became increasingly concerned that undue budgetary restrictions at this critical period could wreck the project. On January 6, 1921, Pearce convened a meeting of the professional staff and declared it for the first time to be a legally constituted medical faculty.

Meanwhile progress was being made on a number of other fronts. An outstanding faculty had been assembled for the basic sciences and the clinical departments (to be described in the succeeding chapters); the first seven medical students, including five from the Premedical School, had been admitted on October 1, 1919; the nurses' training school opened in 1920;* and the last two classes of UMC had completed their training.

---

* See Chapter XI for the story of the nursing school.

The clinical programs had been crammed into the old men's hospital of the UMC, and June 24, 1921, was a glorious day, as the first patients were moved into the new hospital; a week later the first female patients were admitted. Throughout that summer other units were completed and occupied by the basic science and the clinical departments. Visitors began to arrive for the week-long dedication ceremonies scheduled for September 15 to 22.

At this happy time, financial support became a point of deep concern. Houghton returned from New York with a directive that there must be substantial reductions in the budget. Led by Pearce, however, there was unified opposition to this instruction. After four days of detailed study of the budget during dedication week, the trustees, swayed by the grandeur of the events, and appreciating the realistic needs of the college, approved the full amount originally requested. They also endorsed Pearce's proposals for greater local autonomy. But the complex administrative relationship between the program on Hatamen Boulevard in Peking and the offices at 61 Broadway in New York continued to be a cause for concern.

THE DEDICATION CEREMONY

When George Vincent went to China in June 1919 to make a first-hand assessment of the foundation's most important and most complex program, he visited Shanghai, Canton, Moukden, and Seoul, as well as Peking. In discussions with Pearce and Greene, Vincent proposed that there should be an international medical congress in conjunction with the dedication of the new medical center. Pearce, always the candid pragmatist, urged that the program be kept as simple as possible since the congress would mean additional work for his overburdened staff. Further, he would need the services of the visiting doctors in opening the patient-care programs. Vincent's proposal was subsequently endorsed by the trustees of PUMC and the CMB, and a special meeting of the China Medical Missionary Association was added to the dedicatory program. The active cooperation of the Chinese government was solicited and assured.

There has never been a comparable assemblage of intellectual might, of prestige, of diplomatic rank, and of global representation for the dedication of a medical school as that which converged on Peking that week in September 1921. In the academic procession that began at 4:00 p.m. on the 19th, some were elegantly robed and hooded in academic tradition; others were in clerical garb, in mandarin robes, or in frock coats and top hats.

At the request of the Rockefeller Foundation, Francis W. Peabody and Welch returned to Peking to attend the ceremonies. (Peabody would also serve as the first visiting professor.) The foundation felt that it would be particularly desirable to have members of the two China medical commissions present, and they joined a delegation, led by Mr. and Mrs. John D. Rockefeller, Jr., and a group of twenty-seven distinguished guests from England and Ireland as well as the United States, including President Vincent and Victor G. Heiser, director of programs in the Far East for the International Health Board, who represented the Rockefeller Foundation.

In her Peking diary, Mrs. Peabody recorded a feminine view of the splendor of the dedication:

> The color of the academic dress was stunning, and the ladies paled beside it. Dr. Tuffier of Paris was unquestionably the most brilliant, for he wore a veritable crown, and his hat was trimmed with ermine with red about it, and crossing his breast were innumerable medals. . . . Sir William Smyly [of Dublin] wore a gown of scarlet and a scarlet hood. Even those with black gowns had them so covered with bands of red or green velvet that they were scarcely less brilliant. A sprinkling of bishops added another touch, and the British and American ministers were the only ones who brought us down to earth by their sombre cutaways.[3]

Foreign ministers came from countries as distant as Brazil, Norway, Denmark, Cuba, and Mexico. From the Chinese government came Ma Lin-yi, minister of education, Chi Yao-san, minister of the interior, and W. W. Yen, the minister of foreign affairs, who also represented the president of the republic, Hsu Shih-ch'ang. The reaction of the throng of missionaries who came from across China must have been bittersweet as they compared the beautiful and opulent edifices now being dedicated with their inadequate facilities and their Spartan existence. A familiar figure to the missionaries and old China hands was Thomas Cochrane, who had come on from London to see the remarkable changes wrought on the site of the UMC he had founded fifteen years earlier.

General Leonard Wood, a physician and governor general of the Philippine Islands, was accompanied by Dr. Antonio Sison, professor of medicine at the University of the Philippines. Other Asian representatives included Sahachiro Hata of the Kitasato Institute in Tokyo and D. A. de Waart, director of the Government Medical School in Batavia.

Other physicians of distinction from the United States included Florence R. Sabin, professor of histology at Hopkins, and George E. de Schweinetz, professor of ophthalmology at the University of Pennsylvania and president of the American Medical Association. From Canada came A. B. Macallum, professor of biochemistry at McGill; from France, Marin-Theodore Tuffier, professor of clinical surgery at the University of Paris; and from Ireland, Sir William J. Smyly, obstetrician and gynecologist to the British royal family.

The frontispiece of the 400-page volume of addresses and papers from the dedication week shows more than 600 persons of many nationalities carefully arranged in a courtyard against the backdrop of the central hospital building of classical Chinese design. Shown in the photograph are visitors, students, faculty, administrative staff, interns, nurses, laboratory assistants, hospital attendants, janitors, cleaners, cooks, laundrymen, gatekeepers, and other servants. Scattered through the book are pictures of the academic procession, of various areas in the physical plant, and of illustrations used in the scientific lectures.

When the guests at the dedication walked through the main gate of the medical school their first sight was a series of beautifully curved roofs of green tile, with the eaves decorated in traditional Chinese style. The columns supporting the roof were a brilliant red and the overhead beams were in hues of red, blue, green, and gold. They entered a court representative of historic Pcking, bounded by three buildings that housed the laboratories of anatomy, physiology, and pharmacology. In the chemistry building were the library and the director's office. To the north of the court was a two-story building that housed other administrative offices and quarters for house officers. Opposite stood a two-story building in which were located an auditorium—the largest in Peking—that seated 350, a social hall, and the offices of the Department of Religous and Social Work.

The 250-bed hospital complex lay to the north of the medical school buildings, and was connected with them by a tunnel. The first floor of one of its three-story buildings housed the admission wards and an obstetrical outpatient clinic, while the second and third floors were occupied by clinical units for obstetrics and gynecology, and a few pediatrics beds. In two other two-story buildings were the medical and surgical wards, with twenty-five beds on each floor. Pathology occupied a smaller structure. A separate building south of the administration building was for private patients. The main outpatient clinic, roentgenology, clinical laboratories, operating rooms, and offices and research laboratories for the clinical departments occupied a separate four-story structure.

Thirty-six residences were divided into a north and a south compound; the old residence of Prince Yü, its beauty untouched save for the addition of central heating, was to be Houghton's residence.

One of the most important events occurred on the first day of the ceremonies when Houghton was officially installed as the director of PUMC. The affection and esteem that many of his colleagues felt for him were unique; one described him as "a saint with a smile."*

Rockefeller's Pledge

Naturally, John D. Rockefeller, Jr. held the spotlight. He opened his address by reading a cable from his father:

> My highest hopes are centered on the Peking Union Medical College which is about to open its doors. May all who enter, whether Faculty or Students, be fired with the spirit of service and of sacrifice and may the Institution become an ever-widening influence for the promotion of the physical, mental, and spiritual well-being of the Chinese nation.[4]

Rockefeller, describing himself as his father's representative, then traced the events that led to the selection of China for this great adventure in medical education and research. He ascribed it in part to his father's long-held interest

---

* Aura E. Severinghaus 1970: personal communication.

in the country, and reviewed the events leading to the final decision to concentrate the major effort in Peking. The high cost of the physical plant was attributed to World War I and to the inexperience of the CMB in dealing with construction problems in the Orient. He suggested that the founders of the new school must look forward to the day when every aspect of the program was in the hands of the Chinese.

Having in mind his primary commitment to the missionary bodies, Rockefeller stated that recruitment would be based not only on scientific capabilities but on "the finest idealism."[5] He pledged continuing cordial cooperation with the missionary boards but always in the context of the primary dedication to excellence in education and the care of the patient:

> In fullest sympathy with the missionary spirit and purpose, we are desirous of furthering it as completely as may be consistent with the maintenance of the highest scientific standards in the Medical School and the best service in the hospital.[6]

DEDICATION LECTURES

The evening lectures given during dedication week dwelt on topics of broad medical interest. Edward H. Hume, dean of Hunan-Yale, reviewed the development of Western medical education in China and cited grim statistics on the nonavailability of physicians. In Canada the ratio was 1:1,050 population; in Britain, 1:1,100; in the United States, 1:720; in Japan, 1:1,000; but in China it was 1:120,000. Hume went on to discuss the countless deficiencies in medical education in China: what was needed, he said, were more schools and more doctors; the strengthening of financial support to the eight missionary medical colleges; higher standards through effective governmental control; the development of a medical curriculum based on the disease problems of China; increased training programs for auxiliaries; the reform of premedical education; and the expansion of opportunities for medical education for women. Hume pointed out that there were only twenty-four medical schools in China: eleven were operated by Europeans or Americans; eleven, which followed the Japanese pattern for second-level schools, were government owned; and two were jointly Chinese- and foreign-controlled.

In another evening address, de Waart traced the development of medical education in the Dutch East Indies, beginning with the training of *doktor djawa* as medical assistants and vaccinators.

Opening his discussion of the Rockefeller Foundation's program for the control of hookworm, Heiser presented graphic statistics on the situation in the southern part of the United States and compared it to that of the nutritional problems in the Far East:

> One hundred thousand persons die each year in the United States because they swallow some portion of the discharges of other people. One hundred thousand die each year in the Orient from beri-beri.[7]

He went on to report that the success of the hookworm program had been so dramatic that the southern states themselves, responding to public demand, had in a decade increased their annual expenditures on health by a factor of ten—from approximately $250,000 to over $2.5 million.

In the mornings there were lectures by the visiting physicians—Peabody on vital capacity, Sabin on hematopoiesis, de Schweinetz on visual fields in lesions of the pituitary, and Hata on chemotherapy. Wu Lien-teh discussed the lessons that had been learned from the Manchurian devastation by pneumonic plague, during which he had led the public health teams. There were also operative clinics, case demonstrations, and seminars held by the clinical departments.

The impact of the dedicatory ceremonies was best expressed by the students:

> At the beginning of our third year, we witnessed the great occasion of the College dedication ceremony in which we were brought into contact with a large number of eminent scientists from all over the world. The inspiration and idealism which their presence afforded can never be forgotten. When we look back upon these opportunities we must consider ourselves particularly fortunate that we were prepared for the study of medicine under such conditions.[8]

NOTES TO CHAPTER SIX

1. Mary E. Ferguson, *China Medical Board and Peking Union Medical College*, p. 44.

2. Raymond B. Fosdick, *The Story of The Rockefeller Foundation*, p. 106.

3. F. G. Peabody, *Francis Weld Peabody, 1881–1927*, p. 53.

4. Peking Union Medical College, *Addresses and Papers, Dedication Ceremonies and Medical Conference*, p. 57.

5. *Ibid.*, p. 63.

6. *Ibid.*, p. 64.

7. *Ibid.*, p. 142.

8. Peking Union Medical College, *The Unison*, vol. II (*1927*): p. 82.

CHAPTER SEVEN

The Golden Years: 1921-31

The ten years between 1921 and 1931 stand as the golden decade of the Peking Union Medical College. The caliber of the faculty and the students at least equaled the standard of excellence set by William Welch and Simon Flexner. The status of patient care was equally high. The quality and quantity of research was unsurpassed, placing special emphasis on the health problems of China. No significant difficulties arose concerning financial support from New York; there was mutual confidence and essentially every request was met in full. PUMC became the premier medical center in Asia, the equal of the leading academic medical centers in Europe and North America.

At the same time the college was a self-contained island focused on scientific and educational accomplishments in a country that was beset by domestic and international disturbances, including running and pitched battles between military units, at times in or near Peking, and kidnappings by roving gangs of bandits. Nationalism was reaching new heights of expression and students in other institutions were preoccupied with political questions. Transportation was frequently disrupted, making the movement of both personnel and supplies hazardous.

When Chaing Kai-shek moved north in 1927 the foreign missionary groups evacuted their personnel to India, Ceylon, and Korea. The staff of PUMC, however, was unaffected by the continuing turbulence that lasted throughout the 1920s. For the faculty from the United States the fighting only heightened their sense of adventure.

CLOSURE OF THE PREMEDICAL SCHOOL

The long-range program to strengthen premedical education in other schools paid its earliest dividend in September 1925 when the first students to complete their premedical education elsewhere were admitted from Canton Christian College. This marked the end of the Premedical School; it was officially closed in June 1925, having educated 205 students, 100 of whom had enrolled at PUMC.

The last dean of the Premedical School, Aura E. Severinghaus, looking back on his five years in Peking, emphasized the caliber of the students:

> They were just wonderful . . . a uniformly brilliant group . . . there was very little difference in their scholarship.*

On the scientific side, Severinghaus, a cytologyst, worked with Ernest Carroll Faust and Henry E. Meleney in studies on the sexual cycle of *Schistosoma japonicum*. He returned in 1925 to the anatomy department at Columbia University College of Physicians and Surgeons.

In 1942 Severinghaus was appointed assistant dean for admissions, students, and education at P and S under Dean Willard Rappleye, from which vantage point he led two national studies on preparation for medical education that were decisive factors in strengthening premedical education in the United States.

PREMEDICAL EDUCATION AND ADMISSIONS

With the closing of the Premedical School in the summer of 1925, Stanley Wilson of the chemistry faculty and Ma Kiam, a teacher of Chinese, transferred to the faculty at Yenching University; much of the teaching equipment in the Premedical School was given outright to Yenching. Yenching soon became the chief magnet for premedical students, providing two-thirds of the students admitted to PUMC. A general belief that Yenching students were favored for admission was a continuing source of concern for the PUMC faculty, who believed that representation from a wider range of schools was desirable, but they were never able to erase the fixation on Yenching.

Following the closure of the Premedical School, three years of college education continued to be the requirement for admission to PUMC; regular college courses were preferred to those that might be modified toward a "special premedical education." The Annual Announcement of PUMC included a partial list of institutions in China that the faculty considered to be teaching the premedical sciences at an adequate level; the 1929–30 announcement listed eleven such institutions.

The premedical requirements in biology, chemistry, and mathematics continued to be similar to those of the leading American schools, but there was a greater emphasis on physics and stiff requirements in Chinese and English (Table I).

---

* Aura E. Severinghaus 1969: personal communication.

TABLE I. PREMEDICAL REQUIREMENTS AT PEIPING UNION MEDICAL COLLEGE*

Acceptable preparation for admission is defined as follows:

I. The middle school course of six years, including the following subjects: Chinese literature, six years; English, six years; mathematics, including algebra, geometry, and trigonometry, two years; science (biology, chemistry, or physics), one year; Chinese and Western history, each two years;

and

II. Work in an institution of collegiate grade approved by the Committee on Admissions. The courses taken should include:

1. Chinese—the equivalent of five clock hours weekly throughout one academic year.†

2. English—the equivalent of six clock hours weekly throughout one academic year.

3. A modern language other than English—five clock hours weekly throughout one academic year. As a substitute for this requirement in modern language, appropriate credit may be accepted in one of the following groups.

   a) Physical chemistry and higher mathematics
   b) Psychology and education
   c) Economics and political science or sociology

4. Biology—nine clock hours weekly throughout one academic year, of which six clock hours shall have been in laboratory exercises. The work should include invertebrate zoology and vertebrate dissection. General embryology is recommended.

5. Chemistry—nine clock hours weekly throughout two academic years, of which six clock hours shall have been in laboratory exercises. The courses should be distributed approximately as follows: one-half in general chemistry, one-fourth in analytical chemistry, and one-fourth in organic chemistry.

6. Physics—eight clock hours weekly throughout one academic year, of which four clock hours shall have been in laboratory exercises.

* Reprinted from *Peiping Union Medical College, Annual Announcement 1929–30* (Peiping: July 1, 1929) p. 34.
† The academic year was thirty-six weeks.

The Committee on Admissions made a preliminary screening of all applications, giving special consideration to letters of recommendation as well as to the transcripts of academic records. Through periodic visits to the leading schools offering premedical education, and through frank discussions on criteria for selection, the admissions committee was assured of objective and reliable evaluations in the letters of recommendation from premedical teachers. After initial screening the selected applicants were invited to take the entrance examinations, which were held in Peking and Shanghai, as well as elsewhere if indicated. The examinations were in biology, chemistry, physics, Chinese, and English; only an occasional unsuccessful student was allowed to repeat them.

CURRICULUM

The medical curriculum was similar to that of the handful of progressive schools in the United States. (Appendix I gives details of the curriculum for the academic year 1929–30.) Special emphasis was placed on the teaching laboratory and on the partnership of student and teacher in the study of the patient; the amount of time devoted to lectures was minimal. While some American schools continued to teach physiology in the second year, at PUMC it was concentrated in the freshman year with anatomy and biochemistry. During the first year, also, there were two hours of instruction a week in English, as well as instruction in French or German, and scientific Chinese. Rather than pack every hour with required subjects, the curriculum included an elective period in the middle trimester of the second year and three or four elective weeks in the final year. The greater emphasis on public health called for a full-time, four-week clerkship during the senior year; pediatrics was covered in medicine. Some American medical schools placed the student in the outpatient department (OPD) during his junior year and on the wards in the senior year. At PUMC the student had his first contact with patients on the wards; the OPD was reserved for the final year. This sequence was based on the belief that the shorter contact with patients in the crowded OPD required a more sophisticated student. The emphasis on practical training is illustrated by the program for juniors in the Department of Medicine in 1921. There was a lecture from eight to nine o'clock, followed by work on the wards until noon. At two o'clock the student went to the clinical laboratory to perform blood counts, stool examinations, and urinalyses on his patients.

THE COMMENCEMENT CEREMONY

The first commencement ceremony was held on June 28, 1924, with one nursing and three medical graduates. A special committee, headed by Ma Kiam, turned to ancient ceremonies and costumes for inspiration and produced a unique blend of the Orient and the Occident for the graduates: a mandarin-style jacket, a loose-fitting white shirt, and black slippers. The jacket was vermilion in color, a copy of the style worn by Chinese scholars in ancient times. On each side of the facing there were five green leaves representing four years of medical school and one year of internship; another decoration was an embroidered "water herb," a sacred symbol from classical times.

The ceremonies for scholars of the Chou dynasty were represented by special black caps, without the customary Western academic tassel; in the shape of an oval cylinder, they were surmounted by a flat oblong board with narrow edges in front and in back. Only the nurse, Tsing Hsien-tsang, was attired in a typical American-style starched white uniform and cap.

Although classic Chinese ceremonial costume did not include one, an academic hood for all graduates was designed for the occasion in the PUMC colors of blue and white.

All of the students had voted for the student marshal, Liu Shu-wan, who carried a special ebony mace that followed in the tradition of the *Ta Kuei*, "Great Symbol," for dignity and authority, another remembrance of the Chou dynasty. The original *Ta Kuei* had been a slab of white jade notched at one end; instead of a notch, the PUMC mace had a narrow gold band at one end with the name of the student marshal inscribed on it. Each year thereafter another band with the name of the new marshal was added.

The chief faculty marshal was Jerome P. Webster, assisted by Leslie R. Severinghaus.

Chang Kou-kan, minister of education, extended greetings from the president of the republic, K'un Ts'ao. Sun Pao-ch'i, chairman of the PUMC Advisory Committee, which included seven other distinguished Chinese gentlemen, brought a special message from the committee.

The principal address, entitled "The Significance of International Cooperation," was delivered by His Excellency Wellington Koo, one of the most distinguished Chinese of his generation. Koo had taken his Ph.D. at Columbia University and had returned to China to serve it with honor—as Minister of Foreign Affairs; as ambassador to Great Britain from 1941 to 1946; and as ambassador to the United States after World War II.

The commencement was a splendid, colorful ceremony that epitomized the concept of an American institution deeply rooted in rich Chinese traditions.

LIFE IN PEKING

The excitement of living in Peking was a matchless dividend for the staff of PUMC and their families. Each foray out of the college could be a new artistic adventure. There was the matchless spectacle of the Imperial Palace with its glittering golden roofs just half a mile distant from the college. Other breathtaking vistas alternated with delicate corners of elegance and otherworldliness: one hour by train to the north was the Great Wall, forty feet high and thirty-four feet wide at the top—a must for every visitor to Peking; to the west were pleasant hills; in the hot summers a number of families moved to rented or purchased homes at the seaside resort of Peitai-ho, a one-day journey on the Peking-Tientsin-Moukden railway.

Each year a series of lectures was arranged on a broad theme, and faculty members presented discussions relating to their special field of interest. As an example, in the academic year 1921–22 the topic was H. G. Wells's *An Outline of History*, Charles Packard spoke as a biologist on "The Making of Our World," while Davidson Black, a physical anthropologist, spoke on "The Making of Man."

Distinguished visitors were invited to address joint assemblies of faculty and students. Paul Monroe, the eminent Chinese scholar from Columbia and a trustee of the college, came to Peking in January 1922 and delivered a forceful message to the students, "What China Needs:"

> The great need of China today is a generation of young leaders of character. . . . Above all they need to have a knowledge of modern science . . . science which will give their people better health, which will improve their economic condition, which will develop their national wealth. . . . They need to have a knowledge of how to acquire and how to impart all this knowledge.[1]

In the cultural sphere there were organ recitals and frequent concerts by the orchestra of the Peking Institute of Fine Arts. During holiday seasons, the Peking Choral Society and Orchestra, whose first director was Aura Severinghaus, presented oratorios such as "The Messiah." Severinghaus also assembled a group of male singers who performed on many occasions—at the funeral service for Sun Yat-sen in the PUMC chapel they sang his favorite hymn, "Bringing in the Sheaves."

The Women's Club of Yenching University and the students at the Peking American School presented dramatic programs and there were movies and steriopticon presentations. The most popular entertainments were the variety shows given by the PUMC staff, at which Carrington Goodrich imitated to perfection the calls of the street vendors, and Aura Severinghaus, with his rich basso profundo, sang and clowned in a minstrel show, "Democritus Twigg with Mr. Bones."

In a letter to W. H. Halsted, his mentor, Adrian Taylor, head of surgery, described the opportunities for the outdoorsman and hunter:

> Mountains are all around us, and within a short time we can be in perfectly wild country. Last month several of us went hunting in Mongolia. We had a delightful time climbing very rugged hills, chasing day after day the elusive big horn sheep. . . . During the New Year's vacation I hope to go again to the mountains in the south of Shansi province where wild boar are to be found. On our Mongolian trip we killed just as many grouse as we could use, and I hope to be able to get all the pheasant that we want in Shansi, even if we fail to bring home a boar.[2]

He added a cautionary note on the completely different lifestyle: "The demands of social life in Peking are exacting and one has to guard his time very zealously."[3]

Both American and Chinese holidays were celebrated; Chinese holidays included New Year in February, the Dragon Boat Festival in June, and after 1928 the Republic or Double-Ten Day on October 10. On Thanksgiving Day there was a special religious service in the Marine Guards' Mess Hall at the legation, followed by a reception given by the minister.

In the first edition of the classbook, *The Unison of 1924*,[4] Christmas at PUMC was described by a nursing student, Svea Lindberg; the photographs show a white Yuletide. Intensive preparations had been underway for more than a week and when, on Christmas Eve, Miss Lindberg entered a ward, she opened a door—covered with red paper and Chinese characters that told of the joy of

Christmas—to behold a tree decorated with multicolored electric lights. One door of each ward was converted into a "fireplace" for Santa Claus.

In midafternoon there was a children's party in the outpatient department, and the youngsters appeared "with their little hands sticking out of thickly wadded coats; and their little pigtails fastened with brightly colored thread."[5] In the background, voices sang of Christmas joy. Suddenly, Santa tumbled out of the fireplace with gifts for every child.

On Christmas morning, beginning at five o'clock, the nurses walked through the wards singing carols. Santa appeared again at nine o'clock and went from bed to bed with a gift for each patient, as well as for the doctors and the nurses. When Santa reached the children's ward he found it crowded with toy motorcars, baby dolls, and dogs and cats.

In the earlier years a Christmas party had been given for the Chinese employees, but by 1924 this festivity had been discontinued because of the droves of relatives, friends, and other "freeloaders" who took over.

Throughout the year, religious services were held in the auditorium every Sunday morning. Among the numerous other devotional meetings were those of the International Christian Fellowship and the Students' Christian Association. Regular Bible classes and prayer meetings were conducted for staff and students and the college officially recognized the World Week of Prayer.

Life in Peking had other unusual benefits: wives could turn over their household responsibilities to superb Chinese servants including, for those who needed this service, an English-speaking, "number one boy." The culinary skills of the chefs were supreme, and the tempting odors of Peking cuisine lingered for years afterwards in the olfactory senses of every faculty member. Thus relieved of almost all household chores the ladies were free to enjoy such diversions as the Peking American Women's College Club, the Mother's Club, the Red Cross, and "Things Chinese." Several women studied Chinese or were involved in charitable activities.

Medical scientific organizations for the faculty included the Peking branch of the Society for Experimental Biology and Medicine, which was established in 1922 with Carl Ten Broeck, head of bacteriology, parasitology, and pathology, as chairman, Wu Hsien, head of biochemistry, as vice chairman, and Charles Packard as secretary-treasurer. The Faculty Medical Society and the Peking branch of the China Medical Missionary Association met jointly each month. Chinese members of the staff belonged to the Peking branch of the National Medical Association. In addition there were interdepartmental and departmental journal clubs.

STUDENT LIFE

A students' association for medical, premedical, and nursing students was founded in 1920 for "the development of student initiative and self-expression, encouragement of the spirit of cooperation with the faculty, and promotion of fraternal relations."[6] The association's diversified activities included intellectual, social, athletic, health, and publications programs. Among the latter were the classbook, *The Unison*, an annual known as the *PUMC Handbook*, and a lay health education journal, the *PUMC Popular Monthly*, published jointly with the house staff.

Thomas Cochrane had led the students at the old UMC in founding a Students' Christian Association. The association was continued when the school changed hands and, together with the Department of Religious and Social Work, it was responsible for the daily chapel services and the Bible classes. An early special project had been the solicitation in 1921 of funds for famine relief; in recognition of the success of the undertaking a handsome memorial was presented to the school by the president of the republic, the Honorable Hsu Shih-chang.

The students also had dramatic, public speaking, and music clubs. A Journal Club, with Francis R. Dieuaide as faculty advisor, fostered the students' ability to prepare and present scientific papers.

Athletic activities were led by varsity faculty teams in football, basketball, and tennis; there were also interclass rivalries. The baseball team held its own against the best teams of the American military forces in north China. The ladies were not to be outdone, and the 1924 issue of *Unison*[7] shows pictures of a basketball team composed of female medical and nursing students. In addition, all students enjoyed volleyball, calisthenics, and folk dancing.

The same issue of *Unison*[8] presents another approach to the lighter side of student life. Students had been selected to receive contrived "honorary degrees" based on their nonacademic accomplishments: Ph.D. (Physical Director) to P. A. Yang; Ph.B. (Bachelor of Photography) to H. T. Ch'en; S.B. (Bachelor of Sleep) to H. J. Kang; M.D. (Doctor of Music) to William H. L. Chung; and D.D. (Doctor of Dancing) to Hosmer Johnson.

In 1918 two premedical students, A. P. Chen and K. Ma, conducted classes for PUMC employees

> to supply to the technicians and workmen an elementary knowledge of Chinese, English, and arithmetic which will be of practical use to them, and at the same time endeavor to improve their conditions of living and to correct their superstitious ideas.[9]

An accompanying illustration shows a Chinese peasant intently studying a book as he trudges along balancing a long pole with bales of straw on each end. Other illustrations in *Unison* show students on outings to the western hills, on boating parties, on bus trips, and astride burros.

On the whole, however, the students had little time to enjoy their extracurricular programs. Academic work was the first order of every day, and the demands were heavy. The program in the Premedical School also was rigorous in the first class of six students two had to be dropped for academic deficiencies

In another class, only fourteen out of twenty-three students survived the program. Thus when the students entered the medical school they represented such a highly select group that in 1921 Franklin McLean could write to Alfred Cohn at the Rockefeller Institute:

> We have seven third-year students, and both Peabody and I feel that they compare very favorably with the third-year students at home. They are able to understand, speak, and write English without difficulty and there is no handicap in this respect. These men have had four years in this institution.[10]

The admission of female students had been affected by a lack of proper dormitory facilities, and it was not until 1923 that Wenham Hall was opened as a dormitory for women on a site adjacent to Oliver Jones Hall. The dormitory was named for Herbert V. Wenham, a representative of the London Missionary Society and a skillful surgeon, who died of pneumonia in 1914 after spending eight years in Peking.

HOUSE STAFF

During the early years of PUMC the shortage of qualified house officers was a principal problem, and it was necessary to recruit them from American medical schools; as McLean noted, "the few interns available in China are of practically no use."[11] Harold Loucks, a graduate of Western Reserve, came to Peking as an assistant resident in medicine in 1921; a year later he moved to the surgery department. Thus began a distinguished career in academic medicine and an association with PUMC that terminated only when the school was nationalized by the Communist government on January 20, 1951.

In 1921 Helen Vincent, a Johns Hopkins graduate, accepted an appointment as assistant resident in obstetrics and gynecology. In the same year three graduates of Shantung Christian University School of Medicine were appointed to internships. Ruth Fox, a graduate of Rush Medical College, spent one year as an intern at PUMC at the suggestion of a family friend, Alan Gregg.

After the first commencement in 1924 top PUMC graduates gradually began to fill the internships and residencies; of the thirty house officers that year, twenty-three were Chinese.

RELATIONS WITH THE JAPANESE

An exchange professorship program with the South Manchuria Medical College was established in January 1922 when three professors from Moukden—Kubota, Shuno, and Yamashita—visited Peking to make the arrangements. The first PUMC exchange professor was Charles Young of the Department of Medicine who lectured on his studies on kala-azar. Yas Kuno, who later became Japan's leading physiologist, came to Peking as the first exchange professor from Moukden. Kuno's arrival in May 1922 was delayed, however, because the Moukden-Tientsin-Peking Railway had been disrupted by bandits; the fighting became so generalized that communications were cut off with

Tientsin, the major seaport for Peking. The first sixty soldiers to be wounded in the fighting were admitted to the PUMC hospital.

Another friendly gesture toward the Japanese was made when the facilities of Tokyo Imperial University, a leading medical research center, were severely damaged during the disastrous earthquake on September 1, 1923. An estimated 200,000 people were killed, and financial losses mounted to around $1 billion. On November 23, in response to a gracious invitation from the Rockefeller Foundation, eight medical scientists from the Japanese university arrived at PUMC to continue their research; they remained there until the spring of 1924.

A CHINESE DIRECTOR

With the ascendancy of the Nationalist government, in 1928 J. Heng Liu took a leave of absence from the surgery department to join the Ministry of Health in Nanking. This was a fortunate development for the college because it now had a friendly and understanding voice at a high level of government.

In 1929 the Ministry of Education promulgated regulations that any institution of higher education seeking registration must have a Chinese director and that the majority of its governing board must be Chinese. Thus in the spring of 1929 the trustees of PUMC appointed J. Heng Liu as director and Roger Greene as vice director. Although Liu held the post until 1938 he was on a continuous leave of absence over that nine-year period; the college had fulfilled the government's requirement that it have a Chinese director, but administration continued to be in American hands.

The requirement that the governing board have a majority of Chinese members was satisfied at the annual meeting of PUMC trustees on April 10, 1929; among the Chinese elected to the board were J. Heng Liu and Hu Shih.

MARY FERGUSON

When Mary E. Ferguson was appointed registrar in 1928 PUMC gained an intelligent, dynamic, and lifelong devotee. Mary Ferguson was born in Nanking in 1897 where her father, John Calvin Ferguson, a Methodist missionary educator, had founded the University of Nanking. Along with other missionary children she received her secondary education at Miss Jewel's School in Shanghai and then went to the United States where she attended Wellesley College for two years. In 1919 she came to Peking, where her father was serving as educational advisor in government service.

From 1928 until PUMC closed in December 1941, Mary Ferguson's fluency in Chinese, her literary ability, and above all her intellect, made her a central figure at PUMC.

After spending the war years in the United States she returned to China in 1946, but was recalled to New York in 1950. When the college was nationalized in 1951 Mary Ferguson joined the United Board for Christian Higher Education in Asia.

With Harold Loucks, Miss Ferguson began to collect material for a history of PUMC and the CMB, which they planned to write after her retirement from the united board in 1960. When Loucks became ill, she persevered with the project, and *China Medical Board and Peking Union Medical College*12 was published in early 1970.*

Medical school faculty members frequently comment that there is one lady in the dean's office who really makes the institution tick—Mary Ferguson was certainly that lady at PUMC; the college was, and is, her life!

---

* Author's note: That book, together with Mary Ferguson's wise personal counsel, has been of inestimable value in the preparation of the present volume.

NOTES TO CHAPTER SEVEN

1. *PUMC Weekly Calendar Supplement*, 10 January 1922.

2. Taylor to Halsted, 7 December 1921, Halsted Collection, Archives of The Johns Hopkins University Institute of the History of Medicine, Baltimore, Maryland.

3. *Ibid.*

4. Peking Union Medical College, *The Unison*, vol. I (*1924*): pp. 154–55.

5. *Ibid.*, p. 154.

6. Peking Union Medical College, *The Unison*, vol. II (*1927*): p. 108.

7. Peking Union Medical College, *The Unison*, vol. I (*1924*): p 116.

8. *Ibid*, p. 163.

9. *Ibid.*, p. 111.

10. McLean to Cohn, 5 October 1921, Cohn Collection, Archives of The Rockefeller Institute, New York City.

11. *Ibid.*, 1 February 1921.

12. Mary E. Ferguson, *China Medical Board and Peking Union Medical College.*

Peiping Union Medical College

SCHEDULES OF INSTRUCTION FOR THE SESSION OF 1929–30*

SCHEDULE FOR THE FIRST YEAR

	Monday	Tuesday	Wednesday	Thursday	Friday	Saturday
First Trimester	9–12:30 Anatomy 2–5 *First and Second Weeks* Roentgenology 1 *Subsequent Weeks* Anatomy	9–12:30 Anatomy 2–5 *First and Second Weeks* Roentgenology 1 *Subsequent Weeks* Anatomy	9–12:30 Anatomy 2–5 *First and Second Weeks* Roentgenology 1	9–12:30 Anatomy 2–5 *First and Second Weeks* Roentgenology 1 *Subsequent Weeks* Anatomy	9–12:30 Anatomy 2–5 *First and Second Weeks* Roentgenology 1 *Subsequent Weeks* Anatomy	9–12:30 Anatomy
Second Trimester	9–1 Anatomy 2–5 Physiology 1	9–1 Anatomy	9–1 Anatomy 2–5 Physiology 1	9–1 Anatomy	9–1 Anatomy 2–5 Physiology 1 5–6 Development of Modern Medicine	
Third Trimester	9–1 Physiology 2 2–5 Biochemistry 1, 2, 3	9–1 Biochemistry 1, 2, 3	9–1 Physiology 2 2–5 Biochemistry 1, 2, 3	9–1 Biochemistry 1, 2, 3	9–1 Physiology 2 2–5 Biochemistry 1, 2, 3	9–12 Physiology 2

* Reprinted from *Peiping Union Medical College, Annual Announcement, 1929-30* (Peiping: July 1, 1929) pp. 42-8.

SCHEDULE FOR THE SECOND YEAR

	Monday	Tuesday	Wednesday	Thursday	Friday	Saturday
First Trimester	9–1 Pathology 1 2–5 Pharmacology 1 5–6 Clinical Pathological Conference	9–1 Pathology 1	9–1 Pathology 1 2–5 Pharmacology 1		9–12 Bacteriology 1 2–4 Pharmacology 1	9–12 Bacteriology 1
Second Trimester	9–1 Pathology 1 5–6 Clinical Pathological Conference	9–1 Pathology 1 2–5 Pharmacology 2	9–1 Pathology 1 2–5 Pharmacology 2	9–11 Pharmacology 2	9–12 Bacteriology 1 5–6 Development of Modern Medicine	9–10 Medicine 1 10–1 Bacteriology 1
Third Trimester	9–1 Medicine 1 2–5 Parasitology 1 5–6 Clinical Pathological Conference	9–1 Surgery 1 2–5 Parasitology 1	9–1 Medicine 1 2–5 Medicine 1		9–1 Medicine 1 2–4 Surgery 2	9–1 Surgery 1

SCHEDULE FOR THE THIRD YEAR

	Monday	Tuesday	Wednesday	Thursday	Friday	Saturday
First Trimester	9–10 Surgery 3 10–12 Neurology 1 12–1 Surgery 5 2–4 Surgery 4 *Section A* Ophthalmology 1 *Section B* 5–6 Clinical Pathological Conference	9–10 Medicine 2 10–11 Neurology 2 *Section A* 12–1 Surgery 6 (Orthopedics) Neurology 3 *(Alternate weeks)* 2–4 Surgery 4 *Section B* Ophthalmology 1 *Section A*	9–10 Surgery 3 10–11 Ophthalmology 1	9–10 Medicine 2 12–1 Pediatrics 1 Dermatology 1 *(Alternate weeks)* 2–4 Surgery 4 *Section A* Ophthalmology 1 *Section B*	9–10 Surgery 3 10–11 Neurology 2 *Section B* 12–1 Medicine 2 2–4 Surgery 4 *Section B* Ophthalmology 1 *Section A*	9–12 Medicine 2 12–1 Obstetrics and Gynecology 4
Second Trimester	9–10 Surgery 2 10–11 Obstetrics and Gynecology 1 11–12 Neurology 2 *Section A* 12–1 Surgery 5 2–4 Surgery 4 *Section A* Otolaryngology 1 *Section B* 5–6 Clinical Pathological Conference	9–10 Obstetrics 3 10–12 Medicine 2 12–1 Surgery 6 (Orthopedics) Neurology 3 *(Alternate weeks)* 2–4 Surgery 4 *Section B* Otolaryngology 1 *Section A*	9–10 Surgery 2 10–11 Gynecology 5	9–10 Otolaryngology 1 10–12 Medicine 2 12–1 Pediatrics 1 Dermatology 1 *(Alternate weeks)* 2–4 Surgery 4 *Section A* Otolaryngology 1 *Section B*	9–10 Surgery 2 10–11 Obstetrics 3 11–12 Neurology 2 *Section B* 12–1 Medicine 2 2–4 Surgery 4 *Section B* Otolaryngology 1 *Section A* 5–6 Development of Modern Medicine	9–12 Medicine 2 12–1 Obstetrics and Gynecology 4
Third Trimester	8–9 Hygiene 1 9–10 Obstetrics and Gynecology 1 12–1 Surgery 5 5–6 Clinical Pathological Conference	8–9 Hygiene 1 12–1 Surgery 6 (Orthopedics) Neurology 3 *(Alternate weeks)* 2–5 Medicine 2 (Parasitic Diseases)	8–9 Hygiene 1 10–11 Obstetrics 3 Medicine 2 (Parasitic Diseases)	8–9 Hygiene 1 12–1 Pediatrics 1 Dermatology 1 *(Alternate weeks)* 2–5 Medicine 2 (Parasitic Diseases)	9–10 Obstetrics 3 10–12 Medicine 2 12–1 Medicine 2 (Clinic) 2–3 Syphilis 1 3–4 Obstetrics and	8–9 Hygiene 1 10–11 Obstetrics and Gynecology 4 11–12 Pediatrics 1

SCHEDULE FOR THE FOURTH YEAR
General Exercises

All members of the Fourth Year Class attend the following general exercises throughout the academic year:

	Monday	Tuesday	Wednesday	Thursday	Friday	Saturday
12–1	Surgical Clinic	Orthopedic and Neurologic Clinic (Alternate weeks)		Pediatric and Dermatologic Clinic (Alternate weeks)	Medical Clinic	Obstetric and Gynecologic Clinic
5–6	Clin. Path. Conference				*Development of Modern Medicine	

* 2nd trimester only.

CLINICAL CLERKSHIPS

The class is divided into three sections to serve as clinical clerks on the following schedule:

Section	First Trimester	Second Trimester	Third Trimester
I	Sept. 9–Sept. 28—Public Health* (3 wks.) Sept. 30–Nov. 30—Medicine** (9 wks.)	Dec. 2–Mar. 8—Surgery, Obstetrics and Gynecology*** (13 wks.)	Mar. 10–May 31—Outpatient Department (11 wks.)
II	Sept. 9–Dec. 7—Surgery, Obstetrics and Gynecology*** (13 wks.)	Dec. 9–Mar. 1—Outpatient Department (11 wks.)	Mar. 3–Mar. 22—Public Health* (3 wks.) Mar. 24–May 31—Medicine** (9 wks.)
III	Sept. 9–Nov. 23—Outpatient Department (11 wks.)	Nov. 25–Feb. 1—Medicine** (9 wks.) Feb. 3–23—Public Health* (3 wks.)	Feb. 24–May 31—Surgery, Obstetrics and Gynecology*** (13 wks.)

* 75 credit hours.
** Medicine—180 credit hours; Neurology—45 credit hours.
*** Four weeks in Obstetrics and Gynecology (100 credit hours); nine weeks in Surgery (225 credit hours) by rotation.

The outpatient clerkship is conducted on the following schedule:

	Monday	Tuesday	Wednesday	Thursday	Friday	Saturday
10–12	Pediatric Clinic	Syphilis Clinic		Syphilis Clinic	Pediatric Clinic	
2–4	Dermatologic Clinic	Neurologic Clinic	Dermatologic Clinic		Neurologic Clinic	
4–5	Chinese	Chinese		Chinese		

CHAPTER EIGHT

The Golden Years: The Basic Sciences

ANATOMY

The first professorial appointment was in anatomy, and it was filled admirably—but for too brief a time—by Edmund Vincent Cowdry, who arrived in Peking in September 1918. A Canadian with a Ph.D. from the University of Chicago, Cowdry was teaching histology at Hopkins under Franklin P. Mall when he was tapped for Peking.

Of special interest was a survey of the teaching of anatomy and the state of education in anatomy in China that Cowdry published in 1920.[1] Through personal visits to nineteen medical schools, and questionnaires to the seven others, he was able to give an accurate picture of the sad state of medical education in all medical schools in China except the University of Hong Kong and the South Manchuria Medical College in Moukden. The eight Chinese-sponsored medical schools were an army college, a naval college, the National Medical College, and five provincial institutions. Cowdry believed that their existence indicated the desire of the Chinese to assume responsibility for their own needs in medicine, but he was concerned by the schools' lack of adequate facilities.

Cowdry was also disturbed by the condescending attitude of the missionaries toward Chinese doctors. As an example he quoted a missionary doctor as saying, "It is difficult to cooperate with them because they are only heathens anyway."[2]

The root of the problem in medical education in China, Cowdry believed, was the age-old conviction that medicine was a fourth- or fifth-rate profession. Another contributing factor was the Chinese attitude toward illness, described by Cowdry as "apathetic and fatalistic . . . believing that it is a visitation of providence in punishment for transgressions."[3]

Of the nineteen anatomical laboratories that Cowdry visited, only four had adequate physical facilities: those at the University of Hong Kong; at Aurora in Shanghai; at South Manchuria in Moukden; and his own at PUMC. In his judgment all the schools, save Peking, were tragically understaffed. For the twenty-six medical schools Cowdry reckoned there were no more than twenty-four full-time teachers of anatomy.

Library resources were also totally inadequate, except in Peking. In 1919 the China Medical Board made an appropriation of $65,000 to James I. Ballard, the assistant librarian at the Boston Medical Library, and sent him to Europe to purchase books for Peking. With this flying start, resources accumulated rapidly; by 1921 there were 22,000 volumes and 450 journals in the stacks and reading rooms of PUMC, as well as a superb collection of the Chinese pharmacopeia and other native medical works. It became the leading medical library in the Far East, and surpassed all but a handful of medical libraries in American schools. The lack of library resources at other Chinese schools, however, drastically handicapped their students and made research by their faculty all but impossible.

The striking inadequacy of many of the teaching programs was clearly exemplified by a statement made by one missionary school teacher:

> We don't teach histology, embryology, or comparative anatomy, as our scope is to form practitioners only. Besides the intellectual standard and previous scientific education of our scholars are not high enough to allow us to emphasize pure science.[4]

Despite their insistence on Mandarin as the language of instruction, many foreign teachers could speak no Chinese. Their instruction was presented by means of blackboard drawings with English legends: a Chinese interpreter would then explain the sketches to the students. The following morning the students were required to reproduce both the drawings and the English legends.

Because of the severe shortage of cadavers, dissection of the human body was possible in only twelve of the twenty-six medical schools; at the end of a year and a half Cowdry had been able to procure only four bodies. When the first cadaver was carried through the rear entry, the technicians and dieners fled and no inducement could persuade them to return.

With staff and cadavers in short supply in the Chinese-sponsored medical schools the percentage of time allotted to lectures was too high—at one school it was 100 per cent. At PUMC only 10 per cent of the total teaching hours was allotted to lectures; 90 per cent was spent in the teaching laboratories.

During his three years in China Cowdry established a collection of embryos from mission hospitals to study the development of the internal organs at successive stages of fetal growth.

Cowdry was instrumental in the founding of the first Chinese scientific society, the Anatomical and Anthropological Association of China, which held its first meeting at PUMC on February 26, 1920.

Cowdry returned to New York in late 1921. The immediate reason was the illness of his wife, but he may also have been disturbed by the limited opportunities in Peking in his chosen field, cytology. He became a member of Simon Flexner's Division of Pathology and Bacteriology at the Rockefeller Institute, and in 1928 moved to Washington University in St. Louis as professor of cytology and later of anatomy.

Cowdry's father, Nathaniel H. Cowdry, who had had no biomedical training, made an important contribution to the Chinese materia medica. After retiring from a successful business career in Canada, the senior Cowdry turned to studies of medicinal plants in his son's laboratory in Baltimore, where he developed such a deep interest in botany that he and his sister decided to accompany his son to PUMC and study Chinese botanicals. Working out of PUMC they gathered what was described as "probably the finest collection that has yet been made of Chinese medicinal plants."[5] Their studies, with excellent plates, were published as "Plants from Peitaiho,"[6] sponsored by the Royal Asiatic Society of China. On Nathaniel Cowdry's death, E. V. Cowdry, in fulfillment of his father's expressed desire, presented the collection to the Department of Pharmacology, where it was enlarged, classified, and catalogued.

Edmund Cowdry's colleague in anatomy at PUMC was a Toronto classmate, Davidson Black, who had studied with the famed English anthropologist, G. Elliott Smith, and with the distinguished neuroanatomist, C. U. Ariens Kappers, director of the Central Dutch Institute of Brain Research. While Cowdry was an outstanding histologist, Black was an outstanding anthropologist and, to his enduring fame, a key figure in the discovery of Peking man. Describing their relationship Cowdry said: "Black had ambitions in anthropology and seldom used a microscope, while I was looking through one at cells most of the time."[7] Cowdry's designation was in anatomy, while Black's title was professor of neurology and embryology, an arrangement favored by Simon Flexner because, in Cowdry's words, "he [Flexner] said it was important for each of us to keep out of each other's way."[8] Black accepted the appointment at Peking with the understanding that he could pursue his anthropological studies through scientific expeditions to central China and to Tibet.

On the day of their arrival in 1919, Black and his wife were given an impressive lesson in Chinese efficiency. They were met by the Cowdrys and escorted to their new residence in the PUMC compound only to find, to their dismay, that there were no doors, no window frames, and no furniture. After a few words with the caretaker, Cowdry and his wife succeeded in diverting the Blacks into a tour of Peking. When they returned in the evening, the doors and windows were in place; the house was more than adequately furnished; and they were greeted by a beaming "Number One Boy" holding open the just-installed front door.

One of Black's first research projects was in collaboration with Bernard Emms

Read; Black described it somewhat laconically in a letter dated December 5, 1919:

> During the last month I have had a large female camel living in the basement. Read, our physiologist chemist, is doing the nitrogen metabolism on this beast and I shall take what remains.[9]

Read subsequently published a paper entitled "The Secretion of Urine in the Camel."[10]

When Cowdry resigned in the winter of 1921 Black was designated head of the Department of Anatomy. A short time later, in April 1921, in a letter to New York, Richard Pearce, acting director of PUMC, raised the question, which he did not pursue, of whether there might be too much anthropology and not enough real anatomy in that department. This was at a time when the movement in anatomy in the United States was toward histology and away from anthropology. Yet Pearce admitted that scientific progress in the anatomy department of PUMC was greater than in any other department.

In early 1922 Black was offered a professorship in anatomy at Toronto, but when he replied that he was committed to his search for prehistoric man for at least two more years the offer was withdrawn. A completely dedicated scientist, Black's working schedule called for him to arrive at the laboratory in the late afternoon and to carry on through the night. And he was adamant that no one but himself be allowed to handle the beloved skulls for his comparative studies.

Kappers, the father of the theory of neurobiotaxis, which stimulated studies in comparative neurology, was visiting professor in the Department of Anatomy from 1923 to 1924. A year after his return to Holland one of his students, A. B. Drooglever Fortuyn joined the department to teach neuroanatomy and biostatistics. Fortuyn's research was on genetic variability in the common mouse, *Mus musculus*.

Samuel H. Detweiler came to PUMC in 1920 from Yale, where his research had been on the retina, the transplantation of limbs, and the spinal cord. During his three years at PUMC he continued these studies. He left Peking in 1923 to go to P and S, where his research in neuroembryology and related fields of experimental embryology was outstanding.

Peking Man

Calcified structures had for many centuries been one of the most popular medicines in the Chinese formulary. The sources included antler from deer, tusks from East Africa, and "unicorn" horns, which were actually the single horn of the narwhal, *Monodon monoceros*, from the Arctic seas that were peddled as "unicorn" horns in China and Japan by the Dutch.

"Dragon's teeth" and "dragon's bones" (*lung-ku*) were also held in high esteem. A major source was the fossil remains in a limestone cliff, Chouk'outien, thirty miles west of Peking, popularly known to foreigners as "Chow Gate Inn." Every apothecary shop in Peking displayed jars of the teeth from fossil remains, and the study of the contents of the jars was one source of information for Western anthropologists in their search for the antecedents of *Homo sapiens.*

The significance of Chouk'outien for anthropological studies goes back to 1901 when a Swedish paleontologist, K. A. Haberer, found a fossilized tooth from that area in an apothecary's jar; two years later it was identified by Max Schlosser as being from origins close to *Homo sapiens.* But it was not until ten years later that a Swedish geologist, J. G. Anderssen, began to excavate the Chouk'outien area scientifically; in 1921 he opened a fissure cave that contained fossil remains.

This find initiated a major study of Chouk'outien led by Davidson Black and the National Geological Survey of China, represented by W. C. Pei and C. C. Young. Black's laboratories became the base for the studies, which kindled the excitement not only of the investigators but of the other faculty members. On October 16, 1927, Birger Bohlen, a Swedish paleontologist, found a molar tooth in situ, which he delivered to Black in his laboratory that night. Black's studies of the tooth showed it to be from a separate genus popularly known as Peking man; he designated it scientifically as *Sinanthropus pekinensis.*

In December 1927 Black went on furlough to the United States and Europe, carrying the brown tooth of Peking man in his vest pocket as a showpiece. On his return to Peking in the autumn of 1928, he began a three-year leave of absence in order to devote all of his energies to the study of *Sinanthropus pekinensis.*

To coordinate the anthropological studies, in the summer of 1929 the Cenozoic Research Laboratory was established by the National Geological Survey with support from the Rockefeller Foundation; the site at Chouk'outien was purchased by the survey to preserve it for scientific studies. It attracted such internationally renowned scientists as Elliot Smith, with whom Black had studied in London, Teilhard de Chardin, and the Abbé Breuil of Paris.

On December 1, 1929, W. C. Pei found an almost complete skull with a jaw of *Sinanthropus* at Chouk'outien. After wrapping it carefully he placed it in the basket of his bicycle and pedaled hastily along the thirty miles of dusty road to PUMC and Black.

In all, as many as forty individual specimens were finally identified. Davidson Black's studies of the skull indicated little doubt that Peking man's brain was much like that of man today.

Stone tools and weapons were found, as well as bones of mighty animals presumably killed and eaten by Peking man. Since the bones had been broken by the hand of man it was clear that Peking man had been a hunter and had lived on meat. He knew the use of fire and the art of making stone implements from flint and quartz. The animal world that surrounded him half a million years ago included huge stags, giant boars, and the sabre-toothed tiger.

But Black was not destined to enjoy his worldwide fame for long. In 1933 he suffered his first anginal attack, and an electrocardiogram showed advanced myocardial disease. He persevered in his schedule of working through the night, and on March 15, 1934, the night watchman found his body beside his bench. Roy Chapman Andrews, the anthropologist and explorer, had this to say of Black: "Peking man and his cave ranks as the most important discovery in the whole history of human evolution. . . . Enormous credit is due to the scientific acumen and energy of the late Davidson Black."[11]

In 1935 the Rockefeller Foundation, with the approval of the National Geological Survey, invited the eminent German anatomist-anthropologist, Franz Weidenreich, to succeed Black as honorary director of the Cenozoic Research Laboratory and leader of the studies. As military conflicts mounted in 1941, however, Weidenreich moved to New York City and the American Museum of Natural History, taking with him casts of Peking man and numerous sketches and photographs.

The relics of Peking man were casualties of World War II and their loss was probably the greatest anthropological disaster of our time. Following the instructions of the geological survey the skull and other specimens were removed from the laboratories at PUMC and, with misgivings, turned over to the United States Marines on December 6, 1941, for safe transport to the United States. In the turmoil surrounding the first days of World War II, after leaving Peking the locker containing the specimens disappeared.

There is considerable speculation as to their ultimate fate. Japanese anthropologists came to Peking and searched for them exhaustively, but unsuccessfully, in the belief that they had been hidden by the American enemy. Since the American and Japanese military would have had no idea of the value of the "bag of bones" in a trunk, the skull and other specimens of Peking man may have ended up in the ashes of a Japanese bonfire or have been tossed into the waters of the harbor at Chingwantao, where the trunk had been destined for shipment out of Peking. Or, ironically, their ultimate destination may have been as "dragon bones" in an apothecary jar.

PHYSIOLOGICAL CHEMISTRY

When Wu Hsien was appointed associate professor and head of the new Department of Physiological Chemistry on July 1, 1924, he became the first Chinese department head at PUMC.* Wu, a brilliant scholar and a good teacher, was proud and rather aloof. He epitomized the comments of several former students that the Chinese professors at PUMC were usually more demanding than the foreign professors, and less concerned about the students' welfare.

---

* In the early years, physiology, pharmacology, and physiological chemistry were combined in a single department.

In 1910 in his native Fukien, Wu had passed the preliminary provincial examination for study in the United States under the Boxer indemnity program; this qualified him to go to Peking, with several thousand other candidates, to take the final examination. Wu was one of the 160 successful students, and he enrolled at the Massachusetts Institute of Technology in the fall of 1911.

Patriotic recognition of the woeful state of China's navy led him to study naval architecture, but he soon transferred to the natural sciences with a major in chemistry and a minor in biology. In the fall of 1917 he moved to Harvard Medical School as a graduate student in biochemistry under Otto Folin, and together they developed the classic Folin-Wu method for blood analysis: it allowed the preparation of a protein-free blood filtrate from a 10 cc. sample of blood, in which essentially all of the important constituents of blood could be determined. The Folin-Wu method was soon accepted universally in clinical as well as research laboratories and was elucidated in 1919 in Wu's doctoral thesis, "A System of Blood Analysis, with Special Reference to Uric Acid."[12]

Donald Van Slyke, of the Rockefeller Institute, the leading biochemist of his era, came to PUMC as a visiting professor in the fall of 1922. In a conversation with the author in March 1970, he recalled: "In those three months at Peking I completed experiments that would have required a year in any other laboratory, including the Rockefeller Institute."[*] The experiments that Van Slyke referred to were described by his former student and colleague, A. Baird Hastings, as "the most important scientific research in the history of PUMC, and one of the landmark studies in the history of biochemistry."[†]

Earlier in 1922 Wu Hsien had spent four months in New York with Van Slyke, and on his return to Peking he trained his excellent technicians to perfect the Van Slyke techniques.[†]

During the passage from Seattle to Yokohama, Van Slyke had worked out the experimental method and had predicted the findings of his experiments in Peking. Soon after he and his wife arrived at the Hotel Pekin, Van Slyke wrote a letter to Hastings on the hotel's stationery, describing in detail his proposed experiments and expected findings. Again, in Hastings's words: "He did everything but put down the final mathematical results of the experiments."[‡]

After two weeks in Japan, the Van Slykes traveled to Moukden where, at the request of the CMB, he had accepted an invitation to lecture to the faculty of the South Manchuria Medical College. Leaving their railway carriage at 7:00 a.m., the amazed Van Slykes were greeted by a delegation of professors from the college attired in striped trousers and cutaway coats; holding their top hats across their chests, with traditional Japanese dignity they bowed deeply. Van Slyke was to lecture on his current studies on diabetic acidosis. Before

---

[*] Donald D. Van Slyke 1970: personal communication.
[†] A. Baird Hastings 1970: personal communication.
[‡] Ibid.

leaving the station, Yas Kuno, who had studied at Cambridge and was the only member of the faculty reasonably fluent in English, asked for a brief summary of the lecture; Van Slyke gave him a five-minute resume. Later, after Van Slyke had presented his lecture, Kuno gave the audience a five-minute summary of it in Japanese. As the interpreter at his side translated, Van Slyke recognized that Kuno was giving a verbatim reproduction of the summary he had made at the railway station.

Forty-eight years later, Van Slyke recalled that when he had begun work at PUMC, "Everything was ready to go and every experiment worked."* He attributed part of the success to the assistance of three superb Chinese technicians, who had been trained by Wu Hsien. The blood for the studies was drawn from the neck vein of "a single Mongolian pony" that Franklin McLean had purchased months earlier for his favorite Sunday morning activity, horseback riding.† The experiments of Van Slyke, Wu, and McLean showed that the Donnan equilibrium applies to the distribution of electrolytes between the erythrocytes and the plasma in the blood. Thus physicochemical laws would explain the effects of oxygen and carbon dioxide on this distribution.

On his return to New York, Van Slyke took up his epochal investigations of the metabolic, biochemical, and urinary changes in nephritis that could be measured chemically; these studies brought him added fame. When he died in 1971, "Van," as he was known to his associates, was eulogized as the greatest biochemist in American medicine. He always held a special place in his heart for the fruitful three months he had spent in Peking.

In 1923, Daisy Yen, who had studied nutrition at Columbia with Henry C. Sherman, was appointed assistant in the department; she and Wu Hsien were married the following year.

Early in 1925, Wu again went on leave to work in New York with Van Slyke and Hastings on the denaturation of proteins. Van Slyke took this opportunity to suggest to Simon Flexner that Hastings go out to PUMC on an exchange basis while Wu was in the United States. Flexner would have none of it, however, insisting that visiting professorships be reserved for senior scholars with greater scientific accomplishments than had Hastings.

In 1930–31, Hastings, now a professor of biochemistry working with McLean in Chicago, accepted an invitation to serve as visiting professor at PUMC. Forty years later he recalled vividly and with deep affection his months at the college, which he described as "the Rockefeller Institute in a Chinese palace— and with a medical school. It was Western medicine in a Chinese palace."‡ The opportunities for metabolic studies could be equaled only at the Rockefeller Institute for several reasons: the proximity of the wards, the excellent labora-

---

* Donald D. Van Slyke 1970: personal communication.
† Franklin C. McLean 1967: personal communication.
‡ A. Baird Hastings 1970: personal communication.

tories, and the superb Chinese technicians. Special attractions for the patients under study were the spotless wards and comfortable beds of the hospital. They were quite willing to remain in the hospital for several months rather than return to the squalor of their dwellings.

Hastings took full advantage of these unique opportunities. By dividing his time between medicine and biochemistry he completed clinical studies on fluid and electrolyte abnormalities in nephrosis and on the edema of protein malnutrition. In the laboratories he continued his studies on the exchange of chloride and carbon dioxide that were to bring him international renown.

Beyond the scientific opportunities and the beauty of Peking, there was for Hastings and other visiting professors an added lure; in his words, "you could live like a king!"*

In 1935 Hastings moved from Chicago to Harvard as Hamilton Kuhn Professor of Biological Chemistry. He continued to keep in close touch with PUMC through the excellent young graduates of the school who were sent to him for research experience.

PHYSIOLOGY

In 1920 Ernest W. H. Cruickshank was the first appointment in physiology, with the rank of associate professor. One of a long family of medical Cruickshanks from Scotland, in 1911 he entered postgraduate training as a Carnegie Research Fellow in the Institute of Physiology of University College, London, where he remained until 1915.

Cruickshank had studied the distribution and action of the cardiac fibers of the vagus nerve. At PUMC his studies turned to alkalosis and tetany. A rather dour man, Cruickshank stayed apart from his colleagues on the faculty; Carrington Goodrich found him "lonely but lovable."† He left PUMC in 1925.

Meanwhile attention turned to a brilliant young Amoy Chinese, Lim Khoseng (Robert), who was working in the laboratories of the distinguished Edinburgh physiologist, Edward A. Sharpey-Schafer. Lim was born in Singapore in 1897, the son of an eminent physician, Lim Boon-kang. Moving to Scotland at an early age, Lim fought with the Indian Army in World War I. Subsequently, like many other British colonialists who sought careers in medicine, Lim enrolled at the Faculty of Medicine at Edinburgh. After graduating he taught physiology to medical students, many of whom were war-hardened veterans of the war; when they felt that he was too demanding they held him head down at the top of the stair well.‡ Lim had been working with Sharpey-Schafer for four years when he was recommended for consideration for a faculty post at PUMC.

Some of the more conservative PUMC faculty members felt that Lim at the age of twenty-seven was too young and untested for a senior appointment. He

---

* Ibid.
† E. Carrington Goodrich 1972: personal communication.
‡ John B. de C. M. Saunders 1972: personal communication.

was therefore given a one-year trial period under the critical eyes of Anton Julius ("Ajax") Carlson at the University of Chicago. Lim was one of a handful of researchers who had mastered the highly difficult technique developed by Pavlov for preparing a gastric pouch for the study of factors affecting gastric secretion. At Chicago he continued these studies with Carlson and with Andrew Ivy, both of whom were concentrating their efforts on studies in gastrointestinal physiology. Before the year was over, Carlson reported to the CMB that Robert Lim was eminently qualified to hold a senior faculty position in any medical school, in the West or in China.

Thus the program in physiology at PUMC received a great fillip with the arrival in 1924 of "Bobby" Lim. He was short, charismatic, and loaded with energy and enthusiasm. He came to Peking with Sharpey-Schafer's daughter as his wife and far more facility in English, which he spoke with a broad Scottish burr, than in Chinese. "If you closed your eyes you thought that you were talking to a Scot, not a Chinese," was the comment of one of his colleagues.* Despite his Scottish background Lim was intensely dedicated to the cause of a free and democratic China. He was literally worshipped by the students; when they reminisce about the old days at PUMC they turn first to Bobby Lim, remembering him as an excellent teacher with only a single shortcoming—his pronounced Scottish burr: "We were accustomed to American English, not Scottish English!†"

At PUMC Lim continued his studies on factors affecting gastric secretion and extended them to the relationship between the constituents of the blood and gastric juice; he established with Ma Wen-chao of the anatomy department, a collaborative cytological study on changes in the Golgi apparatus in relation to gastric secretion.

While Lim's research and teaching were important, they were by no means his only activities. He was a major force in the general development of the school, throwing the weight of his intelligence and his personality into a wide range of programs. On February 27, 1926, he led the formation of the Chinese Physiological Society and served as its first chairman. Bernard Read was secretary-treasurer; Wu Hsien and H. G. Earle of Hong Kong—later head of the Henry Lester Institute of Shanghai—were directors.

Bobby Lim was remarkably skillful with his hands—he was ambidexterous— and was an accomplished calligrapher and artist. He put these abilities to good use at the time of the Shanghai Incident in 1927 when word reached Peking that the governor of the British settlement in Shanghai had ordered his Sikh guards to "Shoot to kill!" if they were harassed by Chinese. Lim's patriotism was aroused by this and one day, with a medical student, Loo Chih-teh, he locked the doors and closed the shutters of the physiology laboratory. Over several

---

* Wang Shih-chun 1971: personal communication.
† Yu Tao-chun 1971: personal communication.

hours he painted a number of posters which he and Loo plastered around Peking after midnight. Under large characters that read "Shoot to kill!" the posters showed a Sikh guard in British regimentals firing at an impoverished Chinese who was falling at his feet.*

PHARMACOLOGY

When the final arrangements were being made for the sale of the UMC, the London Missionary Society had made a special request that the chemist, Bernard Read, should be retained on the staff. A 1908 graduate of the London College of Pharmacy and a devout Christian, Read had been recruited by Thomas Cochrane a year later as a lecturer in chemistry and biology at UMC. Primarily a pharmaceutical chemist, Read wished to remain in China primarily to explore the vast native materia medica. Members of the CMB, especially Flexner, had reservations as to Read's qualifications for the new program. To test him—and to train him—Read was therefore awarded a CMB fellowship that required him to spend part of his time with Walter Jones, a professor of physiological chemistry at Johns Hopkins, and an atheist. Jones's fall from righteousness had followed a debate with the famed agnostic Robert Ingersoll when Jones had agreed that if he lost the debate he would also lose his soul.†

Read found a more congenial spiritual environment when he moved to the laboratories of E. P. Underhill at Yale, where he earned a master's degree in pharmacology. Since his record was satisfactory at both Hopkins and Yale, and since the CMB wished to maintain a harmonious relationship with the London Missionary Society, Read was awarded a second fellowship in 1922. He returned to Underhill's laboratories and earned a Ph.D. for his studies on the metabolic effects of chaulmoogra oil, at that time the sole agent in the treatment of leprosy.

Working in the laboratories at PUMC, Chen Ko-kuei and Carl F. Schmidt introduced ephedrine to Western medicine. These studies stand as the most important example of a highly effective and widely used pharmacological agent isolated from indigenous sources—a unique accomplishment based on a co-operative research team: Chen, a Shanghai Chinese, and Schmidt, a Pennsylvania Dutchman.

Born in Shanghai in 1898, Chen had won a Boxer Indemnity Scholarship for the study of pharmacy at the University of Wisconsin. His interest turned increasingly to research in the biological sciences, however, and after receiving a degree in pharmacy he entered graduate studies in the Department of Physiology under Walter Meek. In 1923 he earned a Ph.D. through his studies on the autolysis of muscle.

---

* Loo Chi-teh 1969: personal communication.
† Katherine E. Read 1971: personal communication.

Because of his mother's illness, Chen returned to China where he secured an appointment as senior assistant in the Department of Pharmacology, Physiology, and Physiological Chemistry at PUMC. Here he joined Schmidt, who had graduated in medicine at the University of Pennsylvania in 1918. After his internship, Schmidt worked with Alfred Newton Richards, chairman of the Department of Pharmacology, in classical studies on the effects of adrenalin on the glomerular circulation of the frog's kidney. It was at the suggestion of Richards that Schmidt went out to PUMC in 1922 as an associate, with the primary mission of developing an educational program in dynamic pharmacology.

The ephedrine story at PUMC begins with a Chinese herbalist who attended Chen's family in Shanghai. One weekend Chen asked for a list of the ten most toxic preparations in the Chinese formulary; at the head of the list he received was *ma huang*—literally, yellow astringent—which was used in the treatment of asthma.

When he returned to Peking, Chen purchased *ma huang* at an herbal shop near PUMC and injected it into a dog that Schmidt had prepared for the medical students' laboratory exercises. The kymograph showed a sharp increase in the animal's heart rate and a rise in blood pressure, in contrast to the decrease that is the usual response to a foreign agent. Chen and Schmidt then undertook their classic studies, which demonstrated the cardiovascular effects of ephedrine, the similarity of its action to that of Adrenalin® (epinephrine), and, of major practical significance, its pharmacological effectiveness when taken orally. Soon ephedrine became one of the leading drugs in the therapeutic armamentarium of physicians in America and Europe.

When the great Indian poet and philosopher Rabindranath Tagore visited China in 1924, he proclaimed the importance of clinging to traditional medicine instead of adopting the scientific medicine of the West. In reflecting this abiding devotion that many Hindus hold for their indigenous medicine, Tagore was especially interested in the ephedrine-*ma huang* research and held a long conference with Chen to learn the details of his studies.* Tagore hoped that the Indian formulary might yield a medicine as important as ephedrine to buttress his belief in indigenous herbs.

Schmidt returned to the University of Pennsylvania in June 1924, after declining Houghton's offer to become head of pharmacology. Schmidt's research interests turned to the physiology and pharmacology of respiration, and in 1939 he succeeded Richards as head of pharmacology at Pennsylvania, a post he held until his retirement in 1959.

After Schmidt's departure from PUMC, Chen found the scientific climate in pharmacology less attractive, and in 1925 he entered Johns Hopkins as a third-year medical student. He was awarded the M.D. in 1927, and from 1929 until his retirement he was director of pharmacological research for the Eli Lilly

---

* Chen Ko-kuei 1971: personal communication.

Company and professor of pharmacology at the University of Indiana Medical Center.

After serving as visiting professor of pharmacology in 1923, Reid Hunt, professor of pharmacology at Harvard, came away from Peking with lavish praise for the school. In his report to the Rockefeller Foundation he spoke of the splendid spirit of cooperation of all instructors and students:

> I have never seen an institution apparently so efficiently conducted. . . . I do not know of any place in the United States where graduate students can get such excellent opportunities. . . . I feel that I have never seen a more useful, if as useful, institution as the Peking Union Medical College, or one so full of promise, or one yielding such a return on the investment.[13]

Hunt made special reference to the PUMC studies on schistosomiasis of Ernest Carroll Faust and Henry E. Meleny, and to those on kala-azar of Charles W. Young.

BACTERIOLOGY, PARASITOLOGY, AND PATHOLOGY

Carl Ten Broeck, a 1913 graduate of Harvard Medical School, came to Peking in 1920 as the first head of the combined department. He had established his scientific career as the key assistant to Theobald Smith, the leading American investigator of the pathology of animal diseases, at the Rockefeller Institute's new Department of Animal Pathology which opened at Princeton on July 1, 1914.

A Swede from Uppsala, Johannes H. Bauer, was Ten Broeck's assistant. He had first trained for the priesthood, and his previous career had included studies at the Imperial University of Moscow and one year of service as physician-in-charge of the antityphus train of the American Red Cross in Vladivostok.*

Ten Broeck and Bauer were drawn to studies of tetanus through a piece of felt that had covered a bedsore in the sacral area of a patient on one of the surgical wards. The felt was heavily contaminated with feces, and culture revealed the presence of tetanus spores. A search of published reports uncovered only two papers reporting the presence of tetanus spores in human feces: one on Italian peasants reported spores in 5 per cent, while a study on British soldiers who had lived in muddy trenches at the western front reported a prevalence of 33 per cent. Ten Broeck and Bauer were able to isolate tetanus spores from the feces of 33 per cent of the patients admitted to the PUMC hospital, but they believed that the figure was low because they had examined only a single, pea-sized specimen. They also showed that tetanus spores probably multiply actively in the intestinal tract, which raised the interesting question of why there was not a higher incidence of clinical tetanus. Ten Broeck speculated that the presence of the spores in the intestinal tract might confer a degree of immunity, and

---

* Bauer was an eccentric; for example, he spoke Russian, Chinese, French, and Spanish, but refused to speak in his native Swedish.

that perhaps the deliberate introduction of spores into the gut might represent one means of immunizing against the disease.

Ten Broeck returned to the Princeton laboratories of the Rockefeller Institute in 1927. Two years later he succeeded Theobald Smith as director of the Department of Animal and Plant Pathology, in which position he served until 1947 when the laboratories were integrated with the institute.

Johannes Bauer joined the laboratories of the Rockefeller Foundation's International Health Division where, working with E. G. Pickels, he improved the stability of the driving mechanism of the ultracentrifuge, and made other adjustments that adapted the instrument for virus research. These were important developments in the program to prepare yellow fever vaccine.

Ten Broeck was succeeded as head of the department at PUMC by Lim Chong-eang, who had joined the faculty in 1922. Born in Penang in the Malay States and educated at the University of Hong Kong, Lim came to PUMC from Johns Hopkins where he had received the doctorate in public health for his studies on the culture of vaccine virus. At Peking he continued and expanded these studies into a program through which his department prepared immune sera for hospitals and clinics in north China.

In 1921 Samuel H. Zia, one of Hans Zinsser's prize students, joined the department. His research was on the immunological and immunochemical aspects of infection, and on the prevalence of murine typhus in Peking.

Since 1866, when Patrick Manson arrived in China, the country had been of unusual interest to students of parasitology and tropical medicine. The factors contributing to the high incidence of parasitic infection included pollution of food and water with human feces (night soil); the ingestion of raw food, especially fish; and unsanitary personal habits, particularly promiscuous defecation.

With such opportunities for research available, a young parasitologist, Ernest Carroll Faust, was one of the first applicants for an appointment to the faculty at PUMC. Primarily through his work at Peking, Faust became the great pioneer of American parasitology, in a mold comparable to that of Manson for British science.

Faust began his career at the University of Illinois in Urbana, where he earned his Ph.D. and taught parasitology from 1912 to 1919. When his request for an appointment at PUMC was received, he was invited to New York and interviewed by George Vincent, president of the Rockefeller Foundation. After a discussion of Faust's interests and the developments at PUMC, he accepted the customary two-year appointment. Dr. and Mrs. Faust sailed from San Francisco on December 8, 1919, as passengers on a transport crowded with Chinese coolies returning from service on the western front in the Chinese Labor Battalion.*

---

* Ernest Carroll Faust 1971: personal communication.

In 1920 Henry E. Meleney, a graduate of Columbia University College of Physicians and Surgeons, joined the Department of Medicine at PUMC. Since he expressed an interest in schistosomiasis, Faust decided to make a parasitologist out of his new colleague, and he was eminently successful. Subsequently, John F. Kessel, Marshall and Arthur Hertig, and Khaw Oo-kek joined the parasitology program, which became one of the most productive research activities of the college. Their studies give a picture of the truly massive problems caused by parasitic diseases in China at that time.

Faust and his colleagues undertook a series of comprehensive surveys and studies on parasitic diseases of north, central, and south China. Their subjects included healthy and hospitalized human beings, as well as mammals, birds, amphibia, fish, molluscs, and arthropods. The numerous reports that flowed from these studies stand today as signal contributions, not only to our knowledge of the diseases of China, but to our general knowledge of parasitology.

In 1926 Faust summarized their surveys and research. He listed malaria, amebiasis, and kala-azar as the most important protozoan diseases; the leading helminthic diseases were oriental schistosomiasis, clonorchiasis, fasciolopsiasis, hookworm, and filariasis.

Parasitic diseases were seen so frequently at PUMC and had been so carefully mapped out geographically that a frequent comment to entering patients was, "Tell me where you come from in China and I will tell you your parasites."*

Schistosomiasis

Fifty years after he had initiated his studies in Peking, and at the twilight of a brilliant career, Faust looked back to the work with Meleney on *Schistosomiasis japonica* as his most important research contribution. In 1924 the studies were collected in a massive monograph dedicated to Henry S. Houghton who "as a former medical missionary at Wuhu, Anwhei Province, China, undertook the first scientific study of schistosomiasis japonica in China."[14] In his prefatory note Faust cited Meleny as the first scientist to identify the molluscan host, *Oncomelania hupensis*. Further research showed it to be the intermediate host throughout the vast Yangtze flood area in central China, while *Katayama nosophora*, named for the Japanese parasitologist, was the vector in coastal waters where the disease also occurred. The prevalence of schistosomiasis was of such magnitude throughout the Yangtze flood area that 100 million Chinese were endangered by the disease.

Faust and Meleney were the first scientists to give a detailed report on the morphology, biology, and life history of *Schistosoma japonicum* in China. In dogs that had been experimentally infected, eggs appeared in the feces as early as twenty-nine days later. They also reported the first accurate data on the size of the eggs.

---

* Khaw Oo-kek 1970: personal communication.

The route of the infective larvae, circariae, from the skin to the lungs was known to be by way of the lymphatics. The principal manifestations of the disease were, however, based on involvement of the liver and the intestinal tract; the route from the lungs to the abdominal viscera was not known. Faust and Meleney showed that after the circariae reach the lungs they enter the pulmonary veins, pass to the arterial circulation, and are then deposited in the gastrointestinal capillaries and the portal veins.

The blood of patients was found to have a high serum-globulin level—as high as in kala-azar. Because the latter was primarily a disease of north China, as schistosomiasis was of central China, the high globulin levels could be used not only for screening for both diseases, but for tentative clinical diagnosis.

For therapy they recommended sodium- or potassium-antimony tartrate, noting that of the three varieties of the disease, *japonicum* infections are the most resistant to antimony therapy, and most often associated with toxic reactions.

While molluscicides and other measures were proving effective in controlling *Schistosomiasis japonica* in Japan, Faust and Meleney recognized that such relatively advanced approaches would not be practicable in China because of the vastness of the problem. Instead, they recommended a three-pronged, more fundamental approach—control of feces disposal; avoidance of wading in ponds and other fresh water courses; and intensive therapy of proven cases.

Clonorchiasis

The principal studies on clonorchiasis were carried out by Faust and a young Chinese graduate of the Faculty of Medicine at Edinburgh, Khaw Oo-kek, who joined the staff in 1925. Clonorchiasis, caused by the Oriental liver fluke, *Clonorchis sinensis* (Cobbold), was the "most important of the fluke infections in China" because of its high prevalence in dogs, horses, cats, and other mammals.[15] Human disease was confined almost exclusively to Kwangtung and Swatow in south China where it was widely prevalent. For example, 50 per cent of the sailors from south China who were imprisoned in Hamburg in World War I had *Clonorchis sinensis* eggs in their stools, as did a group of Chinese who were examined while in quarantine in San Francisco at about the same time; both groups were from Kwangtung and Swatow. On the other hand, although nearly one-third of the dogs and cats in north China were infected, the prevalence of human infection in that region was less than 1 per cent. The consumption of raw fish was the crucial factor in human infection. Faust and Khaw showed that practically every fresh water fish in south China was capable of serving as the second intermediate host. Raw fish was a popular delicacy in south China, and the fish, heavily contaminated with *Clonorchis*, usually came from commercial ponds that had been fertilized with night soil. The problems in controlling the disease were enormous. Faust and Khaw recommended the avoidance of native dishes and of raw fish as the best preventive measure.

Fasciolopsiasis

Fasciolopsis buski is a giant fluke found in central and south China as far north as the Yangtze valley, with a specially high frequency in two coastal provinces south of Shanghai, Chekiang and Kwangtung. Faust estimated that 5 per cent of the population in these provinces had the fluke although only a small percentage showed symptoms. While the hog is the most frequent reservoir, Faust found the dog also to be an important source. C. H. Barlow and Claude Henon, with guidance from Faust, worked out the life cycle of *Fasciolopsis buski*.* After passage from a hog, man, or dog, it enters a snail which then encysts on a variety of aquatic plants, especially water chestnuts, or caltrop (*Trapa natans*), and water bamboo. In humans the parasites usually attach to the mucous membrane of the duodenum or jejunum where they produce inflammation, ulceration, and abscess formation. The infection responds promptly to hexylresorcinol (Crystoids®), tetrachlorethylene, or stilbazium oxide.

Kala-azar

Visceral leishmaniasis, also known as kala-azar, primarily a disease of children and adolescents in north China, was one of the most common medical problems on the wards of PUMC. Charles W. Young, who was in charge of the Kala-Azar Field Studies Unit, led a survey which showed that the disease was confined to the region north of the Yangtze, and Faust suggested that it had been introduced by way of the northwest trade routes.[16] Seventy per cent of the cases were in persons under the age of twenty.

Young found that the diagnostic Leishman-Donovan bodies could be most readily demonstrated through smears and cultures taken from punctures of a greatly enlarged spleen; similar preparations from the peripheral blood were less frequently diagnostic. Splenic puncture was a dangerous procedure for routine diagnostic work, however, because of the possibility of bleeding from the tense and congested organ, so sternal puncture became the preferred method.

Working with Young in the field studies unit in 1925 and 1926 were two brothers from Minnesota, Arthur T. and Marshall Hertig, both budding entomologists. After a year in China, Arthur Hertig returned to the United States to study medicine at Harvard. He then entered an academic career in pathology, and in 1952 was appointed Shattuck Professor of Pathology at Harvard, partly because of his excellent studies on reproductive embryology. Marshall Hertig continued his studies on tropical diseases as an entomologist, first at the National Institute of Hygiene and Public Health in Lima, Peru, and then at the Gorgas Memorial Institute of Tropical and Preventive Medicine and the Gorgas Memorial Laboratory in Panama.

Another approach to the diagnosis of kala-azar came from the studies of

---

* In 1921 Barlow deliberately infected himself with *Fasciolopsis buski* and, in 1944, while working in the Ministry of Public Health in Cairo, Egypt, with *Schistosoma haematobium*.

Sia Ho-p'ing (Richard), of the Department of Medicine, and Wu Hsien. They showed that the striking increase in blood globulin levels could be applied as a diagnostic procedure through existing precipitation-flocculation tests, especially Ray's hemolysis test; positive reactions were also elicited in malaria, tuberculosis, schistosomiasis, and trypanosomiasis. In addition Sia and Wu found a marked increase in the total serum protein in active cases of kala-azar.

The ability to reproduce a human disease in a laboratory animal is an important research tool, especially in studies of pathogenesis and treatment. In 1924, Young and Jocelyn Smyly demonstrated that leishmaniasis could be reproduced in both the striped hamster, *Cricetulus griseus*, and the giant hamster, *C. triton*. Henry Meleny then undertook a series of studies on the histopathology of kala-azar in the hamster. He found that the fundamental and specific tissue reaction is the production of a large mononuclear phagocytic cell, variously known as clasmatocyte, an endothelial leukocyte, or a macrophage.

James R. Cash, who became head of pathology in 1924, with the collaboration of his colleague, Hu Cheng-hsiang, identified large concentrations of Leishman-Donovan bodies in the pigmented, granulomatous patches that develop in the skin and subcutaneous tissues of hamsters. They suggested that the disease could also be transmitted through droplets from the mouth or nose.

Amebiasis

In 1924 John Kessel and Olof Swensson made a survey of the prevalence of amebic disease in China. Although both amebic dysentery and liver abscesses could be found throughout the country, there were regional differences as represented by the high prevalence in the central Yangtze valley and in Wuchang Province. The remarkable tolerance of the human tissues to *Entamoeba histolytica* was demonstrated by Faust, who found that although 50 per cent of the patients in one mission hospital had *Entamoeba histolytica* in their stools, only 15 per cent had dysentery. Similar studies by other investigators showed that such symptomless carriers may discharge 35 million parasites daily. But the difficulty in managing the disease was demonstrated by the fact that 35 per cent of those harboring the amebae had no clinical manifestation and could disseminate the parasite uncontrollably.

Kessel and Faust found a relatively higher proportion of acute dysentery or liver abscess in tropical and semitropical south China, while in the north there was a higher proportion of carriers. They were also impressed by the relatively high prevalence of amebic disease in foreigners, whose resistance did not approach that of the Chinese. Using the intestinal ambebae of man, Kessel was able to induce experimental infections in rats and mice and to describe their distinguishing characteristics.

Clinical studies of PUMC Student Health Service patients by Kessel and Otto Willner, head of the service, in 1925 showed that emetine was the treatment of choice for acute cases, while sodium-iodoxy-quinoline sulfate (Chiniofon®) was the safest and most effective agent in chronic cases and in carriers.

Hookworm

The massive hookworm problems in China attracted the attention of the International Health Board of the Rockefeller Foundation, which was studying the disease on a worldwide basis. In 1923 and again in 1924 the foundation sent out the China Hookworm Commission led by William W. Cort of the Johns Hopkins School of Hygiene and Public Health, who had studied hookworm in the West Indies for the board. The commission was organized as a joint study of the foundation and PUMC, with John B. Grant of public health representing the medical college; the report was published in 1926.[17]

The Cort Commission found that hookworm was as massive a problem in China as in India. The central issue was the ancient, organized system of soil fertilization and pollution with night soil in the rural areas where the farmers saved it. City dwellers also saved their excreta, however, and sold it to the farmers who would plod through the streets with open pails, "honey buckets," of night soil at each end of a long pole. The excreta was then composted with straw and clay to a dry state or stored in wet form in large jars called *kongs*.

Hookworm was a major problem in central and south China, but not in the north. While stool examinations in Peking showed that as high as 28 per cent of the specimens contained the parasite, clinical disease seldom occurred because of the relatively rigorous nature of the climate. The disease flourished in more tropical climates lying between 36° north latitude and 30° south latitude.

The commission found that the incidence of hookworm disease was especially high among the millions of adults and children engaged in sericulture. Night soil was the prime fertilizer for the mulberry trees whose leaves were used to feed the silkworms, and the hookworm larvae easily pierced the skin of the barefooted, barelegged children and adults harvesting the leaves during the rainy season. On the other hand, hookworm did not represent a hazard for the millions who toiled in the rice paddies, although they too were exposed to night soil, because as soon as the rice fields had been fertilized they were flooded, and the eggs could not develop when covered with water.

Because of the dimensions of the hookworm problem in sericulture, the commission realized that they were up against an almost insoluble challenge. Night soil was an economic necessity—more than 24 million tons were used each year; it was an essential part of the Chinese culture that could not be abandoned. Beyond identifying the unique nature of the problems and urging adequate therapy for proven cases there was little the Cort Commission could recommend.

Malaria and Blackwater Fever

In 1926 Faust reported that malaria was found throughout south and central

China—from the extreme south to as far north as Peking, and from the east coast to the western boundary of Szechuan Province; it was most severe in the south and progressively less so toward the north. There were major areas where as high as 90–100 per cent of the populations were infected with malaria parasites.

Although in 1926 deadly blackwater fever, caused by infection with *Plasmodium falciparum*, was virtually unknown, it later became a problem in Peking, especially among opium addicts: highly virulent strains of the parasite were passed from addict to addict through the needles used to inject opium.

Several of the leaders in the PUMC parasitological studies continued to be authorities on tropical medicine when they returned to the United States. In September 1928 Faust was appointed professor of parasitology and head of the Division of Parasitology in the Department of Tropical Medicine at Tulane University. He turned his research to studies on tropical diseases affecting men and animals in Central and South America and in Puerto Rico. In 1937, with C. F. Craig, he published *Clinical Parasitology*,[18] the eighth edition of which appeared in 1971.

Meleney moved to Vanderbilt University medical school in 1927 as associate professor of preventive medicine and public health, and in 1941 to New York University as head of the Department of Preventive Medicine. For his early work at Peking he was decorated with the Rosette of the Order of the Brilliant Star by the Chinese Nationalist government.

Kessel served for twenty years as chairman of the Department of Bacteriology and Parasitology at the University of Southern California and then established a program in tropical parasitology at the new medical school at UCLA.

Reinhard J. C. Hoeppli, a Swiss graduate, succeeded Faust as the leader in parasitology at PUMC. As a physician, Hoeppli was more interested in the reaction of the host, whereas Faust had emphasized the parasite. Hoeppli studied the lesions produced by parasitic nematodes; tissue reactions to parasites using a transparent chamber in the rabbit's ear; and dermatological lesions of kala-azar in the dog.

Ralph G. Mills, a 1907 graduate of Northwestern, became the first head of pathology in 1920, having previously served as director of research at Severance Union Medical College in Seoul. The first specimens for the pathology museum were inherited from the laboratories of the UMC and of Harvard of China.

When William T. Councilman, head of pathology at Harvard Medical School, came out to Peking as visiting professor in 1923, he recognized the problems in developing a proper course in pathology because of the serious shortage of autopsies. The students had no hesitation in stating their side of the case:

> Because of ignorance and misunderstanding our autopsy service is not all that can be desired. If we could only get people to understand that the chief purpose of an autopsy is to correlate the clinical findings with the anatomical changes we would have less difficulty. . . . If we are to train good practitioners of medicine we must autopsy more of our patients that do not get well.[19]

J. Heng Liu of the Department of Surgery hit upon a novel approach to the autopsy problem, based upon the Chinese tradition that a comfortable coffin was essential for life hereafter. For a period, a coffin was donated to a patient and placed beside his bed so that he could be assured that it was well-fitting; in return his family agreed to a postmortem examination. At times a nurse making her evening rounds would come upon an empty bed only to find the patient lying in his coffin testing its comfort. This procedure angered the Peking police who, as guardians of Chinese culture, offered a rough-hewn coffin, gratis, if an autopsy was refused.

James R. Cash, a 1919 graduate of Hopkins, succeeded Mills in 1924. Cash had followed the footsteps of other young American pathologists to Vienna, where he worked beside and taught English to a young Czechoslovakian pathologist, Hans Smetana. When Cash was appointed head of pathology, Smetana accepted his invitation to join the department.

In the same year Cash recruited a young Chinese pathologist, Hu Cheng-hsiang, who had started his medical education at the Harvard Medical School of China. When that school closed in June 1916, Hu was among the eleven students awarded scholarships by the CMB to continue their studies in China, Japan, or the United States. He was one of six who moved to Boston to continue under the Harvard banner, and he graduated in 1921. He then trained in pathology at the Mallory Institute where he established a friendship with another Harvard graduate, Shields Warren, who was destined to be one of America's leading pathologists.

James Cash was an outstanding teacher, an excellent pathologist, and, in the words of one of his colleagues, "a delightful person to have on a medical school faculty."* During the seven years that he spent at PUMC, Cash's principal research interest was in the pathological anatomy of kala-azar.

In early 1925 Cash performed one of the most unique autopsies in history—on the corpse of Sun Yat-sen. This singular event was dictated in part by the continuing Chinese insistence on maintaining the human body intact after death. When Sun Yat-sen came to Peking in early 1925 he was a dying man. The ministrations of Chinese practitioners had been useless, and he was admitted to PUMC. Examination revealed an abdominal mass with ascites, and the family finally agreed to a laparotomy. Widespread carcinomatosis was found in the peritoneal cavity, and when a biopsy showed the malignancy to be of hepatic origin, the abdomen was closed.

Although Sun was terminally ill, the family removed him from the hospital so that he could die at home. He expired on March 12, 1925, and with the greatest reluctance the family agreed to a partial examination of the abdomen, but only with the assurance that no organs would be removed.

---

* Vernon W. Lippard 1971: personal communication.

When Cash entered the morgue he found the body ringed by a detachment of Chinese soldiers in uniform, with arms at the ready, to assure that the terms of the agreement would be fulfilled. The incision was opened; a sliver of the tumor was removed for microscopic study; and the abdomen was closed—the terms of the agreement had been scrupulously carried out. After a Christian memorial service in the PUMC auditorium, the college's truck, now draped as a hearse, carried the body to the Pi Yun Temple in the western hills. In 1929 Sun's body was moved to its last resting place, an enormous mausoleum in Nanking.

After the Japanese captured Peking in 1937 they seized upon a ridiculous propaganda stunt to ingratiate themselves with the Chinese people and embarrass PUMC as an American institution. They announced that Sun Yat-sen's corpse had not been returned to the family intact after the examination at the medical college and that he had not therefore had a proper burial—the missing organs must be returned to his mausoleum. When the organs had been recovered there would be a great procession to carry them to Sun's final resting place. Unfortunately for the Japanese there were no stolen organs at PUMC; Cash and Paul Stephenson of the anatomy department, who embalmed the body, had scrupulously adhered to the agreement. The only tissue that could be discovered was a microscopic section mounted on a glass slide. Irate and with deep fear of public humiliation, the Japanese had the single microscopic slide packed and sealed in an enormous chest that was borne off to Nanking with much ceremony and with the boast that the parts of Sun's corpse that had been removed by the deceitful foreigners had now been restored to his body.

A unique field expedition led three members of the faculty to a Trappist monastery under Belgian auspices located 100 miles north of Peking. Reports had reached the college of a mysterious and fatal disease, characterized by high fever and disseminated furunculosis, that had invaded the monastery. A relief team was assembled consisting of Carl Ten Broeck, Harold Loucks, and Hans Smetana. Their first problem was to get out of Peking, for the city had been encircled by the armies of three warlords. The American consul arranged a *laissez-passer* with great difficulty because of the state of belligerency. They traveled by rail to Chiweila where they mounted three sturdy Mongolian ponies for the final leg of their journey; for Loucks and Smetana, who were good horsemen, this was the most exciting part of the safari; for Ten Broeck, who was in no sense an equestrian, it was the most difficult.

As they approached the monastery they anticipated serious difficulties in elucidating the course of the disease because of the traditional Trappist oath of silence. Instead they were shortly surrounded by a group of shouting priests who, having seen one-half of their group die, were in mortal fear for their own health. In Hans Smetana's words, "they let loose vocally."*

* Hans Smetana 1971: personal communication.

The team found that the etiological agent of the disease was a highly lethal *Streptococcus hemolyticus* to which the remaining friars had already developed an immunity; the epidemic was therefore on the wane.

For a pathologist primarily interested in morbid anatomy, PUMC, with its paucity of autopsies, left much to be desired; for an experimental pathologist such as Smetana, who was interested in scientific research, it was, in his words,

> a scientist's paradise . . . the scientific opportunities were tremendous . . . there was no piece of scientific equipment that was too expensive, once we had proven the need for it.*

Smetana left Peking in 1927 and after a period in the pathology department at Columbia moved to the Armed Forces Institute of Pathology where he served as senior pathologist.

Cash accepted an appointment as Walter Reed Professor of Pathology at the University of Virginia and moved from Peking to Charlottesville in 1928. He was succeeded as head of pathology at PUMC by Hu Cheng-hsiang.

PUBLIC HEALTH AND HYGIENE

John B. Grant, a great pioneer and innovator in the field of public health, was born in his father's missionary hospital in 1890 in Ningpo, China. Of Canadian descent, Grant graduated from Acadia College in Nova Scotia, and completed the study of medicine at the University of Michigan. Guided into public health, in part through one of his professors, Victor C. Vaughan, Grant took graduate work in public health at Johns Hopkins and then joined the International Health Board (IHB) of the Rockefeller Foundation. In 1921 he was assigned to establish a program in public health at PUMC and to represent the IHB in the Far East.

John Grant was at least twenty-five years ahead of his time in the public health programs that he launched at PUMC. Most American medical schools are only now beginning to emulate Grant's community-based programs. He was endowed with great drive and a singular capacity to inspire students and colleagues, as well as a will to develop and administer programs of action.

Victor Heiser, director for the Far East of the IHB, who watched Grant in action for twenty years, described him as "an extremely able young man whose popularity in China and Japan was unparalleled. He was one of the best administrators developed by the Rockefeller Foundation."[20]

When Grant arrived in Peking in 1921, he knew he would be starting from scratch and he enjoyed the challenge. The most populous nation in the world had no national or municipal public health services, and Grant soon found himself taking the lead in building a national public health service in China. At the same time he needed to establish a strong educational and research base at PUMC.

---

* Ibid.

While the programs of his colleagues on the faculty were centered around hospital patients, Grant chose the community. He had no intention of sticking to the traditional teaching of public health, with lectures and demonstrations on hygiene and communicable disease control, and only occasional field trips. For Grant the paramount need was to move education in public health out of the medical school and into a community that would serve as his clinic, his classroom, and his research laboratory.

The first public health program in China based on scientific medical principles was the Manchurian Plague Prevention Service established in 1912. The Central Epidemic Prevention Bureau came into being in Peking in 1919, after an epidemic of pneumonic plague in north China two years earlier. But these programs were limited in their scope. With so little to build on, Grant and Henry Houghton concluded that it would take several years to determine priorities and opportunities and launch an educational program at PUMC.

Grant turned to a variety of sources for advice and to establish liaison. In 1922 he sent out a circular letter to the members of the China Medical Missionary Association soliciting suggestions on how public health and hygiene might be advanced in the country; he met with UMC alumni and other Chinese trained in Western medicine to listen to their opinions; and he worked with W. W. Peter, secretary of the Council on Health Education in China, who had been developing programs in health education since 1914.

In the meantime Grant was assigned to work with Otto Willner in the PUMC College Health Service and to teach hygiene and public health at the National Medical College in Peking. In 1923 he made an extensive study tour of China for a firsthand look at existing programs in twelve of the eighteen provinces.

Although he judged that both the Manchurian Plague Prevention Service and the Central Epidemic Prevention Bureau had potential as health services, he found it difficult to give a succinct account of the state of public health in China. The programs of the National Health Association and of the Council on Health Education did, however, prove a stimulus:

> The birth of a community health conscience has occurred for there is not a fair sized community visited in a recent tour of twelve of the eighteen provinces which does not possess a group of individuals in various stages of groping toward health efforts.[21]

Grant was especially impressed with the program of the South Manchuria Railway. He estimated its total worth to approach 440 million yen, its chief source of revenue being soy beans; the central laboratory of the railway had identified fifty-one usable soya products ranging from bread and cheese to hay, ink, and explosives. The enterprises of the railway included bituminous coal mines tapping what Grant described as the thickest coal seams in the world capable of producing 16,000 tons a day; steel works; agricultural experimental stations; research bureaus; and a chain of hotels. Grant was especially inter

Prince Yü's Palace.

Vera Nieh as a senior nursing student, 1927.

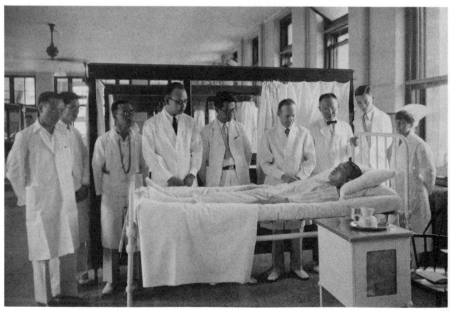

Francis Dieuaide on a teaching round shortly before leaving PUMC in May 1938.

Carl Ten Broeck, professor of bacteriology and head of pathology, 1920–1927.

Faye Whiteside, superintendent of nurses; Dean Gertrude E. Hodgman; Ethel Robinson, assistant superintendent of nurses.

J. Heng Liu, superintendent of the PUMC Hospital, 1924–1934.

Department of Public Health and Hygiene. John B. Grant, center; Marian Yang at his right.

Lim Kha-t'i (now Lin Chiao-chih) as head of the Department of Gynecology and Obstetrics, Capital Hospital, Peking. (Reprinted from *China Reconstructs* June 1972.)

Paul C. Hodges, far left, with students and staff in his 1926 postgraduate course in roentgenology.

Chen Ko-kuei at the time of
his return to Peking, 1923.

The herb shop where Chen Ko-kuei purchased the first
batch of *ma huang*—the source of ephedrine.

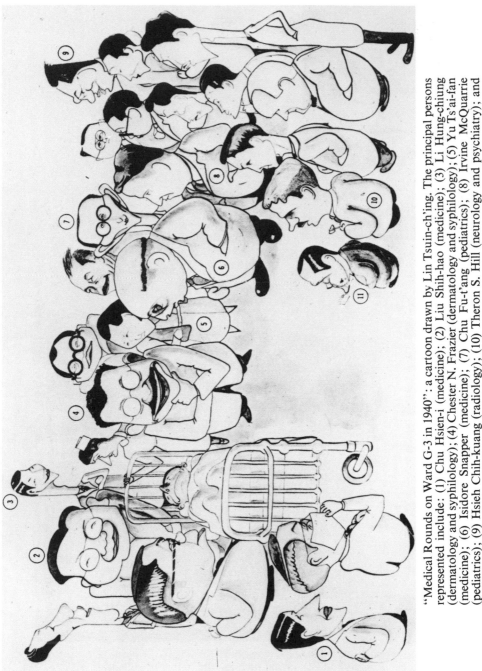

"Medical Rounds on Ward G-3 in 1940": a cartoon drawn by Lin Tsuin-ch'ing. The principal persons represented include: (1) Chu Hsien-i (medicine); (2) Liu Shih-hao (medicine); (3) Li Hung-chiung (dermatology and syphilology); (4) Chester N. Frazier (dermatology and syphilology); (5) Yu Ts'ai-fan (medicine); (6) Isidore Snapper (medicine); (7) Chu Fu-t'ang (pediatrics); (8) Irvine McQuarrie (pediatrics); (9) Hsieh Chih-kuang (radiology); (10) Theron S. Hill (neurology and psychiatry); and (11) Khaw Oo-keh (parasitology and public health).

Franklin C. McLean in the uniform of the United States Army Medical Corps.

Indigenous midwives leaving Marian Yang's North China Midwifery School after training.

Marian Yang in her office with a friend.

The staff of the biochemistry department, 1930. Left to right, S. Wan; W. Y. Li; A. C. Carruthers; A. Baird Hastings; Wu Hsien, chairman; Liu Szu-chih.

A. Baird Hastings in the research laboratory of the biochemistry department, 1931.

Ernest Carroll Faust in his parasitology laboratory.

Oswald H. Robertson, professor and head of medicine, 1923–1926.

Chu Fu-t'ang as a senior medical student, 1927.

Harold H. Loucks, 1927.

Brigadier General Robert K. S. Lim

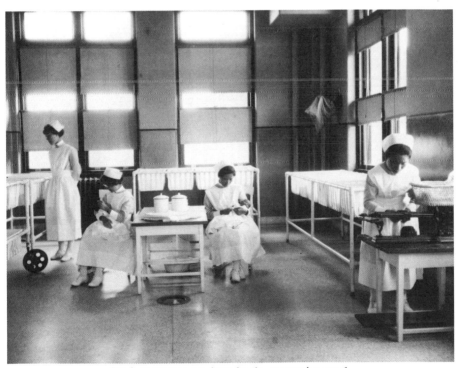

Student nurses on duty in the maternity ward.

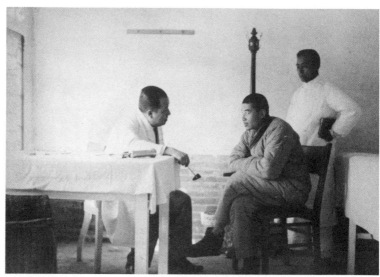

Examining a patient at the Peking Municipal Psychopathic Hospital.

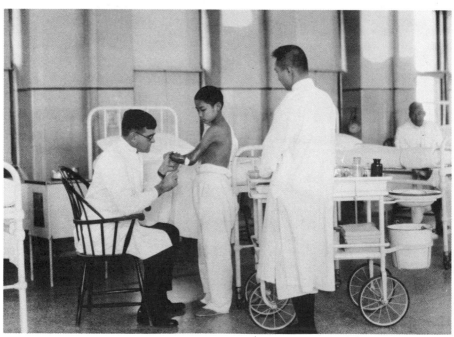

Adrian S. Taylor treating a young patient with burns.

Hans Zinsser (center) with members of the Department of Bacteriology.

J. Preston Maxwell receives a tablet from grateful patients. The large characters read, "Years of helping human beings." The secondary legends state, "This doctor saved many people through his treatments; we remind you not to forget his contributions."

Illustrations

Illustrations courtesy of Archives of the Rockefeller Foundation; The ABMAC Bulletin; Chen Ko-kuei; *China Reconstructs;* John A. Anderson; Francis R. Dieuaide; A. Baird Hastings; Paul C. Hodges Jr.; John C. Snyder; and *The Unison.*

ested in the railway's extensive medical program, which operated fourteen principal and six branch hospitals with a total of 2,269 beds and 137 doctors, serving the railway's officers and employees and their dependents. He described the hospitals as "all well-equipped, costing the railway 1,920,857,000 yen above receipts."[22]

Grant decided that the initial thrust of his program should be in school hygiene and in the establishment of health centers. He predicted that it would take at least ten years before there were tangible advances in public health in China. The Chinese bureaucracy paid little attention to health; indeed the responsibility for municipal health in Peking, which was principally scavenging, was relegated to the police department.

In early 1925, with the full support of Houghton, Grant persuaded the Peking police to join the college in establishing an experimental health center in the city.* The salient points in the cooperative arrangement called for PUMC to contribute 60 per cent, and the municipality 40 per cent, of the station's budget; the Department of Public Health at PUMC would nominate the director of the program.

An abandoned temple was proffered by the municipality, and Grant set about converting it into a community health center, just as John Dudgeon had converted another old temple into a hospital seventy years earlier.

Grant outlined two principal functions for the Special Health Station: to teach preventive medicine and public health to medical and nursing undergraduates and to auxiliaries; and to cooperate with local agencies in demonstration programs in community health practices. Other programs would include epidemiological investigations and the adaptation of modern public health practices to local conditions.

At the beginning there were four divisions: medical services, general sanitation, vital statistics, and communicable diseases; the latter two were later combined. When the full staff had been assembled it included the director and five other physicians, seventeen nurses, one dental hygienist, one pharmacist, three sanitary inspectors, one secretary, and three clerks. Grant was listed officially as advisor to the health station and director of the educational program.

The volume of work burgeoned, and the third annual report in 1928 lists 8,870 sanitary inspections; 1,148 deaths investigated; 57,787 total curative treatments, of which 44,575 were for trachoma; and 25,660 home visits for nursing services.

A study made by the Peking Special Health Station revealed it to be a true microcosm of the paucity of medical services in urban China: in the first 1,000 deaths investigated by the staff, 36 per cent of the sick had received no medical

---

* The center has been variously referred to as the Special Health Station, the First Health Station, and the Peking Police Health Demonstration Station; we will use Grant's term, Special Health Station.

therapy whatsoever. The study also demonstrated the dominance of traditional medicine: 48 per cent had been treated exclusively by native practitioners; only 16 per cent could be described as having been treated with modern medicine.

The program in maternal and child health was led by a remarkable woman, Marian Yang, who after graduation in Britain had taken postgraduate training at the Johns Hopkins School of Hygiene and Public Health. G. Canby Robinson, a visiting professor in 1935, described her as having "qualities of greatness."[23]

At the beginning of Marian Yang's program a survey was made of maternal and infant mortality in the special health area; the results gave evidence of the overall situation of China: the maternal mortality rate was 17.6:1,000 population compared with 3:1,000 in England, 4 in Japan, and 5 in the United States; the infant mortality was 275 compared with less than 75 in both the United States and England. The principal cause of maternal mortality was puerperal infection; of infant mortality, tetanus neonatorium.

Tetanus neonatorium was the constant enemy of every newborn: it was estimated that 50 per cent of the babies born in China died from the disease. The practices of the untrained midwives were appalling: they would sever the cord with any sharp tool lying about or, if none was available, with their teeth; the stump of the cord was then covered with dirt to arrest bleeding, or compressed with a filthy rag. If a woman had difficulty in delivering the baby, as in the deformed pelvis of osteomalacia, the midwife would insert hooks or charcoal tongs into the vagina in an effort to exert traction on the fetus.

The wretched practices of the untrained midwives were brought out strikingly by J. Preston Maxwell, head of the Department of Obstetrics and Gynecology:

> In a village not very far from Peking, there is a Chinese midwife with some reputation. She is deformed, and walks about on her hands and knees. She has been seen to raise herself from this position, wipe her hands down her clothes, and proceed to make a vaginal examination without any further preparation. Moreover there is no attempt made by these women to keep their finger nails in order, and we have had cases under our care with the vaginal wall scored by these dirty nails before they came into our hands. One is only surprised that mortality rates are not higher than they are.[24]

While there were only 500 trained midwives in all of China, there were estimated to be at least 200,000 untrained midwives. The first need, then, in attacking the shockingly high infant and maternal mortality rates was to train midwives. J. Heng Liu, who by now was with the Ministry of Health, appointed a National Midwifery Board on January 28, 1929, to promote midwifery education and to advance the standards of midwifery.

On November 1, 1929, under the auspices of the Peking municipal government and in relationship to the Special Health Station, Marian Yang opened the first modern school to train nurses in midwifery. She also took the bold step of establishing special courses to teach untrained midwives sterile procedures and sanitary practices. At the completion of her training, each midwife was equipped with a basket that contained the necessary instruments, medicines, and dressings to apply the principles and practices that she had been taught at the school.

P'eng Tah-mou (PUMC 1933), who was a district health officer and assistant to Grant at the health station, recalls that the drop in maternal and infant mortality due to Marian Yang's training programs was so impressive that it had helped to persuade J. Heng Liu to place a greater emphasis on maternal and child health in the public health administration.*

Marian Yang also drew up a national program in midwifery that was described by Knud Faber of the League of Nations as "exceedingly useful work."[25] It called for the development of five national normal schools to produce "quality" midwives in a two-year training program. The basic sciences were to be covered in the first year; during the second year each student would be required to deliver at least twenty-five women and administer postnatal care. Midwifery training centers were to be established in each province with the emphasis on a six-month course that would produce "quantity" midwives. Local training courses would be held for indigenous midwives. Marian Yang's imaginative and comprehensive program also called for the establishment of medical consultation stations for prepartum and postpartum care of the poor in each police district of the larger cities. Delivery services would be handled by midwives attached to the stations. Such an encompassing program naturally grew slowly, but in the meanwhile the impact of the pioneering programs that Marian Yang established at the Special Health Station was being felt throughout the country.

Grant knew that another giant step in public health could be achieved by bringing forth a generation that would understand and adopt the best hygienic and sanitary practices. A school health program therefore became a major activity of the Special Health Station. One-third of the 4,000 schoolchildren in the area it served were examined in the first year the station was opened. The most frequent disease diagnosed was trachoma, and there was a high prevalence of dental caries. Preventive inoculations were given to the children; other activities included school nursing services, health education, and the establishment of a high level of sanitation in the schools through frequent inspections and corrective measures.

The Ministry of Health drew heavily on the personnel of the Special Health Station to staff its programs. The vice minister of health wrote in 1929 that the influence of the station on recent developments in public health in China could "hardly be over-estimated."[26] Grant was a close advisor to the ministry and a moving force in the development of health departments in Shanghai and Canton.

---

* P'eng Tah-mou 1969: personal communication.

NOTES TO CHAPTER EIGHT

1. Edmund V. Cowdry, "Anatomy in China," pp. 32–60.

2. *Ibid.*, p. 37.

3. *Ibid.*, p. 38.

4. *Ibid.*, p. 45.

5. Peiping Union Medical College, *Annual Announcement, 1929–30*, p. 57.

6. Nathaniel H. Cowdry, "Plants from Peitaiho," *Journal of the North China Branch of the Royal Asiatic Society* 53 (1922): 158–88.

7. Dora Hood, *Davidson Black*, p. 40.

8. *Ibid.*, p. 40.

9. *Ibid.*, p. 49.

10. Bernard E. Read, "The Secretion of Urine in the Camel," *China Medical Journal* 34 (1920): 18.

11. Roy Chapman Andrews, *Meet Your Ancestors*, pp. 114–5.

12. Hsien Wu, "A System of Blood Analysis, with Special Reference to Uric Acid" (Ph.D. Diss., Harvard University, 1919).

13. *PUMC Weekly Calendar*, 5 February 1924, p. 137.

14. Ernest Carroll Faust and Henry E. Meleney, *Studies on Schistosomiasis Japonica*, p. iii.

15. Ernest Carroll Faust, "Parasitic Infections and Human Disease in China," p. 231.

16. Charles W. Young, "Kala-azar in China."

17. W. W. Cort, et al., *Researches on Hookworm in China.*

18. C. F. Craig and Ernest Carroll Faust, *Clinical Parasitology* (Philadelphia: Lea and Febiger, 1937).

19. Peking Union Medical College, *The Unison*, vol. II (*1927*): p. 50.

20. Victor G. Heiser, *An American Doctor's Odyssey*, p. 401.

21. *PUMC Weekly Newsletter*, 1 May 1923, p. 18.

22. *Ibid.*, 6 February 1923, p. 4.

23. G. Canby Robinson, *Adventures in Medical Education*, p. 247.

24. J. Preston Maxwell, "On Puerperal Mortality and Morbidity," p. 700.

25. League of Nations Health Committee, *Report on Medical Schools in China*, by Knud Faber, p. 33.

26. Mary E. Ferguson, *China Medical Board and Peking Union Medical College*, p. 58.

CHAPTER NINE

The Golden Years:
The Clinical Departments

MEDICINE

Several members of the staff of the Union Medical College were retained in the Department of Medicine of the Peking Union Medical College: H. Jocelyn Smyly, from Dublin; John H. Korns, who had trained at Rush Medical College; and Charles W. Young from Johns Hopkins, an "old China hand" who had been in Peking since 1906 and who had served as dean of UMC.

Oswald H. Robertson, age thirty-three, who had already made his mark in medical science, joined Franklin McLean in 1919. A 1915 graduate of Harvard, Robertson went to the Rockefeller Institute where he studied the life span of the erythrocyte with Peyton Rous and Joseph R. Turner, Jr. In the course of their investigations they tested a number of preservatives and found that Locke's solution, when supplemented with dextrose and sodium citrate, would maintain viability in the red cells for thirty days.

To evaluate this finding Robertson joined the Army Medical Corps in 1917 and was assigned to the 3rd Army of the British Expeditionary Forces on the front lines in Belgium. With blood drawn from camp personnel, which he preserved in the Rous-Turner solution and stored in a jerry-built ice chest made from packing cases, Robertson gave transfusions to the wounded with blood that had been drawn as much as twenty-six days earlier. "His primitive installation was the world's first blood bank. . . . It was 20 years ahead of its time."[1] Robertson also demonstrated that repeated blood transfusions depress the erythropoetic activity of bone marrow.

At PUMC he headed the infectious disease program in the Department of Medicine, where his own research was on factors inhibiting the growth of the

121

pneumococcus. His principal associate was Young, who established clinical and laboratory studies on kala-azar: the Kala-azar Field Studies Unit.

Henry Meleney, as we have noted, joined the department in 1920 and worked with Carroll Faust on schistosomiasis. In the same year Otto Willner, an Austrian who had been a prisoner of war of the Russians, assumed responsibility for the student and staff health program.

Francis Weld Peabody, who returned to China for the dedication ceremonies in 1921, established himself as a visiting professor in the department. He gave a clinic on Saturday mornings and teaching rounds for three hours on Tuesdays; as one of the monthly lectures, Peabody presented his clinical studies on respiration. He also visited other medical schools and hospitals in China.

Mrs. Peabody found home life at PUMC a delight:

> It is needless to say that we are in the seventh heaven; for we had quite given up the hope of having a house of our own in Peking, and the fun of living behind high garden walls. . . . It is a great thing to live where the No. 1 boy gets the other servants and is responsible for them, so that we give no more thought to the matter.[2]

On his return to the Thorndike Memorial Laboratory at Harvard in 1922, where he had recently been appointed as the first director, Peabody sent a report of his impressions of PUMC to Franklin McLean and his colleagues. Essentially he had nothing but praise for the program, and he epitomized his impressions with the statement: "The minor character of the suggestions which I can offer is the best indication of my satisfaction with the way the work is being carried on."[3]

Peabody also prepared an article for *Science* on the Department of Medicine at PUMC.[4] In ensuing years, reprints of the article were sent to prospective faculty for the college. It began with the comment that Western medicine in China had been based on surgery and the surgical specialties, while internal medicine had never had a chance to develop because demands on Western doctors, largely missionaries, were for urgent surgical problems. In addition, facilities for applying modern methods of medical diagnosis were seldom available.

> Under these circumstances, it is of interest to watch the development at the Peking Union Medical College of a medical clinic which in its personnel and equipment would take high rank on any continent.[5]

Among the special advantages at PUMC, he cited the organic connection between the hospital and the preclinical sciences, the location of the Department of Medicine, only a few steps from the library, and a laboratory for routine clinical examinations adjacent to each ward. The staff was large enough to allow ample time for study and investigation, and cases were selected for admission primarily for their value for teaching or for clinical investigation.

Peabody then gave an interesting picture of the disease problems of China, painting on a broad canvas and stressing the misconceptions held in the West:

> Tuberculosis, and especially pulmonary tuberculosis is very common . . . lobar pneumonia is probably somewhat less common than in northern United States. Typhoid fever, in spite of much that is said about the Chinese having an inherited or acquired immunity to it, is common and the mortality is about what we expect in America. Syphilis abounds in all its manifestations . . . and the extraordinarily interesting neurological clinic in Peking contains its full quota of syphilitic cases. Dysentery, both bacillary and amoebic, occurs with great frequency in the summer and autumn, and malaria, usually the tertian form, is not uncommon.[6]

Peabody went on to note the frequency of scarlet fever, smallpox, relapsing fever, and typhus fever. Every patient with an enlarged spleen was suspected of having kala-azar and it was not unusual to have four to six patients in the wards undergoing treatment simultaneously. While there were many cases of acute and chronic nephritis with a clinical picture similar to that in the West, Peabody had the impression that essential hypertension, acute rheumatic fever, and exophthalmic goiter were seen far less frequently than in the West.

Diabetes mellitus was believed to be very rare in China, but a mild form readily controlled by diet was quite frequent in patients past middle age:

> A cirrhosis of the liver with ascites, said to occur characteristically in farmers, is another interesting and new type of disease entity . . . there are numerous patients with all sorts of neuroses and psychoses. In general, therefore, the medical clinic in Peking is marked particularly by the great variety of disease. One finds most of the diseases that we are accustomed to see in America, and in addition a good many new types.[7]

Peabody concluded with a statement that PUMC matched the world's best medical schools:

> To many people in America, China may seem to be remote and Peking an outpost of Western civilization, but to those who know the situation the Peking Union Medical College is progressing hand in hand with the foremost medical schools of the world on the frontier of scientific medicine.[8]

In the meantime McLean was becoming increasingly concerned that the clinical departments might be so overwhelmed by demands for patient care that their educational and research programs would be stifled. He expressed his concern in a letter to his favorite advisor, Alfred Cohn of the Rockefeller Institute:

> There is a great danger of our becoming a sort of service station, or Mayo clinic, for the whole of the foreign population of China . . . called upon for all sorts of general office practice . . . we are turning down most of the requests for visits in patients' homes . . . but the problem is enormous.[9]

In the same letter McLean reported that the contagious disease unit had been opened prematurely in the preceding week to isolate a medical staff secretary who had contracted smallpox. Ten days later he wrote:

> Between plague to the north of us, typhus to the south of us, and smallpox in our own staff (also scarlet fever today!), we are all being kept pretty busy.[10]

It was at this time that McLean began to have doubts about his own future at PUMC:

> This is not the place for me permanently for I don't believe that I shall ever be in a position here to settle down to what we recognize as the functions of a professor of medicine.[11]

In the fall of 1921 McLean expressed disappointment to Cohn that his name had been omitted from a paper prepared for the American Society for Clinical Investigation. The incident led McLean and Cohn to recognize the serious problems inherent in any effort to establish the cooperative research programs that McLean had dreamed of between the Rockefeller Institute and Peking. The distance was simply too great: "The worst feature of the whole situation out here is this difficulty of keeping in touch with work at home."[12]

The crowning period for McLean at Peking came in the fall of 1922 when he collaborated with Donald Van Slyke and Wu Hsien on studies on the physicochemical aspects of the distribution of electrolytes between cells and plasma (see Chapter Eight, p. 100).

McLean Leaves Peking

McLean's growing concern about scientific isolation, heightened by the stimulus of working with Van Slyke, were major factors in his decision to leave Peking and resume his collaboration with Van Slyke at the Rockefeller Institute. McLean's farewell to Peking in June 1923 was climaxed by his marriage to Helen Vincent, an obstetrical resident at PUMC, in Tientsin on June 11, 1923, on the homeward journey.

As his boat docked in New York, however, McLean's plans for a future at the research bench were altered drastically when he was handed a cable from Ernest Burton, head of the First China Medical Commission and now president of the University of Chicago. It offered McLean an opportunity he could not turn aside; for the second time in his still short career he would assume leadership in developing a major academic medical center—this time at the University of Chicago.

McLean was the chief architect of the plant and the plan at Chicago; as at PUMC he stressed excellence and scientific medicine. He introduced a program which at the time was highly controversial: all members of the faculty were full-time; their sole income was their university salaries; and they were not permitted to accept any fees for the care of patients. Today this system or a modification of it is favored by almost all American medical schools.

In 1933—ten years after leaving PUMC—McLean gave up administration and returned to full-time research on calcification. After his retirement from Chicago in 1953 he continued to be active as a medical scientist. One of his most enduring contributions was the opening of the doors of medicine to black Americans who wished to be doctors—in this he was *the* pioneer. Franklin McLean died on Septmber 10, 1968, at the age of eighty.

Helen Vincent McLean turned from obstetrics to the newly developed field of psychoanalysis and gained national recognition through her work with Franz Alexander at the Institute of Psychoanalysis in Chicago.

Oswald Robertson succeeded McLean as head of medicine on February 7, 1923. A few months later, he joined Henry Houghton and a nurse in a hurried trip to Tsinan in response to a message that Lucy Aldrich, sister-in-law of John D. Rockefeller, Jr., had been kidnapped by bandits. A cable, now in the United States National Archives, was dispatched to Washington from Tsinan at midnight on May 6, 1923, by Schurman, the American minister in China:

> Express train which left Shanghai Saturday morning held up by bandits near Lincheng, Shantung, about 2 o'clock Sunday morning, 19 of 26 foreigners held captive . . . British subject killed; bandits being pursued by small military force. Situation serious, little information received but foregoing from American on scene. Schurman.[13]

A footnote added later states that Miss Aldrich was one of the seven Americans who had escaped—or else she had ransomed herself. And one can only smile at the thought that whatever the circumstances the bandits lost one of the richest sources of ransom in the world!

Lee Chung-en (C.U.), a graduate of the Faculty of Medicine at Glasgow, joined the Department of Medicine in 1923. He worked with Charles W. Young on the kalar-azar program and succeeded him as leader of the unit when Young left Peking in 1928.

Since McLean had been both director of PUMC and head of the Department of Medicine, it was perfectly natural for him to "headhunt" in Peking for the faculty for Chicago. One of his prize catches was Robertson, who left PUMC in 1926 after contracting typhus while returning from a duck-hunting trip with Francis Dieuaide. Their only available transport back to Peking was in a freight crowded with soldiers—and lice.* After an extended convalescence Robertson went to Chicago as professor of medicine. Robert F. Loeb, recalls that when "Robby" came to his first Atlantic City meetings after returning from PUMC, his friends were struck by the change in his mien and in his manners, which were now decidedly Chinese! (Similar comments were made about other men who had taught in Peking.) Robertson continued his record of scientific achievement at Chicago through his studies on microbial diseases. During World War II he ~~ed~~ a major research program on airborne infection.

At about the same time, McLean, with the counsel of Alfred Cohn, was on the trail of Francis Dieuaide, Robertson's heir apparent at PUMC. He also had his eye on Paul C. Hodges, head of roentgenology at PUMC, and Anna Wolf, superintendent of nursing.

---

* Francis Dieuaide 1972: personal communication.

Dieuaide, who had been a medical resident and assistant at Johns Hopkins, joined the Department of Medicine at PUMC in 1924. His wisdom, his outstanding clinical abilities, and his studies on heart disease had already established Dieuaide as a young man with a bright future in academic medicine. Fortunately, he chose to fashion his career in China, despite attractive offers to return to America. Beyond the unique medical challenges at PUMC, the rich and fascinating Chinese culture offered Dieuaide an opportunity to apply the full range of his remarkably broad interests and abilities.

In a letter to Cohn in March 1927, Robertson, now in Chicago, described Dieuaide in glowing terms:

> A man of unusual capacity and of great possibilities. With a suitable environment and particularly one free from the administrative pressure of his present job, he should go far.[14]

On March 18, 1927, McLean offered Dieuaide an appointment at Chicago as associate professor of medicine. Cohn, who had been in Peking as a visiting professor when Dicuaide joined the staff of PUMC, suggested that if Dieuaide agreed to move to Chicago he should first spend a year working with him in electrocardiography at the Rockefeller Institute. In April, however, Dieuaide advised McLean that he had decided to remain in Peking for another year.

Dieuaide's decision was of the greatest importance for the future of the school. A small, slender, reticent man, Dieuaide's manner belied his remarkable talents. As his colleague, Harold H. Loucks, stated: "PUMC owes more to Francis for scientific excellence than any other person."* His colleagues on the faculty, the students, the house officers, and the visiting professors recognized Dieuaide as the intellectual leader and linchpin of the college. It was to him that members of the staff and administration turned for wisdom; in a sense he sacrificed his own talents in cardiovascular research for the benefit of others who placed such heavy demands on his time. His colleagues felt that Roger Greene never made a move without consulting Dieuaide. Robertson had been quite correct in noting the "administrative pressure" that continued to be an important and mounting factor throughout the fourteen years that Francis Dieuaide spent at PUMC. Nevertheless he was able to build an excellent Department of Medicine.

David L. Edsall, dean of Harvard Medical School and a trustee of the Rockefeller Foundation, went out to PUMC as visiting professor in the Department of Medicine for six months in the academic year 1926–27. Well over six feet tall, Edsall had an imposing bald head and a prominent forehead. Dieuaide recalls that the Chinese held Edsall in special awe because his physiognomy resembled that of Wen Ch'eng, the Chinese god of literature.† His appearance

---

* Harold H. Loucks 1972: personal communication.
† Francis Dieuaide 1970: personal communication.

was particularly striking when he stood beside the slim, short Dieuaide. Edsall worked closely with Dieuaide, attending rounds and giving a number of lectures. He left Peking sold on the school and, as a trustee of the foundation, he was an ardent and important voice in support of the program.

An early recruit to the Department of Medicine was Hobart A. Reimann, who joined the faculty in 1927 after three years at the Rockefeller Institute working on the classification of Friedländer's bacillus. Reimann continued his interest in microbial diseases and studied the differences in the immunological responses of typhus fever and typhoid fever, both of which were common in Peking. Typhoid carriers were a problem and Reimann showed that the Weil-Felix reaction, which was diagnostic for typhus, was not affected by the coexistence of typhoid bacilli in the intestinal tract. He also reported on the frequency of thrombocytopenia in typhus and pointed out that it may continue to cause purpuric manifestations after all other clinical signs of the disease have subsided. Reimann returned to the United States in 1929 and after a period at the University of Minnesota was appointed professor and head of medicine at Jefferson Medical College in Philadelphia.

While McLean was recruiting faculty for Chicago from Peking, Dieuaide was recruiting for PUMC from Hopkins. His prize catch was Chester S. Keefer, who came to Peking in 1928 for what he later described as "two of the most interesting and productive years of my life."* A review of the publications that emanated from Keefer's two short years at PUMC shows that they characterized the high productivity that marked every phase of his outstanding career. One of his studies was on the anemia of malnutrition, which he found was best treated with whole liver and iron rather than liver extract and iron; he stressed the importance of the combined therapeutic approach rather than a choice between liver and iron, especially in anemia due to hookworm infection.

Keefer extended his hematological studies to kala-azar and, with Khaw Ookek, reported that in that disease all of the formed elements of the blood are reduced in number. He found that due to the decrease in platelets, purpuric manifestations were frequent. Treatment demanded a broad approach: blood transfusions, dosages of liver and iron, correction of nutritional deficiencies, and the elimination of intercurrent infections—as well as specific therapy for kala-azar.

The frequency of beriberi heart disease also attracted Keefer's attention, and a study of the cases at PUMC showed that patients who develop beriberi heart disease had only minimal involvement of the nervous system.

In 1930 Keefer went to Harvard and the Thorndike Memorial Laboratory, and in 1940 was appointed head of medicine at Boston University. As a member of the Committee on Medical Research of the National Academy of Science, he led the penicillin program during World War II.

---

* Chester S. Keefer 1970: personal communication.

The first graduate of PUMC to join the department was Liu Shih-hao, class of 1925, who, after serving successively as assistant resident, assistant, and resident in medicine, was appointed associate in medicine in 1930. During this period Liu had developed an interest in metabolic studies, and in 1926, one year after graduation, he had prepared his first paper—a review of research literature on parathyroid hormone. Two years later, while still at PUMC, he published his studies on calcium and phosphorous metabolism in tetany in the prestigious *Journal of Clinical Investigation*.[15]

Beginning in 1928 Liu spent two years at the Rockefeller Institute working on metabolic studies with Van Slyke; in 1932 he was awarded a second fellowship to work with Van Slyke.

Richard H. P. Sia, who had pioneered in the Department of Medicine in 1919, was introduced to the pneumococcus by Robertson during the latter's seven years at PUMC. In 1931 Sia went on leave to work with Oswald Avery and Martin H. Dawson in New York on the fundamental immunochemistry of the pneumonococcus. Avery and Dawson had observed that a strain of pneumonoccus could be changed from nonvirulence to virulence by passage through animals or by growth on selected culture media. Later, Dawson and Sia were successful in causing dead pneumococci to transform living pneumococci from a nonvirulent to a virulent strain. This experiment was one step in the chain of studies that showed that deoxyribonucleic acid is the transforming substance, and that DNA is the carrier of the genetic code. A. Baird Hastings described this work as "the classic but insufficiently recognized studies on which subsequent research that earned three Nobel Prizes was based."*

In 1928, while Francis Dieuaide was on sabbatical leave, Hilding Berglund of Stockholm served as visiting professor. Because of his domineering manner and fiery temper the Chinese held Berglund in special awe. One act of Berglund's that lingers in the memories of his Peking colleagues was the day he became so angry he slammed the telephone down on a desk with such force that the glass top was shattered into fragments. The departmental secretary, appalled but unhurt, submitted his resignation on the spot, and did not resume his duties until Dieuaide returned from sabbatical. After Berglund left Peking he became head of the Department of Medicine at the rapidly rising University of Minnesota Medical School.

Pediatrics

The development of pediatrics at PUMC began in the fall of 1923 with the arrival of L. Emmett Holt, America's most distinguished pediatrician, as visiting professor. In the words of his biographers, he was at that time "the grand old man of American pediatrics."[16] As the family pediatrician he had long

---

* A. Baird Hastings 1970: personal communication.

standing ties with the Rockefellers; his status as a practitioner was assured by the fact that he was also pediatrician to the Guggenheim aristocracy.

Holt modestly described himself as a "middleman" of science, standing as the link between the research worker in the laboratory and the practicing physician.[17] Yet it was to Holt and to Christian A. Herter that Rockefeller turned in March 1901 for advice on the desirability of establishing the Rockefeller Institute. Holt and Herter were subsequently appointed as the first two directors of the institute.

Holt was also a pioneer in exploring scientific fundamentals in pediatrics. In 1910, with a grant of a few hundred dollars from the Rockefeller Institute, he had set up a laboratory in which he carried out the first reliable studies on the blood chemistry of infants and the mineral content of human milk.

Holt's *Diseases of Infancy and Childhood*[18] was the standard textbook in the field, but his most enduring fame came from *The Care and Feeding of Children*,[19] a "bible" for hundreds of thousands of young mothers; the book went into seventy-five printings and was translated into Spanish, Russian, and Chinese.*

In letters to his son, L. Emmett Holt, Jr., and to his daughter, Evelyn, Holt described his busy life at PUMC. Two mornings a week he saw private patients, gratis, and found this arrangement more satisfactory than the fee-for-service basis he had followed in New York. On Monday and Friday afternoons at 5 o'clock he presented lectures, and on Saturday mornings he presided over a pediatric clinic. In a letter to his son, he reported that he was doing more teaching than he had expected.[20] On November 16, 1923, he presented the monthly public lecture in the PUMC auditorium, to an audience of close to 400, on the topic, "What Preventive Medicine Has Done for Children." The social life was demanding: "We have had calls and invitations—many, almost too many—already."[21]

In a letter to his friend Nathaniel R. Norton, Holt described the pediatric material at PUMC as small but interesting—intestinal parasites were common; there was a great deal of tuberculosis.

> The diets which the children past infancy get in China would surprise you. No milk, butter or cheese; eggs very seldom and meat usually only on special festivals. They live chiefly upon *mantou*, which is a steamed bread dough, rice and millet without sugar, butter or milk—but with vegetables in fair amount, especially cabbage, and some vegetable oils. Cabbage soup which is little else than the water in which the vegetable is cooked is a staple article in all homes. Cabbage apparently is the one food stuff which protects them against the deficiency diseases—scurvy and beri-beri are both very rare here.[22]

He noted that rickets was rare, and was impressed with the low incidence of dental caries. Eighty-six per cent of 100 children whom he examined at a Peking

---

* The Chinese translation was done by Archibald P. Ch'ien at PUMC, who was secretary to Roger Greene and later to L. Carrington Goodrich.

orphanage showed no dental caries; in Japan he had found that only 2 per cent of the children had healthy teeth. There was a comparable disparity in the incidence of caries between Chinese and American children.

Holt's period at PUMC helped to focus attention on the need for a strong program in pediatrics in a country where 90 per cent of the patients were infants and children. Academic pediatrics in the United States was just coming into its own as a discipline separate from internal medicine. Whereas infant feeding had been considered the principal role of the "baby doctor," medical scientists with a sophisticated approach to communicable diseases, to nutrition, and to metabolic disorders, were slowly bringing pediatrics to rank as a leading clinical department in a small but increasing number of medical schools. The number of pediatricians with the academic background required at Peking was, however, still sharply limited.

Emmett Holt was sixty-eight years old when he came to PUMC and his health was failing. His cardiac reserve steadily diminished and he died in Peking on January 14, 1924, a few hours after suffering a heart attack

Ernest S. C. Tso and Ruth A. Guy were the first pediatricians to join the staff on a permanent basis. Arriving in Peking in 1924, Ruth Guy's primary interest was in nutrition and she was given a joint appointment on the staff of the Peking Special Health Station. She initiated a series of studies comparing the cereal-legumen vegetable diet of the poorer classes with the milled cereal-meat-vegetable diet of the more well-to-do. The poor derived their caloric energy almost entirely from cereals such as yellow corn and millet ground with soybean flour, and their food was cooked in sesame or peanut oil. Their vegetable sources were sharply limited: spinach in the early spring; small green cabbage in the late spring; kohlrabi and string beans in the summer; and Chinese cabbage in the autumn and winter. Ruth Guy reckoned that this diet at most yielded 2,100 calories a day compared with a minimal daily requirement of 2,400 calories. Further, the total protein intake was estimated to be only 88 g. a day, almost exclusively from vegetable sources. The inadequacies of the diet were accentuated by the fact that the men, and frequently the women, were engaged in harsh physical labor.

There were stringent rules against nepotism at PUMC and Ruth Guy gave up her post in pediatrics in 1929 to become Mrs. Francis Dieuaide. She continued in part-time work on nutrition at the Special Health Station, and on studies with Tso of suitable replacements for breast milk.

In 1929 Chu Fu-t'ang (PUMC 1927), an assistant resident in pediatrics, collaborated with Tso on a review of the cases of typhoid and paratyphoid fever admitted to the pediatrics service. The scale of the typhoid problem was aptly described by Dieuaide when he said that "on any summer day the medical and pediatrics wards could be filled with typhoid patients."* Chu and Tso analyzed

---

* Francis Dieuaide 1970: personal communication.

sixty-five children with typhoid, 20 per cent of whom were under the age of two years, and found a mortality rate of 6.2 per cent, a surprisingly low rate for youngsters who had been suffering from moderate to severe malnutrition when they contracted the disease. It was a tribute to the superb nursing care at PUMC.

The academic program in pediatrics gained a major boost in 1928 with the arrival of A. Ashley Weech. After graduation from Hopkins in 1921, Weech had spent seven years as a member of the house staff and the junior faculty at Hopkins. His principal studies were on keratomalacia and epituberculosis. He found a widespread Vitamin A deficiency in Chinese children and adults, and observed that a frequent complication was keratomalacia leading to blindness.

While beriberi was a major problem in south China, it was less common than in many American cities. Weech attributed the rarity of scurvy to the popularity of cabbage, with its high Vitamin C content.

Weech reported four cases of young Chinese children with epituberculous infiltration of the lung. They presented the typical clinical picture of insidious development in young children: extensive lobar infiltration, usually of an upper lobe, sputum negative for tubercle bacilli, and ultimate recovery. The accepted explanation for the syndrome was an allergic response of sensitized lung tissue to tuberculin. Weech, however, cited experimental studies to show that, except for the absence of tubercle bacilli, epituberculous infiltration was no different than other tuberculous pulmonary exudates in which the course is progressive.

Weech's secretary, Brown Chang, remembers him not only as an excellent pediatrician but as a fine vocalist who sang in church choirs and other choral groups.* Weech's fondest memories are of the occasions—and there were a number of them—when he was invited to sing "O Promise Me" at Chinese weddings: "They loved it—and so did I."†

The greatest academic satisfaction for Ashley Weech was to work with his resident, Chu Fu-t'ang. Chu was a brilliant student and scientist who had a special concern for his patients: "He was one of the few residents in my career whom I knew would lie awake at night worrying that a baby might be in pain."‡

Weech returned to the United States in 1930 and continued his career in academic pediatrics at Columbia University College of Physicians and Surgeons. In 1942 he was appointed head of the Department of Pediatrics and of the Research Foundation of the Children's Hospital at the University of Cincinnati College of Medicine.

Dermatology and Syphilology

Chester North Frazier, who had received the M.D. at Indiana in 1914, joined the PUMC faculty in 1922 as the first head of the Division of Dermatology and

---

* Brown Chang 1972: personal communication.
† A. Ashley Weech 1972: personal communication.
‡ Ibid.

Syphilology.* Frazier was to be the pioneer of modern dermatology in China: "It is said that there are few if any Chinese dermatologists who do not owe the greater part of their training to Dr. Frazier."[23] He represented the best of scholarship in dermatology: through biochemical and physiological studies he approached it as a part of internal medicine. Thus one of his first research projects on fluctutations in the serum globulin levels in leprosy was carried out with Wu Hsien in the Department of Biochemistry.

Neurology

In 1926, Andrew H. Woods, professor and head of the Division of Neurology, summarized his studies of the 3,135 neurological cases he had seen at PUMC over a period of four years. Beriberi was the etiological factor in 30 per cent of the cases diagnosed as neuritis, and there was a high incidence of beriberi neuritis among students from the rice-eating southern and central provinces. Tuberculosis was the cause of 41 per cent of the cases of meningitis, and spondylitis deformans due to acid-fast infection was seen frequently. The meningococcus was the causative agent in 50 per cent of the patients with meningitis. Twenty-six per cent of all Chinese and 19.5 per cent of all foreign neurological patients had central nervous system syphilis. Epilepsy was very common, due in part to the frequent epidemics of encephalitis.

Woods also served as the psychiatrist at PUMC. He cited three major reasons for neuroses and other abnormal behavior patterns in the Chinese: fear of public disapproval; "loss of face"; and, in women, loss of their husbands' affections.

Woods died in Peking in 1928; he was succeeded as head of neurology by Ernest De Vries.

SURGERY

Although the post as head of surgery was accepted by Ernest G. Grey, a 1911 graduate of Hopkins, he died soon after the appointment was made. William Stewart Halsted, head of surgery at Hopkins, and the father of modern American surgery, who had trained Grey, described him as "a man who might well have succeeded me at the hospital."[24]

Attention then turned to Adrian S. Taylor, an Alabaman who, after graduating in medicine from the University of Virginia in 1905, had joined the Southern Baptist Mission in Yangchow. In 1915, after ten years in China, Taylor was awarded the first CMB fellowship for postgraduate study. He elected to go to Harvard, feeling that he had been away from the cutting edge of medicine for so long that he should spend one year reviewing advances in the basic and clinical sciences while he had been in China. Although he had to supplement his grant by working at night in an orthopedic hospital, Taylor's record was so excellent

---

* A handsome man, his colleagues described him as a "dandy," with carefully-groomed mustache, wearing a boutonniere and spats and carrying gloves and a cane.

that the CMB extended the fellowship so that he could train at Hopkins under Halsted. Subsequently he replaced a young resident at Hopkins, Jerome P. Webster, who was in uniform as a medical attache working on famine relief at the American Embassy in Berlin. (In 1921 Webster was to join the Department of Surgery in Peking to head the development of a proper residency program.)

Franklin McLean described Adrian Taylor as "the best surgeon in China."[25] Beyond his surgical skills, however, which included neurosurgery, Taylor was highly respected by his colleagues as an individual. Hodges recalls him as "rather short, with dark piercing eyes. He was always right to the point—a religious man—but he never exhibited his religion."* Taylor came away from Baltimore devoted to Halsted; his sterling qualities in turn drew Halsted's respect and friendship, and they maintained an illuminating correspondence after Taylor's return to China. Taylor also established an enduring friendship with Mont R. Reid, one of Halsted's assistants, who was destined for a distinguished academic career in surgery.

When Taylor came back to China in the fall of 1920 he first visited his brother, the only doctor at the Baptist hospital in Yangchow where Taylor had served before his fellowship to Harvard. Instead of the dispensary with a few beds that he had left in 1915, Taylor found a new 125-bed hospital that had been built with a grant from the CMB. The highest hopes of the board must have been fulfilled, for through the grant Adrian Taylor's brother had gained "the co-operation and friendship of the Chinese community" and was "leading a busy and happy life with the people in that great city."[26]

Taylor's first report to Halsted on PUMC was auspicious:

> The physical equipment is almost ideal. The faculty of well-trained, earnest young men is gradually being assembled, and I look forward to our work here with the greatest hope and enthusiasm."[27]

The surgery department was still based in the old hospital of the UMC, and although it was crowded, Taylor found the equipment to be fairly good and the caliber of the surgical program satisfactory. The manual skills of the young Chinese men who served as assistants at the operating table drew his special praise.

During Taylor's years at Baltimore, Halsted had intensified his efforts to introduce silk as the ideal suture material, and Taylor returned to China an ardent champion of silk sutures. Young surgeons and visitors at PUMC in turn went back to the United States as advocates of silk, leading Jerome Webster to comment that "silk was largely introduced to American surgery through the operating rooms of Peking Union Medical College.†

Taylor also shared Halsted's interest in the surgery and physiology of the

---

* Paul C. Hodges 1970: personal communication.
† Jerome P. Webster 1971: personal communication.

thyroid gland. While at Hopkins he had worked in the Hunterian Laboratory of Experimental Medicine, and when he came to PUMC he established a "Hunterian Laboratory" in his department. Here he studied the use of thyroid transplants in restoring thyroid function after ablation of the gland.

Taylor's skills in thyroid surgery were applied shortly after his arrival in Peking: he wrote Halsted that on his first day at the hospital he was called to examine a "well known" American who had an exophthalmic goiter.[28] After controlling the hyperthyroidism he performed a subtotal thyroidectomy. Shortly thereafter he operated on a European who had a large adenomatous goiter with secondary hyperthyroidism.

Taylor was the first surgeon in China to systematically use the Carrel-Dakin's solution in treating the many patients who came to the surgical clinics only after serious complicating infections had developed, and the several soldiers and bandits who were usually on the wards with infected gunshot wounds.

Carrel-Dakin's solution (sodium hypochlorite buffered with sodium bicarbonate) had been developed during World War I by Alexis Carrel of the Rockefeller Institute, who had directed a military hospital in France, and Henry B. Dakin, an English chemist.

At the time of Taylor's arrival in Peking, the solution was the most widely used method of treating surgical infection in the West. With the assistance of Chinese pharmacists whom he trained personally, Taylor was able to prepare the solution using sulfuric acid imported from Japan. In his clinics and lectures on Carrel-Dakin's solution, Taylor emphasized the importance of meticulous care in its preparation. Beyond use of the solution in ordinary surgical infections he found that it improved but did not cure the many tuberculous fistulae that were seen at PUMC.

J. Heng Liu, a 1913 Harvard graduate, joined the surgery program at PUMC in 1918 after serving at Harvard in Shanghai. When Taylor arrived, Liu was about to leave for the United States on a CMB fellowship to study the techniques of research on tumor transplants with James B. Murphy at the Rockefeller Institute. Liu returned to PUMC in 1922 and opened a tumor laboratory in the Department of Surgery. His distinguished career in medicine and public health in China led to his appointment in 1928, after the Nationalists took power, as the first vice minister of health under Hsueh Tu-pi.

The opportunity to study surgical infections at PUMC opened a distinguished career in surgical bacteriology for Frank L. Meleney, the brother of Henry, who came to Peking in 1920 from Columbia University College of Physicians and Surgeons, where he had served for a year as instructor in surgery. In the first two papers he wrote in Peking, beginning in 1924, Meleney described a method for testing streptococcal lipase and the viability of the streptococcus in culture. In a third article he described the clinical syndrome and the bacteriological findings in a series of cases of fulminating and highly fatal streptococcal gangrene

Frank Meleney and Carl Schmidt in pharmacology sailed to the United States together on June 15, 1924. Meleney rejoined the Department of Surgery at P and S and continued his studies on surgical bacteriology, including the role of the anaerobic streptococcus in surgical infections and on bacteriophage.

In an introduction to Meleney's book on surgical bacteriology, Allen O. Whipple, his chief at P and S, described him as the most important contributor to surgical bacteriology since Lord Lister.[29]

Taylor described Jerome Webster's arrival in Peking in the summer of 1921 as

> ... the great event of the year. ... He is living in the hospital as resident in surgery, and already the service has taken on a new tone since he has been in charge. The young Chinese doctors have not understood the responsibility of a residency in a large hospital.[30]

Webster turned his attention to plastic surgery, and in another letter Taylor described to Halsted how Webster had performed a very skillful repair on a harelip complicated by a lipoma in the cleft.

PUMC was already establishing a reputation throughout China, and a Russian millionaire with a large unhealed X-ray burn on his back was referred to Taylor and Webster from a Japanese hospital in Harbin, Manchuria.

Taylor took special pride in describing to Halsted the comments of Tuffier, the famous French surgeon, during the dedication of PUMC in September 1921: "He seemed to be very much pleased to see the effort we are making to carry on your ideals here in China."[31]

The excellent instrument shop at the college provided opportunities for several innovations in surgical technique. Through the resources of the shop, Webster devised an ingenious and relatively simple instrument that made aseptic end-o-end anastamosis of the large bowel a safe procedure. Taylor in the meantime worked with technicians in the shop to nickelplate the reels of silk he had brought from Hopkins, which would make it easier to unwind the wet silk. He then sent samples of the new reels to Baltimore for testing.

Taylor was the first surgeon to introduce modern neurosurgical techniques to China. In a letter to Halsted of February 24, 1922, he described a cerebellar extension for an operating table that he had devised with Webster and the craftsmen in the instrument shop.[32]

The care of wounded soldiers and bandits was not limited to the wards of the teaching hospital; at times Taylor and other members of his department were called out to the field. In December 1925 Taylor led a surgical team to Tientsin where they cared for some 4,000 casualties; they worked around the clock to perform over 700 surgical procedures under circumstances as demanding as those of the battlefield.

Because of the strong Chinese tradition against violating the human body, and a natural fear of the knife, many patients admitted to the surgical wards were at first adamant against any surgical procedure. Webster recalls, however, that this attitude was often changed to one of complete submissiveness by the use of a scrubbing brush: "They were scrubbed so thoroughly, so vigorously—usually for the first time in their lives, and on a marble platform—that it literally took the starch out of them—they agreed to almost any procedure."*

Webster returned to New York in 1926 where, after two years in the laboratories of Frank Meleney, he joined the surgery department at P and S. He turned his full attention to plastic surgery and, with John Staige Davis at Hopkins, led the development of that specialty in the United States.

Webster came back to China in the fall of 1949 to conduct a six-week course in plastic surgery in Shanghai under the cosponsorship of the Ministry of Education and the American Bureau for Medical Aid to China. But because of the rapidly deteriorating situation in Shanghai, and the violent food riots, the course was not completed.

After two decades in China, in 1927 Taylor decided to leave PUMC permanently. He was tired, and his daughter, who had a congenital orthopedic deformity, was believed to require surgery. He returned to his native Alabama, practiced surgery for two years, and then moved to the Clifton Springs Sanitorium in New York State. Hugh Linder of Birmingham, who served as his surgical resident for three years, recalls that Taylor developed an illness that was probably encephalitis; when he recovered he told Linder: "The fever burned out my brain so I must do no more surgery."† His final position was as medical consultant to the U. S. Steel Company in Birmingham.

With Taylor's departure there was need for a neurosurgeon and Kwan Sungtao was sent to the University of Pennsylvania School of Medicine to train with Charles H. Frazier.

The post as head of surgery was offered to Mont Reid, but he chose to remain in Cincinnati. Instead, his colleague Max M. Zinninger accepted the appointment in 1928. Zinniger was an able, completely dependable man who served at PUMC for two years.

In the meantime Harold Loucks, a younger member of the department whose quiet, self-effacing manner and intelligence approached that of Dieuaide, was carrying a major teaching responsibility for students and house staff. A graduate of Western Reserve, Loucks had come to PUMC in 1922 as assistant resident in medicine, but after one year had moved to surgery. An ardent outdoorsman and hunter, in the summer of 1925 Loucks joined Roy Chapman Andrews on his expedition to Mongolia

Loucks shares with others vivid memories of and a special pride in the work of PUMC during the battle of Nanyuan in December 1925, when the college mobilized overnight a surgical and medical unit to handle several thousand

---

* Ibid.
† Hugh Linder 1970: personal communication.

casualties in the field.* Feng Yü-hsiang, the "Christian General" and warlord, had launched a major campaign against the troops of Marshal Chang Tso-lin, an ex-bandit and a Manchurian warlord, who was threatening Peking. General Feng's objective was to drive Chang back to Tientsin and eventually to Manchuria. The campaigns around Peking had, however, cost the Christian General between 15,000 and 20,000 casualties, and many of the seriously wounded had died on the field at Nanyuan through lack of medical care.

Feng therefore came to the authorities at PUMC with a request that the college send a unit to care for the survivors. It was a request that could not be turned aside. J. Heng Liu and Mont Reid, who had come out to Peking as a visiting professor in 1925 while Taylor was on leave, organized medical and surgical teams at PUMC, with volunteers from the language school and from other hospitals, and an emergency hospital was established in an abandoned barracks south of Peking. Nursing and medical students were bused back and forth daily. Reid and Liu led the surgical teams—it was a unique opportunity for Reid whose major interest was in wounds and wound healing. Henry Meleney was in charge of the medical team, and Nicholson Eastman from obstetrics was on general duty. Ruth Ingram, superintendent of nurses, who was fluent in Chinese, moved out to direct the nursing services at Nanyuan.

Paul Hodges, head of roentgenology, set up X-ray and fluoroscopy units and every patient was fluoroscoped for bullets and shrapnel before being wheeled into the operating room. To reduce the incidence of postoperative respiratory complications, chloroform was used as the anesthetic agent. In all, some 3,000 operations were performed, with a surprisingly low mortality rate. Cases requiring further surgery and prolonged hospitalization were moved to PUMC to be cared for under Loucks's supervision.

With deep gratitude, General Feng decorated the principal staff members of the emergency hospital with cloisonné medals bearing his likeness. It was, in the words of Loucks, "an invaluable experience for both the staff and the students; an experience in which PUMC could take pride."† It also served to introduce both medical and nursing students to the situation they would face years later in a wartorn China.

In 1930 Loucks succeeded Zinninger as head of surgery. Loucks's primary interest was in abdominal surgery, and in the same year he published in the *National Medical Journal of China* a review of eleven cases of hydatid cyst caused by the tapeworm, *Echinococcus granulosis*, that he had operated on at PUMC.[33] Before 1925 only eight cases of the disease had been recorded among the native population and three among foreigners in the whole of China. Echinococcus disease, for which the dog is the principal host, was therefore considered to be rare. Loucks pointed out, however, that sheepherding with dogs was com-

---

* Harold H. Loucks 1972: personal communication.
† Ibid.

monplace in northern and western China, and that dogs were the principal scavengers in both urban and rural areas. He concluded that echinococcus disease was far more widespread than was believed. Loucks's studies made surgeons in north and west China alert to the possibility of echinococcus disease in patients with hepatic masses.

OBSTETRICS AND GYNECOLOGY

J. Preston Maxwell, professor and head of obstetrics and gynecology, was described by his associate, Gordon King, as "a man of tremendous will, a devout Christian, a good surgeon, very affable, and a forceful teacher."† His piety made him take the lead in religious services and practices at the college—and his colleagues respected him for it.

Preston Maxwell was a member of a Scottish Presbyterian medical missionary family that served with distinction in China. His father, James L. Maxwell, had come to Formosa as a pioneer medical missionary in the spring of 1865. On his return to England he led the London Missionary Society's program to provide hostel accommodations for children of missionaries coming to London to study. Preston Maxwell's brother, James L., Jr., had followed his father to Formosa in 1901, and in 1910, with W. H. Jefferys, he published a valuable reference source, *The Diseases of China, Including Formosa and Korea*.[34] In 1923 he moved to the mainland as executive secretary of the China Medical Association.

For more than a decade before his appointment at PUMC in 1919, Preston Maxwell had served as a superintendent of a mission hospital at Yungchun in Fukien Province.

At PUMC Maxwell was not content simply to practice the arts of obstetrics and gynecology at a high level: his studies on osteomalacia in pregnancy stand as classics on that disease.

The old obstetrical unit of UMC had been torn down to make way for the new physical plant, thus limiting for several years the number of maternity cases for teaching obstetrics and gynecology. In the first year of the clinical program, 1921–22, only ninety-seven deliveries were made in the hospital and four by the home delivery service; even four years later the number had risen to only 267 hospital and thirty-three outside deliveries.

Calcium deficiency was widespread in north China; its most striking clinical manifestation in adults was osteomalacia, *yao t'ui t'eng*—literally, back and thigh pain. In 1923 Maxwell pointed out that no cases of osteomalacia were to be found south of the Yellow River save for an area in Hunan province. In Shansi and Kansu provinces in the north, and in Manchuria, however, he reckoned that 5 per cent of the women over the age of puberty had the disease—hence the popular name, "Shansi pelvis," for pelvic deformities in advanced cases.

---

† Gordon King 1972: personal communication.

The women in the north spent most of their time indoors and had little exposure to the sun, especially in the winter. They therefore had a severe deficiency of Vitamin D, which meant that they absorbed little of even the small amount of calcium in their diets. As her limited supply of calcium passed to the fetus during pregnancy the mother's bones collapsed into gross and crippling deformities, making childbirth difficult and at times impossible. The lack of fertility was of such magnitude that an estimated 400,000 women were moved into north China to maintain an adequate birth rate.*

After delivery it was the custom for a Chinese mother, who ate only the scraps from the table, to nurse her baby for at least a year because no other food was available for the child; if the babies were not breast-fed they were certain to die. This was brought out strikingly whenever mothers found it necessary to sell their breast-milk to buy food for the other children.

Breast feeding, however, placed an even greater drain on the mother's calcium stores than pregnancy, and her skeletal deformities became more pronounced. From his patients at PUMC, Maxwell compiled excellent descriptions of the clinical picture, the course, and the management of osteomalacia in pregnancy. The radiographic resources and the metabolic laboratories provided him with unique opportunities for collaborative studies on the disease. Working with Paul Hodges and Hsu Chien-liang, he divided the radiographic deformities into three types: chest, pelvis, and long bones. Severe kyphoscoliosis was also common, and in advanced cases the bones were at times so transparent that it was difficult to obtain a satisfactory radiogram. The autopsy specimens and roentgenograms from Maxwell's studies are still used to illustrate the disease in standard texts of obstetrics.[35]

Chu Hsien-i and his colleagues in the metabolic laboratory showed the essential role of Vitamin D in absorption of calcium from the gut: when patients with osteomalacia were fed diets deficient in Vitamin D, there was a prompt increase in fecal calcium levels. Roger R. Hannon and Liu Shih-hao found that the abnormal calcium-phosphorus excretion could be corrected promptly by therapy with 100,000 units of Vitamin D and five g. of calcium lactate daily, combined with a balanced diet. Infants with fetal rickets who were breast-fed by mothers with osteomalacia were also treated successfully with Vitamin D.

Nicholson J. Eastman, a 1921 graduate of the University of Indiana Medical School, who was destined for a distinguished career in academic obstetrics in the United States, was Maxwell's associate in the obstetrical department from 1924 to 1929. His principal educational contribution during this, his first of two appointments at PUMC, was to build a proper residency program.

Eastman's successor was Gordon King, a handsome, brilliant, charismatic English Baptist medical missionary. A graduate of the London Hospital Medical School, King had then trained in surgery. He reached Peking in August

---

* J. R. McKelvey 1971: personal communication.

1926 for a year of study at the North China Union Language School before taking up his duties at the medical school in Cheeloo. His program was interrupted in the spring of 1927 by Chiang Kai-shek's military victories, and, as total war seemed imminent, all foreign missionaries were evacuated to other countries in Asia. King wished to remain in China, however, and when Maxwell offered him a three-year appointment he accepted it enthusiastically. In so doing he switched from surgery to a distinguished and multifaceted career in academic obstetrics.

King had been studying liver function in surgical problems using the new dye test with tetra-idiophenolphthalein and the levulose tolerance test. At PUMC he applied the levulose tolerance test to the study of toxemias in pregnancy and demonstrated impaired liver function in a significant percentage of patients with eclampsia and pre-eclampsia.

In 1930 King reported on a study of thirty-three cases of eclampsia at PUMC. He emphasized the fact that eclampsia was a critical problem in China, that the incidence at PUMC was one case in 71.4 births, and that the general incidence was estimated to be one in 500 labors. Over 75 per cent of the patients admitted to PUMC with eclampsia had had no antenatal care whatsoever. The fetal mortality was 44 per cent and the maternal mortality 12.1 per cent, despite intensive obstetrical and supportive care, applying the most effective therapy in use in the West.

King was also a pioneering advocate of the use of spinal anesthesia in gynecologic patients, in part because he knew that his residents might subsequently be required to perform surgery without adequate anesthetic support.

Gordon King remembers most vividly a female resident, Lim Kha-t'i (PUMC 1929), who began a distinguished medical career in Nationalist China that reached its zenith in the People's Republic of China, where today she is considered a heroine as a doctor and a member of the party. In the words of one of her students, Alice Hsu (PUMC, 1933), who is herself a highly successful obstetrician-gynecologist in Hong Kong: "Kha-t'i was very bright, very popular, both as a person and a doctor—and very short."* She was also a woman of great self-confidence. In addition to her outstanding clinical skills, Lim Kha-t'i's popularity was enhanced by the fact that Chinese women preferred, as they still do, a female obstetrician-gynecologist. Nor was her popularity restricted to a Chinese clientele; American women who resided in Peking before 1950 remember her vividly as their choice, for she was efficient, understanding, and had a special rapport with patients.

When Gordon King left PUMC in November 1931, his post was filled by Amos Wong, who had returned from fellowship training at Hopkins.

King was appointed professor of obstetrics and gynecology at Cheeloo, where his outstanding qualities of leadership were soon recognized, and he was ap-

---

* Alice Hsu 1971: personal communication.

pointed dean. In November 1938 King accepted an appointment to the chair of obstetrics at the University of Hong Kong. Here he published a series of notable studies on hydatid mole and choriocarcinoma, which have a higher prevalence in the south than in north China.

King recalls that on two occasions he was "occupied" by the Japanese on Christmas Day: in Cheeloo in 1937 and again when Hong Kong fell on December 25, 1941. After two "underground" graduations had been held for senior medical students at the University of Hong Kong, King urged the other classes to escape to free China to continue their studies. In February 1942, he himself decided to go to free China to teach, and his students found a guide who would take him from Kowloon to Chungking. Led from Hong Kong Island to the rendezvous by a female medical student, King, with his hat pulled down and collar turned up, slipped past the Japanese soldiers who were closely guarding the Star Ferry and crossed to Kowloon. He followed his student and when she turned her head slightly toward a bystander, King knew that she was indicating the man who was to be his guide. King and his escort passed through the major Japanese post at the airport in the New Territories by timing their arrival to coincide with the changing of the evening guard. By junk, sampan, train, bus, and foot, King thus escaped to Chungking.

His principal anxiety was not for his own safety but for the welfare of the 350 students from the University of Hong Kong, including 150 medical students, who were studying at universities that had moved to the Chungking area. In their zeal to escape semitropical Hong Kong, they had failed to bring along adequate clothing for the harsher climate of western China, and King persuaded the British Embassy to put up funds to purchase simple, quilted peasant outfits for them.

In 1944 King was ordered to London to train in military medicine as a prospective leader of the British forces that would invade Hong Kong. The events at Hiroshima and Nagasaki in August 1945 made the invasion unnecessary, however, and three days after the Japanese surrendered the colony King returned to Hong Kong as deputy director of medical services.

After considerable negotiation, the General Medical Council in London finally approved the education that the Hong Kong medical students had received in free China. Their graduation ceremony was held with customary pomp and dignity in the Great Hall of the university—but the ceiling was the Hong Kong sky, for the roof of the Great Hall had collapsed when residents of Hong Kong had pulled down the timbers for use as firewood during the war.

The university reopened in 1947 and Gordon King served as dean and acting vice chancellor as well as professor of obstetrics. He left the colony in 1956, lured to Australia by Stanley Prescott to establish a medical school; Prescott, who had taught physiology at Cheeloo with King was now vice chancellor for the new university at Perth. After establishing the school at Perth, King was called upon to found still another medical faculty, this time in Nairobi, Kenya. In 1972 he returned to Hong Kong as medical director of the Family Planning Association, which he had established many years earlier as the Hong Kong Eugenics Society—at a time when "family planning" was not considered a proper term.

ROENTGENOLOGY

After earning a master's degree at Wisconsin, Paul C. Hodges had come out to Harvard in Shanghai to teach physiology. When the school closed he returned to Washington University in St. Louis, earned a degree in medicine and took a residency in roentgenology. Hodges assumed the chairmanship of roentgenology at PUMC in 1919.

A recognized master of radiological instrumentation throughout his career, Hodges decided early to develop diagnostic X-ray units for the mission hospitals. The young medical missionaries coming to China were aware of the value of radiological support, but lack of funds and of expertise in using the units then available in the West precluded their introduction in China. Hodges soon recognized that while PUMC with its own generators had no voltage problems, the mission hospitals were at the mercy of the frequent wide fluctuations in voltage in the Chinese power lines.

The need of the mission hospitals for X-ray machines was brought home most vividly to Hodges in the spring of 1922. In May of that year there was heavy fighting in the Peking area and the Presbyterian Mission Hospital at Paoting requested an X-ray unit and surgical support. Hodges recalls that it was necessary to add a special boxcar to the regular train to transport the X-ray unit, and that he was crowded into a compartment with General Chang Tsung-cho, director of ammunitions for the national armies.*

Soon after, on May 12, a team of fifteen persons led by Carrington Goodrich answered a call for surgical and radiological assistance from Kaifeng where there were 3,000 wounded soldiers. Goodrich reported that they completed 150 X-ray examinations, deloused, washed, and dressed ninety-six combatants, and performed forty-one operations. He added a personal note:

> Entre nous, I can't help "pointing with pride" to Dr. Hodges, who went into his X-ray work with the zeal of a holy cause and whose industry has brought the pledged machines to both Paoting and Kaifeng; to Dr. Char [George Char of the surgery department], who ploughed through his operations at the rate of eight a day.[36]

With a grant of $15,000 from the CMB, Hodges proceeded to develop a simple, inexpensive machine that was able to withstand the sharp fluctuations in voltage. The relatively low cost of the units was in part attributable to the fact that it was necessary to import only a few components from the United States

---

* Paul C. Hodges 1970: personal communication.

Under Hodges's supervision, the units were manufactured in China or, when more complex components were required, in Japan. In September and October 1922, Hodges installed his new units in mission hospitals that he had selected on an earlier tour, including those at Paoting and Kaifeng.

It now became necessary to train physicians in the selected hospitals in the theory and use of X-ray equipment, and Hodges organized special postgraduate courses to meet this need. The first course was offered for six weeks, in the spring of 1923, for English-speaking physicians, house officers, and fourth- and fifth-year medical students; enrollment was limited to twenty-five. Each student received as a permanent reference source a fat, profusely illustrated volume of letters. For Hodges an important reward for giving these courses was a letter of commendation from George Vincent, president of the Rockefeller Foundation.

With his intellect, his dynamism, and his capacity for self-expression, Paul Hodges would have been a force on any faculty—and he was at PUMC. But his enduring contribution was the introduction of diagnostic radiology to China.

Hodges went on leave in 1927 with every intention of returning to Peking, but an invitation from McLean to head the department at the University of Chicago was so attractive that he could not decline it. At Chicago he continued to make important contributions to instrumentation and radiological techniques. Although he never returned to PUMC, he maintained a deep affection for China. After his "retirement" from Chicago in 1960 Hodges rejoined former PUMC colleagues at the National Defense Medical Center on the outskirts of Taipei, where he reorganized the radiology department. He supervised the establishment of a radiation therapy center, as well as courses of instruction in the techniques and uses of radiation therapy.

Paul Hodges then sought retirement for a second time and settled in Florida; but again it was short-lived. The new medical school of the University of Florida in Gainesville needed leadership for its embryonic Department of Radiology and soon he was once again deeply involved in establishing a program in academic roentgenology—his third effort.

Hodges's successor as head of radiology at PUMC was Hsieh Chih-kuang, who had joined the staff of the radiology department in 1922. Hsieh's principal studies were on radiological diagnosis of osseous tuberculosis.

UROLOGY

George Y. Char, a native of Hawaii and a 1914 graduate of Harvard in Boston, came to PUMC from Harvard in Shanghai as head of urology. His classmate and close friend in Boston, Jean A. Curran, described him as "a keen and highly personable gentleman."* Char was a *Hakka*, literally, "guest folk," an ethnic group that originated in the north central region of China, probably in Hunan

---

* Jean A. Curran 1970: personal communication.

Province, and drifted southwards from the fourth to the ninth century, settling in Kwangung Province. From there they spread across southeast Asia and as far east as the Hawaiian Islands.

Char made the first study of the nature of the urological problems of eunuchs, a number of whom came to him with urinary complaints; he found that they were caused by ureteral strictures and urinary tract infections following the mutilating procedure used in castration.

In 1927 Char was appointed medical superintendent of the Central Hospital in Peking, where he had served on the surgical staff between the demise of Harvard of China and the opening of PUMC; at the same time, he continued as head of urology at the college.

ANESTHETICS

As in academic medical centers in the United States, the anesthesia program relied on a nurse-anesthetist, the surgical staff, and house officers. Anesthesiology had not yet developed as a specialty for doctors. Helen Holland was the "official" nurse-anesthetist, and each surgical resident had an assignment in anesthetics as part of his training. Because a majority of the surgical residents would not have anesthetic support in their practice, local and spinal anesthesias were the most popular agents. The stoicism of the Chinese made possible a far wider use of these methods than was customary in the West.

When Helen Holland went on leave, she was replaced by Mary Swisher, a nurse-anesthetist from Johns Hopkins, whose career was subsequently interrupted by her marriage to Harold Loucks. It was resumed some years later, however, when she performed heroically as a nurse-anesthetist while a prisoner of war in Santo Tomas in Manila during World War II.

ORTHOPEDICS

E. G. Brackett, head of orthopedic surgery at the Massachusetts General Hospital and a specialist on scoliosis, served as visiting professor in 1922.

George W. Van Gorder, a graduate of Harvard Medical School, had served as a resident at the Peter Bent Brigham Hospital with Harvey Cushing before coming to Peking as a surgical resident in 1920.

After completing a CMB fellowship in orthopedics, Van Gorder led the program at PUMC until his return to Massachusetts General Hospital in 1929. In Boston he worked with Marius Smith-Peterson and Edwin Cave in developing and perfecting the use of the Smith-Peterson nail in fractures of the neck of the femur.

OPHTHALMOLOGY

The first head of ophthalmology was Harvey J. Howard, a graduate of the University of Pennsylvania who had served as head of eye, ear, nose and throat at Canton Christian College from 1913 to 1915, and then at Harvard in Shanghai. It was only natural that his interest should be in trachoma, as this was the leading cause of blindness in China. Howard reckoned that 50 per cent of the eye diseases in north China were due to trachoma, but only 15 to 20 per cent in south China. The dust raised by the high winds of north China—"Peking Dust"—was considered to be the principal reason for the geographical difference.

In 1922 Ernst Fuchs, the renowned Viennese ophthalmologist, who developed ophthalmic pathology along the lines of Virchow's cellular pathology, was visiting professor of ophthalmology. The following year his son Adelbert, whose interest was in geographical ophthalmology, served in a similar capacity. This established a continuing link between the program in Peking and the famed eye institute in Vienna.

The summer of 1925 brought the flagrant exploits of Chinese bandits directly home to PUMC when Harvey Howard was held captive in northern Manchuria for ten weeks by the Black Dragon River bandits. With his twelve-year-old son, Howard was visiting Major Morgan Palmer on his 15,000-acre ranch at Aolaimi in Heilungchiang Province near the Siberian border.

Palmer had been entreated by his farmhands and the local peasants to assuage the bandits who were plundering their lands. The Chinese soldiers garrisoned nearby, however, not only refused to interfere but made no effort to conceal their delight with Palmer's troubles. When Palmer, accompanied by Howard, approached the bandits seeking a truce, he was immediately seized and murdered; Howard was taken prisoner.

The bandits soon realized that they were in deep trouble for having killed Palmer, and with Howard under close guard they kept on the move at night and hid by day. In their frustration over having lost the rich ransom that would have been theirs for a live Palmer, they threatened to kill Howard on several occasions. Adding to Howard's anxiety was the physical discomfort of riding in a rough-hewn wooden saddle, in clothes that were soaked by the frequent squalls.

In an article he wrote later, "My Bandit Clinic,"[37] Howard made light of his at times desperate situation. He also gave an interesting picture of the lifestyle of the bandit gang, and their attempts at self-medication. Several of the bandits had a small supply of powdered deer horn and "dragon's teeth," two prized medicines that were "almost as costly as gold dust."[38] Every member of the gang smoked three to four ounces of opium a week, and several of them developed severe abdominal pains from the gastrointestinal effects of the drug. Howard treated them with abdominal massage and soon all of the bandits were complaining of aches and pains and insisting that he massage them. The low incidence of diarrhea among the bandits was attributed to the fact that they systematically boiled their water—a most unusual practice in rural China at that time. The two bandits who did suffer from diarrhea

> had at first allowed their own medicine men to prick holes in their skin with a shoemaker's needle, and to burn them over the involved region with lighted incense sticks and moxas in order to drive the evil "winds" out.[39]

After traditional Chinese medicine had proven ineffectual, however, they accepted Howard's advice—rest and no food—and their diarrhea soon disappeared. Howard urged them to continue to boil their water and to ingest only food that had been thoroughly cooked.

Howard's chief interest of course was in the condition of their eyes, and he found that 40 per cent of his unwanted patients had trachoma. They delighted in placing Howard's only pair of glasses on their noses, which at first made him fearful that he would contract trachoma. But his fears were soon relieved when he observed that their virtually bridgeless, Oriental noses could not grasp the pince-nez and that the glasses fell dangling from its ribbon around their necks. The high incidence of myopia among the bandits—60 per cent—agreed with the studies Howard had been making on the Chinese for nearly a decade.

Tzu Jih-pen, the "old" bandit ex-chief—who, it developed, was only two years older than Howard—had the most severe case of trachoma of all the men; during the time Howard was held captive Tzu had two acute attacks of superficial keratitis with multiple ulcers. When the gang's "medicine man" was unable to help him, Howard was summoned and was able to relieve the intense pain by the use of almost continuous hot compresses; after each attack Tzu was able to see more clearly.

Months after Howard's release, he received a letter from Tzu, and thus began a fairly regular correspondence between them. The "old" bandit returned to Howard his ring that one of the gang had removed forcibly when he was first captured. As a further evidence of friendship he sent Howard his photograph and requested one of Howard and his family. Another letter said that as soon as the weather permitted he would come to Peking so that Howard could cure his trachoma and find him the right kind of job. But in 1927 before Tzu Jih-pen could come to PUMC, Howard returned to the United States to become head of ophthalmology at Washington University in St. Louis.

Arnold Pillat, a student of Fuchs in Vienna, succeeded Howard as head of ophthalmology.

THE HOSPITAL PHARMACY

The hospital pharmacy was headed by a Scot, John Cameron, who was more than a hospital pharmacist. He had studied and written about the Chinese pharmacopeia and the training of Chinese apothecaries. Many years later Cameron was escort to a fellow Scot, Sir Alexander Fleming, the discoverer of penicillin, when the latter toured the United States. During this trip Cameron naturally sought out old PUMC hands at every opportunity, so it was not surprising that Sir Alexander commented at the end of his tour that it appeared to him that American medicine was controlled by doctors from Peking Union Medical College.*

---

* Chester S. Keefer 1970: personal communication.

POSTGRADUATE COURSES

Continuing education for medical missionaries and for Chinese doctors was an early and important contribution of PUMC. Visiting professors were invited to offer postgraduate courses; the calendar for 1922–23, for example, included a course in orthopedic surgery by E. C. Brackett from Harvard; in ophthalmology by Ernst Fuchs; in pharmacology by Reid Hunt; in surgery by Adrian Taylor; in educational hygiene by John Grant; in obstetrics and gynecology by Preston Maxwell; and in medicine by Oswald Robertson.

The popularity of the courses is indicated by the institutions represented in Brackett's course in orthopedic surgery: Chefoo; the British Legation; North China Union Medical College for Women; Hunan-Yale; the British Legation Guard; Tinghsien; Shanghai; and Tengchow. Harvey Howard offered an annual four-week ophthalmology course in Chinese for Chinese physicians, with enrollment limited to twelve students.

A letter on the impact of these courses appeared in the magazine of the Fenchow Mission Hospital in Shansi Province:

> People at home may not realize what a boon it is to mission hospitals to have a place where it is possible to give the Chinese staff the special training they need in order that the work in mission hospitals may be specialized. In this way sick people get much more expert treatment, the hospital gets a much better name, many of the administrative difficulties of a Chinese staff disappear, and the Chinese doctor develops a much greater degree of efficiency because of the extra responsibility that can be placed upon him. It means that mission institutions will hold a respected position for a much longer period of time among the rising Chinese government institutions. Furthermore, the doctor also has available expert laboratory diagnosis through the mail as well as shorter and longer terms of postgraduate study in Peking.[40]

DEPARTMENT OF RELIGIOUS AND SOCIAL WORK

The Department of Religious and Social Work had as its first leader Philip Allen Swartz, who had served as pastor of a union congregation, the Church of Forest Hills, in Long Island, New York. A principal problem was the recruitment of strong leadership of a caliber that could match the wisdom of the leaders of the medical faculty. As the years passed, the status of the department became a focus of increasing friction between the faculty, the administration, and New York.[41]

FABER REPORT

In the fall of 1930 Knud Faber, a distinguished professor of medicine at Copenhagen and an experienced observer of programs in medical education, made survey of Chinese medical schools for the League of Nations.

In his report Faber noted that there were twenty-two medical schools in China; four governmental; two provincial; thirteen private, including missionary; and three military.[42]* In addition there were about fifteen schools teaching Chinese traditional medicine, although by all odds the largest number of traditional practitioners were trained through an apprentice system. Faber was informed that there were about 1 million indigenous practitioners compared to 4,000 to 5,000 Western-trained doctors. As the latter were concentrated in the big cities and in the hospitals, medical care in China continued to be administered almost entirely by practitioners of traditional medicine. With the population of China then at 400 million, there was one doctor trained in modern medicine for each 100,000 inhabitants.

There was a comparable shortage of hospital beds: of the 500 hospitals listed in the medical directory published by the National Medical Association of China in 1930, half were mission hospitals, the majority with fewer than fifty beds and many with only ten or fifteen.

Faber visited the South Manchuria Medical College and reported that it "has also a high standard, with excellent laboratories and class-rooms for pre-medical and preclinical training and a large hospital for clinical training."[43]

Among the mission schools he found the best to be Shantung Medical School, a "union" of four schools, followed by Moukden Medical College. He considered that all seven of the mission schools were doing good work, however.

Faber reserved his highest praise for PUMC and "the real scientific spirit reigning in the college."[44] He noted that in addition to the program for undergraduate medical students "there is very important postgraduate teaching. During the last year, 117 took postgraduate work or special laboratory work."[45] Faber described PUMC as functioning "to a certain degree as a normal school for teachers of other medical schools," with the graduates "nearly all engaged as assistants or teachers in the same or other colleges and hospitals or are attached to the Public Health Service."[46] He was especially impressed with the program that Marian Yang had established in midwifery. Faber's recommendations included an expansion of the bed capacity of the hospital; further development of the specialties, particularly psychiatry; and the expansion of facilities for John Grant's graduate programs in public health.

Faber summarized his impression with plaudits that clearly rated the school, in the eyes of this distinguished observer, as equal to the leading schools in the United States and Europe:

> With a hospital of 250 beds and extraordinarily well-equipped with all the necessary facilities for preclinical and clinical teaching and research, this is an excellent medical school and its influence on the development of modern medicine in China cannot be over-estimated.[47]

---

* As the actual total was twenty-six schools, four were omitted from the report.

NOTES TO CHAPTER NINE

1. George W. Corner, *A History of the Rockefeller Institute, 1901–1953*, p. 143–4.
2. F. G. Peabody, *Francis Weld Peabody, 1881–1927*, p. 54.

3. *Ibid.*, p. 54.

4. Francis W. Peabody, "The Department of Medicine at the Peking Union Medical College," pp. 317–20.

5. *Ibid.*, p. 318.

6. *Ibid.*, p. 319.

7. *Ibid.*, p. 319.

8. *Ibid.*, p. 320.

9. McLean to Cohn, 1 February 1921, Cohn Collection, Archives of The Rockefeller University, New York City.

10. *Ibid.*, 11 February 1921.

11. *Ibid.*

12. *Ibid.*, 1 December 1921.

13. United States Government Printing Office, vol. 1 (1938), p. 631.

14. Quoted by Cohn in a letter to McLean, March 10, 1927, Cohn Collection.

15. Shih-hao Liu, "A Comparative Study of the Effects of Various Treatments on the Calcium and Phosphorous Metabolism in Tetany: I. Chronic Juvenile Tetany, II. Chronic Adult Idiopathic Tetany," *Journal of Clinical Investigation* 5 (1928): 259–84.

16. Robert L. Duffus and Luther Emmett Holt, Jr., *L. Emmett Holt, Pioneer of a Children's Century*, p. 266.

17. *Ibid.*, p. 266.

18. L. Emmett Holt, *The Diseases of Infancy and Childhood* (New York and London: D. Appleton, 1897).

19. L. Emmett Holt, *The Care and Feeding of Children* (New York: D. Appleton, 1894).

20. Robert L. Duffus and Luther Emmett Holt, Jr., *L. Emmett Holt*, p. 274.

21. *Ibid.*, p. 276.

22. *Ibid.*, p. 282.

23. *Harvard Medical Alumni Bulletin*, no. 69 (June 1948).

24. Halsted to Taylor, 3 January 1921, Halsted Collection, Archives of The Johns Hopkins University Institute of the History of Medicine, Baltimore, Maryland.

25. McLean to Cohn, April 8, 1922, Cohn Collection.

26. Taylor to Halsted, 19 October 1920, Halsted Collection.

27. *Ibid.*

28. *Ibid.*

29. Allen O. Whipple, Introduction to *Treatise on Surgical Infections*, by Frank L. Meleney (New York: Oxford University Press, 1948).

30. Taylor to Halsted, 7 December 1921, Halsted Collection.

31. *Ibid.*

32. *Ibid.*, 24 February 1922.

33. Harold H. Loucks, "Hydatid Cyst, a Review and Report of Cases from North China," pp. 402–96.

34. James L. Maxwell, Jr. and W. H. Jefferys, *The Diseases of China, Including Formosa and Korea* (Philadelphia: Blakiston Son, 1910).

35. Duncan E. Reid, *A Textbook of Obstetrics* (Philadelphia and London: W. B. Saunders, 1962), p. 895.

36. *PUMC Weekly Calendar*, June 1922, p. 109.

37. Harvey J. Howard, "My Bandit Clinic," p. 1669–70.

38. *Ibid.*, p. 1669.

39. *Ibid.*, p. 1670.

40. *PUMC Weekly Calendar*, 4 April 1922, p. 36.

41. Mary E. Ferguson, *China Medical Board and Peking Union Medical College*, pp. 89–102, passim.

42. League of Nations Health Committee, *Report on Medical Schools in China*, by Knud Faber.

43. *Ibid.*, p. 13.

44. *Ibid.*, p. 15.

45. *Ibid.*, p. 15.

46. *Ibid.*, p. 15.

47. *Ibid.*, p. 15.

CHAPTER TEN

Excellence in Adversity: 1931-41

After the Japanese attacked Moukden in September 1931, the operation in China of a foreign institution such as Peking Union Medical College became increasingly difficult. Concern mounted at the Rockefeller Foundation and the China Medical Board as to the future and the goals of the school. In the opinion of Francis Dieuaide and Harold Loucks, however, no major impact from the hostilities was felt until the Japanese seized the Marco Polo Bridge at Lukouchiao near Peking on July 7, 1937; the city was occupied on August 4. Henceforth PUMC was in Japanese-held territory, and the victors were intensely hostile to Americans.

The Japanese onslaught in the summer of 1937 left PUMC as an educational oasis in north China, as other institutions moved to the southwest.

> The four great universities of northern China—Peking National, Tsinghua, Yenching and Nankai—were particularly loathed by the Japanese. They singled out Tsinghua, which had been built with American money, for special treatment. . . . As the Japanese drove further inland, university after university packed up and moved away. . . . Of China's 108 institutions of higher learning, 94 were either forced to move inland or closed down entirely. And yet the entire educational system had been re-established by the fall of 1939, and 40,000 students were enrolled in the refugee colleges.[1]

The colleges and universities were re-established mainly in three centers: Chunking, Kunming, the capital of Yunnan, and Chengtu. At the latter center they

> took refuge on the beautiful campus of the missionary West China Union University, where they were sheltered in relatively adequate quarters and, under the protection of Canadian and American missionaries, preserved their academic integrity almost inviolate; their scholastic standards remained consistently the highest throughout the war.[2]

It was here that the School of Nursing of PUMC was also to find its wartime home.

The residency programs for specialty training expanded as the number of PUMC graduates increased and applicants from the other schools sought training in Peking. The mounting requests for patient care by the Chinese and foreign communities posed heavy service burdens on the clinical staff and diminished the time they could spend on research. Further, the cream of the research opportunities unique to China had already been taken off the top in some fields by the earlier faculty. Medical research required increasingly complex and expensive equipment that was difficult to procure and maintain in a distant and unsettled country. Yet scientific productivity continued at a high level.

The shift from a foreign to a Chinese faculty moved ahead as qualified alumni and Chinese graduates of American schools became available. This trend was accelerated after 1933 when the great depression caused the income of the CMB to drop by 50 per cent. Since the salaries of Chinese faculty were pegged at a lower level than those of Americans, recruitment of Western faculty was trimmed, and the expenses entailed in moving a man and his family from the United States to Peking were thus avoided.

The policy of filling key positions with eminently qualified scientists was not altered. The caliber of the visiting professors continued to be outstanding, with appointments of men such as Walter Cannon, Hans Zinsser, and Eugene Opie.

Chen Ko-kuei returned in 1936 to spend three months in Peking, and in his opinion "PUMC was as good as ever. . . . Dieuaide was the most powerful force on the faculty."*

Several internal incidents, however, shook up the school. One was a selfish effort in December 1934 by several members of the faculty to usurp the headship of a major department. The same people also hurled accusations of malpractice against J. Preston Maxwell, head of the Department of Obstetrics and Gynecology. The conspirators were given an opportunity to present their charges, which proved to be totally unfounded, and they were released from their contracts.

A second period of turbulence was occasioned in 1937–38 by a serious challenge to the original goals of PUMC: excellence based on small classes of carefully selected students. With China's desperate need for doctors and nurses becoming even greater as the country became enmeshed in a total war, Robert K. S. Lim, John Grant, and J. Heng Liu proposed that the college place more emphasis on quantity and less on quality. They also suggested that PUMC should become a normal school at the call of the government. This brought a sharp reaction from other members of the medical and nursing faculties led by Dieuaide and Dean Gertrude E. Hodgman—the latter was "horrified at the

---

* Chen Ko-kuei 1971: personal communication.

thought!"* The forces supporting small classes and excellence prevailed, primarily because as the government moved to Chungking, and PUMC became an island in Japanese territory, other problems of far greater magnitude engulfed the ministries.

ROGER GREENE DEPARTS

A third crisis was the forced departure of Roger Greene in June 1935, as the culmination of a long sequence of differences of opinions and issues regarding administrative relationships. Greene had been resident director of the CMB since 1915, and during the formative years, from 1915 to 1920, in Franklin McLean's frequent absences it was natural for new staff members to turn to Greene for support and advice. This established a pattern in which Greene became far more deeply involved in the affairs of PUMC than was desirable in his other role as representative of the financing agency.

The complexity of Greene's administrative relationship expanded with his election as a trustee of PUMC in 1922 and as acting director in 1929. This resulted in a dual role—he represented the CMB to PUMC and at the same time he represented PUMC to the CMB. As the years passed his primary allegiance turned to PUMC, and the leaders of CMB became increasingly concerned about his adamant support of the college. His devotion to the cause of the college mounted to the point where, in the eyes of the officials in New York, he was unable to function effectively as the CMB's representative. Their attitude was strengthened when in 1933 the CMB found it necessary to reduce the budget for PUMC. That many institutions of higher learning in the United States were forced to cut budgets as much as 20 per cent made little impression on Greene, who was insistent that the level of financial support to PUMC must remain unchanged.

Greene was, in addition, the sitting target for those missionaries who felt that John D. Rockefeller, Jr. was not requiring of the staff the dedication to "a missionary spirit and motive," which he had pledged to do in his letter of March 1915. Egbert M. Hayes, secretary for religious and social work at PUMC, demonstrated the less attractive aspects of this missionary spirit in a critical letter of April 11, 1935, to Rockefeller, in which he complained that:

> After spending almost two years in this place where practically all the department heads and important staff members are either indifferent or antagonistic to religion because of careless living. . . . The policy of the last few years of choosing men and women without regard to their religious experience is now bearing painful fruit.[3]

Some missionaries also felt that the Department of Religious and Social Work was not given proper recognition—they failed to recognize the difficulty of recruiting a suitable secretary for the department. Perhaps the final straw

---

* Gertrude E. Hodgman 1971: personal communication.

came in 1934 when Thomas Cochrane, after a visit to PUMC, called on Rockefeller in New York and informed him that the Christian character of the college was on the downgrade.

Recognizing the nature of his dwindling effectiveness and frustrated by lack of support, Greene yielded to the urging of Alan Gregg and resigned as resident director of the CMB. On July 1, 1935, he stepped down and handed over the reins to a temporary administrative committee composed of Maxwell, Lim, and Wu Hsien.

Greene's resignation was obtained without consultation with the trustees of PUMC, who had great faith in him, and they were irate. Brought to the surface again were the problems of authority and responsibility between Peking and New York. The faculty, in general deeply loyal to Greene, were shaken by his departure and the apparently unilateral manner in which it had been generated.

Henry Houghton, who had moved from Iowa to the University of Chicago, returned to Peking on July 1, 1935, to make a study of the intricate relationships between the college, the CMB, and the Rockefeller Foundation. At the strong urging of Rockefeller, with whom he held ties of mutual respect going back for almost two decades, Houghton reluctantly agreed to succeed Greene, which he did on July 1, 1937. In the same year, Lim Chong-eang was elected dean. The post had been unfilled since A. M. Dunlap's departure in 1930, since administrative responsibilities had been handled adequately by other members of the staff.

ADVANCES IN EDUCATION

By the mid-1930s, the attitude toward education had improved dramatically. T. E. Hsiao, professor of education and director of the Department of Foreign Languages at the National University of Peking, described the striking changes:

> The last two decades in China can be compared with the fourteenth century in Europe. This brief period has witnessed clear evidence of the rise of the modern spirit. There are radical changes in all phases of Chinese life. It is universally recognized by both Chinese and Occidentals that a change in the life, government, social ideals, and religion of the Chinese can only come through some modification of their educational system.[4]

He went on to point out that while the old system of education was undemocratic, limited to a few, and neglected the general elevation of the intellectual level, the new system was democratic—it met the needs of all.

The first serious attempt at educational reform had taken place under Emperor Kuang Hsu (1875–1908), with the founding of the Chian Hsüeh Society for the study of Western learning; the Empress Dowager had, however, put a stop to the movement. Although the 1911 revolution had ordained that education should cultivate virtuous and moral character in the young—moral training supplemented by industrial and military education—"as a matter of fact, the

Revolution of 1911 heralded in a long period of internecine strife, and education has often been relegated to the background."[5]

Hsiao paid lavish tribute to the contributions of Hu Shih, who had sparked the acceptance of the Chinese vernacular, *paihua:* "The work of Hu . . . is roughly comparable to that of Wycliffe and Chaucer in England, and to that which Petrarch and Dante accomplished in Italy."[6]

One notable evidence of the educational advances in China was that the number of children enrolled in school rose from 3 million in 1912 to 12 million in 1935. In the same period the number of universities increased from four to eighty-two, and twenty-nine "special" colleges were established.

THE EDUCATIONAL PROGRAM

The curriculum was a special concern of Francis Dieuaide who took it to be his personal responsibility to keep it in line with that of the leading medical schools in the United States. In 1934 he reported that large blocks of free time had been introduced in the second trimester of the sophomore year, and a three- to four-week elective period in the senior year. As a result the students' use of the library had increased ninefold in a period of ten years. In general the students spent only one-third of their time in the classroom; emphasis was on the teaching laboratory and the study of the patient. While in most American schools the junior year was still crammed with introductory clinical lectures, at PUMC junior lectures and demonstrations had been reduced to two hours a day.

During one trimester, a series of eleven lectures on historical and philosophical aspects of the development of medicine was presented by various members of the staff. All first-year students were expected to be present, and other students were encouraged to attend since the subjects and the lecturers varied from year to year.

Dieuaide took note of the criticism that PUMC placed too much emphasis on complex laboratory procedures and too little on practical medicine, and he accepted the criticism as inevitable in light of the mission of the school.

Internships were available in medicine, surgery, and obstetrics and gynecology. For interns interested in gynecological surgery, there was a combined program with nine months in obstetrics and gynecology and three months in general surgery. Most of the graduates chose the medical internship. By 1933 there were seventeen interns in medicine, eleven in surgery, and two in obstetrics and gynecology.

By 1933, also, the number of young doctors in residency training exceeded that at most teaching hospitals in the United States. Medicine and surgery enrolled one resident, one first assistant resident, and nine assistant residents on each service. Medicine also accepted one assistant resident in pediatrics, one in neuropsychiatry, and one in dermatology and syphilology.

The residency program in obstetrics and gynecology enrolled one resident, one first assistant resident, and four assistant residents. There were three assistant residents in ophthalmology and three in radiology.

After residency most of the graduates were awarded CMB fellowships for further training in leading medical schools and teaching hospitals, primarily in the United States and Canada, such as Chicago, Hopkins, Harvard, and McGill.

ALUMNI CAREERS

From the beginning PUMC was highly successful in achieving its goal of training men and women for leadership roles in medical education and research. In his 1934 report to the CMB, Dieuaide stated that of the total of 141 graduates in the history of the school, 95 per cent were teaching medicine, had research appointments, or were in full-time hospital posts; only seven were in private practice.

The 1937 PUMC announcement listed graduates of the class of 1927 as holding the following positions: commissioner of health for Kiangsi Province; superintendent of the Ch'angchow Red Swastika Hospital; superintendent of the Municipal Infectious Diseases Hospital and Municipal Anti-Opium Hospital in Nanking; assistant professor of dermatology at PUMC; and head of the Department of Public Health at PUMC. For the class of 1926: chief of pediatrics service, Hospital of the Greater Municipality of Shanghai; head of medicine and superintendent of the hospital of Hopei Provincial Medical College; head of the Department of Obstetrics and Gynecology, Central Hospital in Nanking; commissioner of public health, City Government of Greater Shanghai; and staff member, North Manchurian Plague Prevention Bureau.

A SURVEY OF OTHER MEDICAL SCHOOLS

An analysis of medical education in China in 1932–33 was prepared by Lee T'ao of the Division of Chinese at PUMC, based on reports from twenty-seven medical schools enrolling 17,414 students—four supported by the national government; five by provinces; sixteen by private funds; and two by the army. Seven of the schools had no premedical requirements; those in eighteen varied from one-half to two years of premedical studies; only PUMC and the South Manchuria Medical College required three years. The medical school course was from four to four-and-one-half years in duration. A majority of the schools, 75 per cent, required a one-year internship. Government regulations required six years of primary school; six years of middle school; and a minimum of six years for premedical and medical studies.

The requirements of the "special" medical schools, which were patterned after the *semmon gakko* of Japan, were six years of primary, six years of middle school, and four years of medical school—there was no premedical requirement. The size of the classes varied considerably, with the smallest number, twenty-five, at PUMC and the largest, about 100, at Tung Nan Medical College in Shanghai.

A review of hours allotted to the major courses showed that PUMC had the lowest number of hours for anatomy and the highest for public health.

Women were taking up the study of medicine in increasing numbers, and two of the twenty-seven schools, one in Canton and the other in Shanghai, were exclusively for women. Almost 17 per cent (2,923) of all medical students were women, and medicine was described as "the only profession in this country in which women have thoroughly established themselves."[7]

The Commission on Medical Education was founded in 1935 under the auspices of the Ministry of Education, with Chu Chang-keng (PUMC 1929) as its director. The commission was supported equally by the ministry and by the Rockefeller Foundation, each contributing an average of about $10,000 a year. It had three major objectives: standardization of the curricula of the government medical schools to meet China's health needs; the training of teachers for the medical schools; and the preparation of medical textbooks.

AMERICAN BUREAU FOR MEDICAL AID TO CHINA

When the Japanese launched their full-scale invasion of China in 1937, a group of former teachers at PUMC rallied to the support of the Nationalist government. The American Bureau for Medical Aid to China (ABMAC) was established by Frank Meleney, Donald Van Slyke, and Frank Co-tui, a graduate of the University of the Philippines, who was now on the staff of the Department of Medicine of New York University. They were joined by other faculty alumni, principally Aura Severinghaus, Jerome Webster, and Walter Cannon. Gertrude Hodgman, former dean of nursing, became chairman of a sub-committee on nursing and nursing education.

In his presidential address at the thirty-third annual dinner of ABMAC on December 9, 1970, Severinghaus painted a picture of China in the fall of 1937:

> An army of 3 million men, joined by 50 million civilians, were marching from China's eastern areas to the interior, pressed by a military machine of great power, leaving and destroying their homes and belongings, and even the good earth, in order to delay the advance of a determined enemy, vicious and fired up by a sense of sure victory. These marchers were besieged all along the way by malaria, plague, cholera, smallpox, dysentery, typhus and typhoid. With them were only a small fraction of the 6,000 fully qualified doctors who in the preceding peaceful years had ministered to 400 million people.[8]

It was this dreadful picture and their deep emotional attachment to China that stirred the founders of ABMAC to a unique and highly successful effort to raise funds to send medical aid to China. In the first year they raised $100,000 for drugs, vaccines, antibiotics, and quinine; in the four years before the onset of World War II their total contributions equalled $1.5 million. Their persuasive dedication drew the support of such distinguished citizens as Eleanor Roosevelt, Pearl Buck, and Theodore Roosevelt, Jr.

In addition to the purchase of drugs and vaccines, support was given to such programs as the Medical Relief Corps and the Chinese Red Cross, as well as for the purchase and shipment of a vaccine plant to Chungking. Madame Chiang Kai-shek commented: "Before Pearl Harbor the only two forces which convinced the Chinese people that Americans were fond of them and concerned about their welfare were General Chennault's Flying Tigers and ABMAC."[9]

With the outbreak of World War II, Robert Lim, as on-the-scene advisor on China's needs, became a key person in the ABMAC program. As funds reached $1.5 million in 1942 and $2.5 million in 1944, assistance was given to six medical schools that had moved to west China. Special emphasis was placed on audiovisual equipment and publications for medical libraries. Similar materials were sent to Lim's emergency medical school. All ABMAC aid was flown to India and across the "hump" into Chungking.

After the war, support for ABMAC programs fell sharply due to the mounting concern over the future of the United States in China. In addition to his duties as chairman of the Commission on Medical Education of the Ministry of Education, and chief medical officer of the Chinese National Relief and Rehabilitation Administration, J. Heng Liu succeeded Lim as the ABMAC representative in China. With the fall of Nanking to the Communists in 1949, Liu transferred ABMAC's office to Taiwan and thenceforth the program centered on the support of the National Defense Medical Center under Loo Chih-teh (PUMC 1929), and its nursing school under Chou Mei-yu (PUMC, nursing, 1930).

ANATOMY

Gross anatomy was the major academic stumbling block for freshman students at medical schools in the United States, but not at PUMC. Paul H. Stephenson, who had joined the department in 1920 to teach gross anatomy, was definitely on the side of the students—he was "so nice that everybody passed."[*]

Ma Eiko taught histology, and A. B. Drooglever Fortuyn neuroanatomy based on the text on comparative anatomy of the nervous system that he had written with his old chief, Ariens Kappers. Fortuyn's research in genetics continued, and when he went on leave in 1938 he was invited to lecture in medical schools in Germany and in England as well as in his native Holland.

BIOCHEMISTRY

In 1927, Wu Hsien and his wife, Daisy, had begun a series of studies on the nutritional value of the average Chinese diet. They found that the vegetable protein on which the diet was chiefly based had a low biologic value, and that

---

* Yu Ts'ai-fan 1971: personal communication.

the diet was also deficient in fat-soluble vitamins and in calcium. They ascribed the short stature and the lack of general physical development of the average Chinese to these inadequacies.

Immunochemistry was another area of research for Wu, who developed one of the first methods for the quantitative analysis of antigen-antibody precipitates, using a chemical color group such as hemoglobin or iodinated albumin. Wu's studies on the denaturation of proteins contributed to the theory that denaturation is due to the unfolding of the protein molecule.

The growing importance of immunochemistry drew the attention of the CMB to the desirability of strengthening that field at PUMC. Roger Greene recruited a former Tsinghua scholar, Bacon Chow, who had earned a Ph.D. in chemistry in 1932 in the laboratories of James B. Conant at Harvard. While Chow had several offers to remain in the United States, he concluded that "the need was greatest in China, and the research opportunities at PUMC were excellent."* Greene arranged for Chow to spend the year 1935 in the laboratories of Oswald Avery at the Rockefeller Institute before returning to China. Here Chow worked with Walter F. Goebel and they succeeded in preparing an "almost pure antipneumococcus antibody by a method of their own, superior to that of previous workers."[10]

Arriving in 1936, Chow remained in Peking for three years, during which period he gave a strong impetus to immunochemical studies and to interdepartmental cooperation in research projects. He studied the fluctuations in complement levels in pregnancy with Lim Kha-t'i in the Department of Obstetrics; and he and Samuel Zia of the Department of Bacteriology studied complement and precipitin reactions through fundamental immunochemical techniques. It was through the latter studies that Chow attracted the attention of Hans Zinsser who offered him an assistant professorship at Harvard.

In 1938 Chow joined Harry B. Van Dyke, formerly of PUMC, who had just assumed the chairmanship of the new program in pharmacology at the Squibb Institute. They were the first to isolate luteinizing hormone, biologically pure follicle-stimulating hormone, and oxytoxic principle. Chow later became professor of biochemistry at the Johns Hopkins School of Hygiene and Public Health.

In 1944 Wu Hsien established a nutrition institute for the Nationalist government. Shortly thereafter he was sent to Washington to discuss the nutritional needs of free China with the United Nations Relief and Rehabilitation Agency.

In 1948 Wu left China and taught for a period at the School of Medicine of the University of Alabama. At his death in 1959, A. Baird Hastings noted: "Wu was one of the outstanding biochemists of the pre-World War II era. Indeed his name, linked with that of his Harvard professor, Otto Folin, is known throughout the world."[11]

* Bacon F. Chow 1971: personal communication.

PHYSIOLOGY

The Sino-Japanese War brought Robert Lim to the position of national leadership in China's programs in military medicine. His accomplishments under the most difficult circumstances drew the highest praise and firmly established him as one of China's great wartime heroes.

Lim's intense patriotism and remarkable organizational abilities were first demonstrated when the Japanese attacked Shanghai in 1931. He hurriedly but effectively organized the first series of Chinese Red Cross medical units, which handled more than 20,000 casualties.

In the same year his close friend and associate in physiology, Loo Chih-teh (PUMC 1929), was called to full-time military duty by J. Heng Liu on the recommendation of Lim and Grant. Loo was assigned as head of the medical department of the Central Military Academy in Nanking to expand the fledgling military medical program initiated by Lim. For "Dick" Loo this marked the beginning of a distinguished career in military medicine and medical education that spanned more than four decades. As the prospects of a major war became increasingly ominous, Loo was sent abroad in 1935 to study military medical services in the United States, Britain, and Europe.

Despite his increasing commitments to national medical programs, Lim continued to be highly productive in his physiology laboratory at PUMC. With Loo's departure, Lim appointed as his research associate Wang Shih-chun, a medical student in the class of 1935, and together they continued the investigation of factors influencing the secretion of gastric juice. They showed that it is not affected by the degree of acidity; there is a straight-line relationship.

After graduating from PUMC, Wang spent two more years with Lim and was then awarded a fellowship by the Rockefeller Foundation to work with Stephen W. Ranson at the Neurological Institute of Northwestern University. At the end of his fellowship Wang joined the Department of Pharmacology at Columbia University College of Physicians and Surgeons, where he established an international reputation through his studies on vomiting, especially the identification of the chemoreceptor trigger zone in the medulla.

Lim's other research associate was Liu An-ch'ang (PUMC 1928) who had studied with Archibald Vivian Hill, the distinguished British neurophysiologist at University College, London.

Anton J. Carlson, with whom Lim had worked in Chicago, was a visiting professor of physiology in 1935. A second visiting professor was Walter Cannon, George Higginson Professor of Physiology at Harvard, and one of America's leading medical scientists and statesmen. Cannon lived with his daughter, Wilma, who was doing editorial work in the parasitology program, and her husband John K. Fairbank, who was studying Chinese. Fairbank later became director of the East Asia Institute at Harvard, and America's foremost sinologist.

In Cannon's eyes the situation in China in 1935 was similar to that in Spain five years earlier. Students who had enjoyed the advantages of study in progressive foreign universities were returning to their homeland with high hopes of creating in China the career opportunities that they had seen in the Western world. Cannon, a dedicated liberal, believed that China would make striking progress if the liberal forces were allowed a decade of peace. But he feared that Japan too was aware of what was taking place and that she was determined that China would not have those years to free herself from the tyranny of the past. Cannon's fears were prophetic, for even as he and his wife were leaving China for Manchuria, in early June 1935, they passed trainloads of Japanese soldiers moving in to seize Peking.

In his memoirs Cannon lauded Robert Lim as a scientific leader:

> While I was visiting professor of physiology at the Peking Union Medical College in 1935, I had the privilege of associating with Professor Robert K. S. Lim and of working with the remarkable group of young Chinese investigators he had gathered in the physiological laboratory. . . . Although China can boast of a very ancient civilization, she is a young nation in recognizing the importance of modern science. Scarcely more than a score of years ago Dr. Lim established the first active center for physiological research in his native land. He also instituted an admirable periodical for reporting Chinese contributions to his science.[12]

On the personal side, Cannon described Lim as a man who came from intellectual antecedents and who "has the charm, the gracious courtesy, and the wide learning typical of the Chinese scholar. . . . I count my friendship with Dr. Lim as one of my choicest."[13]

Cannon also characterized Lim as "a devoted citizen and an ardent patriot."[14] In alluding to him as an ardent patriot, Cannon was referring to the remarkable saga of Lim as the leader of China's military medical programs during her long and painful years at war. In the spring of 1937, Lim and his family started on a leave of absence in the United Kingdom. When their steamer stopped at Singapore, however, Lim was handed a cable from J. Heng Liu and John Grant entreating him to come back to China immediately. Leaving his family in the Straits Settlements, Lim returned to Nanking where he took command of the Red Cross medical program.

Soon after Lim reached Nanking the Japanese approached the city. Faced with the responsibility of evacuating 600 Red Cross staff members from hospitals, he organized them as mobile medical units, which became the nucleus of the Chinese Red Cross Medical Relief Corps. They retreated to Hankow and then to Changsha where they were joined by a group of nurses, primarily from PUMC, who were attached to the Mass Education Movement led by Chou Mei-yu.

Under Lim's leadership, programs at Kweiyang mushroomed. Another of his admirers, George E. Armstrong, assistant surgeon for the China-India-Burma Theatre and later United States Army surgeon general, stated that, "In Kweiyang [Lim] led in building up the greatest medical center in wartime China."[15] Lim established six Emergency Medical Service Training Schools in which young men were trained as advanced medical corpsmen. Miss Chou was appointed chief nurse for the schools.

In another accolade, Donald Van Slyke credits Lim with the preservation of the Chinese Army:

> Dr. Lim organized for the Chinese Army, under the Chinese Red Cross, the field service which was practically all the medical service the shattered Chinese army had after the fall of Shanghai. After the Chinese defense became somewhat stabilized, Lim introduced a degree of improved sanitation into the Chinese army, without which I doubt whether the Army could have held out.[16]

In early 1942 Lim was transferred to the Chinese Expeditionary Force under General Joseph W. Stillwell, and soon he was leading his medical group in Stillwell's twenty-six-day forced retreat through the jungles of Burma to India. For his heroism during the retreat and his services at Kweiyang, President Roosevelt awarded Lim the Legion of Merit, which Stilwell presented to him personally. In 1946 he was honored with the Medal of Freedom of the United States.

As the end of the war approached, Chiang Kai-shek appointed Lim as Surgeon General of the Medical Services of the Chinese Army with responsibility for leading the health and medical programs in the projected effort at postwar reconstruction. Lim was sanguine about a task that would have overwhelmed an ordinary man:

> China has lost millions of lives, and has endured indescribable hardships during the war, for which she can secure no adequate reparations. Her material losses, however, are light by comparison. China may consider herself fortunate in having emerged from the war with no insurmountable problems of livelihood or rehabilitation, and with the friendship of the three major powers to aid her in their solution.[17]

Lim's program included the establishment of ten general hospitals and a postgraduate training program under which Chinese medical officers would study at medical centers in the United States.

He was responsible for the formation of the National Defense Medical Center in Shanghai in June 1947, which represented a merger of the Army Medical College, founded in Shanghai in 1902, and the six field service schools Lim had established in 1938.

In the spring of 1949 the National Defense Medical Center was moved to Taiwan with other elements of the Nationalist government and re-established on the outskirts of Taipei. Dick Loo succeeded Lim as commanding officer. P'eng Tah-mou (PUMC 1933) served as his deputy, and Chou Mei-yu headed the nursing school. The medical center flourished, with educational programs in dentistry, nursing, pharmacy, and medical technology as well as medicine. There were major infusions of money from the CMB, the United States Department of State through its foreign aid programs, the ABMAC, and the government of Taiwan. Today it is one of the leading educational and research centers in the health professions in the Far East.

Resigning his post as surgeon general in 1948, Lim came to the United States when he returned to research in physiology at the University of Illinois and later at Creighton University. His final position was with the Miles Medical Science Research Laboratories in Indiana. Robert K. S. Lim died in Kingston, Jamaica, on July 8, 1969.

Bobby Lim's accomplishments have been lauded by scholars who have analyzed the Chinese efforts during World War II. Barbara Tuchman refers to him as "one of China's great men."[18] White and Jacoby describe Lim and Dick Loo as belonging to

> The staunch-hearted handful who fought to help the Chinese soldiers—men like Dr. Richard Lu [Loo] of the Chinese army medical service and Dr. Robert Lim of the Chinese Red Cross—suffered agonies themselves as reports came in from the war areas. They could do nothing; they were trapped by the harsh reality of the ignorant, feudal country on the one hand, by corruption and lack of support from above on the other.[19]

When Walter Cannon introduced Lim at a meeting of the ABMAC in 1944, he read a glowing citation that included such plaudits as:

> Pioneer in bringing into a very ancient civilization a respect for modern science....
>
> Leader of an eager and energetic group of investigators engaged fruitfully in productive scholarship....
>
> Head of a department in a first-rank medical school [PUMC] ... a department so admirable that it would do credit to any medical school in the world....
>
> Imaginative provider of aid to the sick and wounded in his country's fighting forces ... and responsible officer in the army of a long-suffering ally whose perils and privations in the struggle for freedom he has fully shared.[20]

In reviewing the extraordinary career of Robert K. S. Lim, it is easy to be carried away by his heroic patriotism and to overlook his outstanding scientific contributions. Lim gained international recognition for his studies on gastrointestinal physiology and on the central nervous system. His contributions to understanding pain included demonstrating that the analgesic action of aspirin is peripheral, and that the drug acts by blocking the pain impulses at the receptor sites. A master technician, Lim adapted to the dog the stereotaxic technique of Horsley and Clarke, and thereby introduced the dog, physiologists' favorite experimental subject, to neurophysiological research. Heretofore, because of the endless variations in the size and shape of the skulls of dogs, they had been ignored in neurophysiological studies.[21]

Chang Hsi-chun, who joined the PUMC faculty in 1927, succeeded Lim as head of physiology in 1938. Chang's research interests included the acetylcholine content of soft tissues, and a collaborative project with the Department of Chemistry at National Tsinghua University on the Vitamin C content of green peppers—a frequent ingredient in the delicious cuisine of north China.

BACTERIOLOGY

Lim Chong-eang, who became head of the department in 1927, was, like Wu Hsien, a rather distant man. The students frequently contrasted his manner with the warm gregariousness of Bobby Lim. Lim Chong-eang, however, became increasingly involved in managerial responsibilities, which he both enjoyed and performed efficiently. In January 1932, he assumed the editorship of the newly-created *Chinese Medical Journal*, which represented a merger of two publications—the *China Medical Journal*, founded in 1907 as a missionary organ and edited by J. L. Maxwell, Jr., the brother of Preston Maxwell; and the *National Medical Journal of China*, first published in October 1915 by the National Medical Association and edited for many years by Wu Lien-teh, founder of the Manchurian Plague Prevention Service. Lim had succeeded Wu as editor of the *National Medical Journal* before the merger.

Under the very capable leadership of Samuel H. Zia, the major research effort in the department turned to typhus fever, of the variety transmitted by the human body louse, a major disease problem in north China and Mongolia. It was endemic throughout the year and usually became epidemic in late winter and spring. The manner of dress during the long cold season made an excellent medium for the propagation of the body louse: garments were padded with cotton, wool, or sheep skin, seldom if ever washed or changed during the winter, and thus provided an ideal breeding place for the louse. At night all members of a family slept on the *k'ang*, with their clothes as a common cover, so the lice moved easily from one person to another.

Typhus fever was a special problem for Westerners; it was described by Balme as "the deadly enemy of the missionary of North China."[22] In contrast to the filthy clothes that carried the louse from one Chinese to another, the ricksha blanket was a special hazard for Westerners who, to protect themselves against the icy winds of Peking, would unsuspectingly pull the blanket up around their necks. The typhus-laden lice deposited by a patient being rushed to the hospital would thus move easily from passenger to passenger, spreading the disease via the blanket.

The clinical picture was identical with that of European, epidemic, louse-borne typhus, with a high continuous fever for two weeks, skin eruptions, and central nervous system manifestations. Zia and Wu Ch'ao-jen of the Department of Medicine reported 450 cases with a mortality of 10 per cent among 5,000 admissions to PUMC over a period of fifteen years.

Wu and Zia noted that in the summer and fall, when body lice are not prevalent, they saw many mild cases of typhus. The clinical picture suggested th possibility of the Mexican (murine) strain or flea-borne typhus fever. Through cross-immunity studies with the Mexican strain they isolated typhus rickettsia of the murine type from five Peking house rats. They were not, however, able to establish any direct etiological relationship between this finding and the mild cases of typhus seen in the summer and fall.

Recognized as the world authority on typhus, Hans Zinsser, professor of bacteriology at Harvard Medical School, had served on typhus commissions in Serbia and Russia, had studied the disease in the laboratory—and in 1929 had contracted it himself. Since 1930 Zinsser had concentrated his rich talents on the culture of the rickettsia, looking toward large-scale cultivation that would make possible the manufacture of a human vaccine. When he came to PUMC as a visiting professor on March 2, 1938, his vaccine was being used in the field in China, Mexico, Hungary, and Rumania. Several members of the department at PUMC had worked in Zinsser's laboratory; in 1934 Zia had spent a year with him learning the techniques for the cultivation of the Mexican and European rickettsiae in the chick embryo.

It was partly the opportunity to work with Zia, Liu Ping-yang, and Liu Wei-t'ung on the preparation of typhus vaccine with his new "agar-tissue" medium that drew Zinsser to PUMC. He carried rickettsial cultures with him on the steamer and transferred them at the National Institute of Health in Tokyo, which was sponsored by the Rockefeller Foundation. In studies on typhus in Peking, Zinsser guided Zia, Liu Ping-yang, and K. H. Pang in the use of his medium, an agar slant of serum-tyrode mixture over which small bits of tissue are laid. They showed that rickettsia of the classical European type that had recently been isolated from patients could be readily propagated by using Zinsser's agar technique. In earlier experiments Zinsser had used older laboratory strains of the rickettsia that could have differed greatly in their growth properties from the recently isolated agent.*

The opportunity to study the culture of China was another magnet that drew Zinsser to Peking. A learned student of the arts, he had studied and enjoyed the treasures of Europe; now he was drawn by the mysterious East. Zinsser was captivated by Peking; in his autobiography he wrote eloquently of the sounds and sights of the city:

> Could I borrow a pen of a Loti or a Gide, I should be tempted to describe Peking, its noises and smells, the evening crowds on Hatamen Street, the files of long-haired, coal-laden camels threading their way along a street that might be a Paris boulevard, among automobiles and rickshaws; its children and beggars; the strange mysterious silences of its twisted alleys after dark; the surprise of passing through gates from sordid lanes into quiet and charming courts and gardens; and the majesty of its palaces.[23]

---

* John F. Enders 1972: personal communication.

He went on to compare Peking with his beloved Paris:

> ... (for, truly, the Winter Palace, with its symmetric immensity is more impressive than Versailles) ... Peking had a charm that no other city except Paris has ever held for me ... I felt immediately at home, and could quite understand how those of my Western friends who had once settled there for a year or two had no desire to leave.[24]

Zinsser left an indelible imprint on every person who associated with him at PUMC, as he did throughout his brilliant career. Robert Loeb described Zinsser as "a man of remarkable charisma; when he walked into a room he was immediately the center of attraction."* He was an instant hit with the PUMC faculty, and a charming photograph in the collection of John C. Snyder, Zinsser's former student, shows him on the steps of the college surrounded by Chinese colleagues whose faces reflect his radiance.

Social evenings with Zinsser were memorable; his breadth of cultural knowledge, his scintillating conversation—and his ability to play a tune on the piano with his back to the instrument—delighted all who had the pleasure of being in his company.

Hans Zinsser was the first visiting professor at PUMC to be honored by the publication of a *festschrift*. Entitled *Pathology and Microbiology*, it appeared as a supplement to the *Chinese Medical Journal,* in March 1938,[25] and consisted of forty-nine articles on pathology, microbiology, immunology, public health, and entomology, most of them written at PUMC.

The mission to China had a tragic aftermath for Zinsser, for while he was sailing back home he realized he was a sick man. He accepted his illness, leukemia, calmly and bravely. W. Barry Wood, Jr., who worked with Zinsser during his fatal illness, recalled that his only complaint was that his enlarged spleen made him so uncomfortable when he sat a horse to ride to the hounds that he had given up one of his favorite sports.†

PHARMACOLOGY

Soon after his arrival in Peking in 1908 Bernard Emms Read began to translate and study the classic of Chinese materia medica, the *Pen T'sao Kang Mu,* (*The Great Herbal*), the leading reference and one of the most popular works on Chinese medicine. The *Pen T'sao* was compiled by Li Shih-chen, a city magistrate, who spent twenty-seven years collecting and analyzing over 12,000 prescriptions from more than 1,000 sources, including all of the earlier monographs on materia medica. It was published at the end of the Ming dynasty, a dynasty characterized by Wong and Wu as "the most glorious in the history of the pharmacopoeia of China."[26]

---

* Robert Loeb 1972: personal communication.
† W. Barry Wood, Jr. 1971: personal communication.

In fifty-two volumes, the *Pen T'sao* lists over 2,000 drugs of which about half are from plant sources, and half are divided about equally between animal, mineral, and other sources. Two especially interesting chapters contain classifications of diseases with recommendations on specific therapy.

With Liu Ju-chiang, Li Yu-thien, Phu Chu-ping, and Yu Ching-mei as his collaborators, Read translated into English volumes twelve to fifty of the *Pen T'sao*, publishing them between 1931 and 1941. They represent a Herculean and valuable landmark contribution to scholarship on Chinese traditional medicine.

As an example of the wide range of indications for native products, the horns of the Sika deer when covered with "velvet" were prescribed for vaginal bleeding, to "quiet" the placenta or the heart; as an aphrodisiac for the male; for convulsions; for diarrhea after an alcoholic bout; as a tonic for bone marrow; and for general weakness. Musk from a musk deer was recommended for malaria, convulsions, snake and rat bites, furuncles, and as an abortifacient. Fresh human placenta was indicated in anemia, emaciation, and general weakness. Any form of infection should be treated with human saliva. Antler from a species of Mongolian deer was of merit in bleeding during pregnancy, pains in the bones and joints, furuncles, carbuncles, breast abscess, and backache associated with kidney disease. The *Pen T'sao* also lists a number of medicinals used today, such as rhubarb, camphor, chaulmoogra oil, and kaolin.

More exotic procedures included the preferred treatment for weakness or chilliness of the legs—to have young boys and girls breathe on the navel of the patient. It was specified that this ritual could only be performed between midnight and noon when "live air was obtainable," since from midday to midnight "the air is dead."[27]

Read's knowledge of materia medical made him a valuable member of the group that prepared the *Chinese Pharmacopoeia I*, published in June 1931 under the auspices of the Chinese National Board of Health. It represented a synthesis of listings from the pharmacopoeias of Germany, Britain, Japan, and the United States, together with Chinese native drugs.

"Asses'-skin glue," as it was described by an early British visitor, was a celebrated and historic medication for a host of dermatological problems in China.[28] One of the Chinese dietitians at PUMC had a recurring skin rash that did not respond to Chester Frazier's treatments. Her mother insisted that she would be cured by asses'-skin glue prepared from a sliver taken from the skin of a donkey whose only source of water came from a well to which he was tethered in Shantung. The skin rash disappeared almost magically with the asses'-skin glue, but when Read analyzed it he found that it consisted solely of clots of collagenous material from the donkey's hide. To his and Frazier's disappointment they were not able to identify any magical new drug to add to the therapeutic armamentarium.

Read's botanical interests led him to study the characteristics of the ephedrine plant, a gymnosperm, *Ephedra*. His principal search was for the male of the species, which, after extensive field trips, he identified in 1927.*

Read's doctoral studies at Yale had been on the preparation and properties of chaulmoogra oil, the only known effective drug in the treatment of leprosy. There were estimated to be more than 1.5 million lepers in China, the largest number in any country in the world. For centuries the natives of India had realized that chewing the leaves and bark of the chaulmoogra tree frequently had a salutary effect in leprosy. When chaulmoogra oil is taken by mouth, however, it causes intense nausea. It was through research led by Victor Heiser in the Philippines that the addition of camphor to the oil was found to make parenteral injection feasible. On his return to Peking from New Haven, where he obtained his Ph.D., Read established a program for the production in quantity of injectable chaulmoogra oil for the mission hospitals that treated the hordes of lepers.

It was in part his complete commitment to strict missionary traditions that led Bernard Read to leave PUMC—he was distressed by what he considered to be the loss of the dominant Christian character in the programs of the college. Read felt that a number of his colleagues on the faculty were intent on destroying the Christian standards first enunciated by his hero, Thomas Cochrane. He continued to remember Rockefeller's guarantee of a religious influence in the institution and communicated to Rockefeller the fact that his pledges were being ignored by the faculty. He was shaken when there was no response to his communication.

In 1932 Read moved to the newly-founded Henry Lester Institute for Medical Research in Shanghai as head of the Division of Physiological Sciences. Interned by the Japanese during the war, Read remained in China after the armistice. He died in Shanghai in 1949.

With Read's departure from PUMC the decision was made to move ahead with the long-held desire to establish a program in dynamic pharmacology on a biochemical and physiological basis. The appointment as head of pharmacology was first offered to Chen Ko-kuei, but when the Eli Lilly Company offered to expand his research program he decided to remain in Indianapolis. An approach was then made to Harry Van Dyke, then professor of pharmacology at the University of Chicago, although there was little hope that he could be persuaded to leave Chicago. Van Dyke had, however, heard of the unique opportunities at Peking from Baird Hastings and other PUMC faculty alumni at Chicago, and since he was anxious to have more time for research and to write a monograph on the neurohypophysis, he accepted the offer in 1932. Looking back almost forty years later he continued to feel that Peking had offered him "the most productive years in my career."†

---

* Katherine E. Read 1971: personal communication.
† Harry B. Van Dyke 1970: personal communication.

Van Dyke recounted the rewards of his six years at PUMC when he gave the 1970 Sir Henry Dale Lecture, which had been endowed in honor of the British pharmacologist who was the 1936 Nobel Laureate in physiology and medicine for his research on acetylcholine as a neurotransmitter:

> The College provided an unusual opportunity for the development of a strong department of teaching and research in pharmacology as a means of furthering medical education in China. . . . I had no fears concerning my academic future. After accepting the offer I never had occasion to regret my decision. The teaching load was not heavy and research work could be prosecuted with fewer distractions than in the United States.[29]

In describing the superb library resources that proved invaluable in the preparation of his scholarly and comprehensive two-volume, *The Physiology and Pharmacology of the Pituitary Body*,[30] he said:

> During my years in Peking, I assembled a comprehensive bibliography and completed nearly all of the writing of two successive volumes on the physiology and pharmacology of the pituitary body. This would not have been possible without the College's fine medical library which was among the best in the world at that time.[31]

Van Dyke found the student body to be "superb," "highly intelligent . . . aggressive but hard working . . . very competent scientifically."[32]

During his six years at PUMC, Van Dyke, an exceedingly well-organized man, a meticulous investigator, and a tireless worker, established a modern pharmacology program based on the highest standards of physiology and biochemistry. His research and his publications on the pituitary caught the eye of the advisors to the Squibb Pharmaceutical Company and in 1938 Van Dyke joined the Squibb Institute for Medical Research. He headed the program in pharmacology until 1944, when he was appointed David Hosack Professor of Pharmacology at the College of Physicians and Surgeons of Columbia University.*

Like Paul Hodges, Van Dyke was a "career orientalist" and after his retirement from P and S in 1963 he taught pharmacology at the National Defense Medical Center in Taipei where he found a number of his former PUMC students and colleagues. He then moved on to develop a Department of Pharmacology in a Far Eastern medical school for the third time in his career—this time at the new University of Malaysia in Kuala Lumpur.

Hamilton H. Anderson, a 1930 graduate of the University of California School of Medicine, succeeded Van Dyke as head of the Department of Pharmacology in 1940. Anderson's interests were in the chemotherapy of parasitic diseases, especially amebiasis, in which he had collaborated with Chauncey D.

---

* David Hosack, 1769–1835, perhaps New York City's leading practitioner and scientist, established the Elgin Botanic Garden, 1810–1811, on a site that is now the mall of Rockefeller Center.

Leake. Before coming to Peking he had worked on parasitic disease in field expeditions in Panama and Brazil. Anderson was the first to use carbarsone, which had been developed by Paul Erlich, in the treatment of amebic dysentery. After repatriation to the United States on the *Gripsholm* on December 1, 1943, Anderson returned to the University of California as head of pharmacology and continued his studies on chemotherapy of amebiasis.

PARASITOLOGY

Reinhard J. C. Hoeppli, who succeeded Faust as head of the parasitology program in 1929, twice a year presented postgraduate courses in general parasitology in Chinese for Chinese general practitioners and medical officers of health.

Over 90 per cent of the dogs in Peking showed signs of kala-azar, and Hoeppli, with Feng Lan-chou and Chung Huei-lan (PUMC 1929), of the Department of Medicine, studied the pattern of canine kala-azar. They found that sections from the skin lesions of dogs were loaded with Leishman-Donovan bodies, which confirmed the suspicion that dogs were an important source of human infection. It was clear that human kala-azar could not be controlled until decisive steps were first taken to eradicate the disease in dogs.

Since *Clonorchis sinensis* is largely concentrated in the distal biliary tree, it was suggested as a possible etiological factor in the high incidence of carcinoma of the liver in China. Working with Hu Cheng-hsiang in pathology, Hoeppli examined liver sections from sixty-six patients with clonorchiasis. They found histopathological changes in the bile ducts in all cases but were not able to establish any significant relationship between this finding and hepatic malignancy.

Hoeppli also pointed out the frequency of primary carcinoma of the liver in areas where *Fasciola hepatica* and *Opisthorchis felineus* were prevalent. In addition, he noted that *Schistosoma japonicum* and *S. mansoni* infections favor the development of carcinoma of the liver.

In 1933 the University of Hamburg, a leading center in tropical medicine, conferred on Hoeppli the honorary *aussordentlicher*, extraordinary professor, degree in recognition of his contributions to parasitology.

Hoeppli is perhaps best known today for his studies in 1932 in which he demonstrated a delayed, cell-mediated response to sensitization to schistosome eggs. An eosinophilic halo is produced surrounding large loads of mature *Schistosoma japonicum* eggs in tissues of experimentally infected animals. The Hoeppli corona, an antigen-antibody complex contains both egg antigen and fixed host globulin.

As a Swiss citizen Hoeppli was not interned by the Japanese and served in Peking as deputy for the consul general of Switzerland. He was an invaluable representative of American interests, especially of PUMC. As a bibliophile, his treasure was the PUMC library for which he had shared faculty responsibility with Chester Frazier. Hoeppli returned to the faculty in 1946 and continued to teach parasitology until 1952, when he moved to the University of Malaya in Singapore as visiting professor of parasitology.* Here he prepared the historical treatise *Parasites and Parasitic Infections in Early Medicine and Science*.[33]

Hoeppli spent his final years in parasitology as resident director of the Liberian Institute of the American Foundation for Tropical Medicine in Harbel, Liberia, retiring to Switzerland in 1963. In 1969 he published *Parasitic Diseases in Africa and the Western Hemisphere*.[34]

The procurement of autopsies continued to be a major problem: if even a grandparent raised an objection, and they usually did, a post-mortem examination was out of the question. In 1939 Hu Cheng-hsiang, head of pathology, showed Eugene Opie, a visiting professor, 144 crocks, representing the total number of post-mortem examinations in the twenty-year history of the college, as well as some specimens inherited from the UMC in 1918.†

Eugene Opie was one of America's leading experimental pathologists. A graduate of the first medical school class at Hopkins, and one of Welch's most brilliant students, Opie had held successive appointments at the Rockefeller Institute, Washington University, the University of Pennsylvania, and Cornell. He came to Peking in 1938 to spend a year before retiring from Cornell—but his "retirement" led to another career at the Rockefeller Institute, in which he was active and productive until the age of ninety-five.

In 1966, almost thirty years after his months at PUMC, Opie recalled them as: "The best months of my life. I enjoyed it; I think of it as the Arabian nights. I enjoyed it enormously.‡ Opie's journey to Peking took him through Yokohama, Nagasaki, and Moukden. When he reached the Chinese border, he was forced to wait for an extended period while the Japanese guards meticulously searched every non-Japanese crossing the border. When they came to Opie he discovered to his dismay that he had mislaid his visa, for which oversight he was searched and fined the yen equivalent of $1.25.

For nine years Opie had been director of the Henry Phipps Institute for the Study, Treatment, and Prevention of Tuberculosis, and he renewed his studies of that disease in Peking. In 1925 John H. Korns of the Department of Medicine had reported that the percentage of positive tuberculins in about 2,000 healthy Chinese youths between the ages of eight and twenty years was distinctly lower than one would expect in similar age groups in Western countries. With so low a percentage of positive tuberculins, Korns could not explain the high morbidity and mortality from tuberculosis.

To elucidate this finding Opie studied all PUMC autopsies from June 1935 to February 1939 to determine the frequency of lesions of the childhood type versus lesions of the adult type. He found that many of the tuberculous lesions

* As Hoeppli was leaving China all of his teaching materials were seized by the government at the port of exit.

† Eugene L. Opie 1966: personal communication.

‡ Ibid.

in Chinese adults were of the primary type of infection usually seen in infants and children, and not associated with a positive tuberculin reaction. Further, the lack of resistance associated with the primary type would account for the high morbidity and mortality among adults.

Opie also found that the tuberculous lesion in adults who had grown up in rural districts and who had later moved to large cities was of the first-infection or primary type; in adults who had grown up in Peking the lesions were of the secondary or adult type.

Opie adopted Chinese traditional medicine as an avocation—not as a practitioner but as a collector. When he returned to New York he carried with him a large exhibit of instruments and equipment used by Chinese practitioners, including a rattan stand on which the patient rested his forearm while the practitioner diagnosed his pulse; an ivory female figurine on which embarrassed female patients could point out their areas of distress; superficial surgical instruments; and acupuncture needles. Opie's collection also included a small bell with a distinctive tone which the practitioner rang to inform villagers that he was at their service.

An envelope of powdered artemisia leaves for making moxibustion cones was procured for Opie by Chen, his number one boy, who proudly told Opie that, no matter what his state of health, he had been going to the same practitioner every Sunday for a number of years to have moxa routinely applied to his knees, back, and elbows.

As he twirled the acupuncture needles, Opie recalled that he had seen two autopsies of patients who had died from peritonitis because the acupuncturist had unwittingly forced the needles through the abdominal wall into the peritoneal cavity.

In 1940, as a special supplement, the *Chinese Medical Journal* published a *festschrift* to honor Eugene Opie. Prepared by the Chinese Society of Pathology and Microbiology it was entitled, *Pathology, Microbiology and Experimental Medicine.*[35]

PUBLIC HEALTH

In the early 1930s the program in public health at PUMC came to full fruition as affiliations were established with several forces converging on the problem of rural development in China. The first liaison was with the Mass Education Movement led by Yen Yang-ch'u (James).

After studying political science at Yale and Princeton, during World War I Yen had joined the YMCA Council in France to work with the Chinese Labor Battalion. He tackled the problem of their complete illiteracy by teaching them *paihua*, the 1,000-character basic Chinese vocabulary. Yen reckoned that it could be learned in ninety-six hours at a cost of about twelve cents per student.*

---

* James Yen 1972: personal communication.

Returning to China in 1923 determined to apply *paihua* to the massive problem of illiteracy, Yen established the Mass Education Movement through the auspices of the Chinese National Association of Mass Education. But it became increasingly obvious that, in Yen's words, "we fed their empty heads but not their empty stomachs."*

In 1929 Yen expanded his movement from the focus on illiteracy to a comprehensive program to upgrade rural life through practical experimentation in a specific district, Ting Hsien—about 100 miles west of Peking, and a long day's journey by unpredictable train service. Ting Hsien, consisting of 472 villages each with a population of less than 1,000, was representative of the other 1,900 counties in China. It was an agricultural area, with an economy based on wheat, millet, sweet potatoes, beans, and cotton. Yen established a research community of sixty-one villages, representing a total population of 44,000, and launched a fourfold reconstruction program in cultural education, economic improvement, citizenship training, and public health. From the beginning, Yen relied on John Grant as his advisor on the public health program in Ting Hsien.

As interim leader of the public health program, in 1929 Yen appointed Yao Hsun-yuan (PUMC 1925). As permanent leader, on the advice of Grant, Yen in 1932 appointed Ch'en Chih-ch'ien (PUMC 1929), who had an M.P.H. from Harvard, and whom Grant had described as "my most brilliant student."†

Looking back forty years later Jimmy Yen considered Ch'en's work at Ting Hsien to be "the greatest contribution to the promotion of public health in China."‡ The desperate medical and public health problems in Ting Hsien, which Ch'en described in his annual report for 1933, were representative of those throughout rural China.[36]

There were no Western-trained physicians in the *hsien;* as in other rural regions, if a village had a doctor he was a practitioner of Chinese traditional medicine—described by Ch'en as "a self-made doctor."[37] Ch'en noted that the handful of Western-trained physicians who had gone to practice in rural areas found the livelihood so meager that they turned to illegal injections of morphine and the promiscuous sale of heroin to bolster their incomes.

Half the villages had no medical facilities whatsoever and 30 per cent of the people who died had received no medical care. Women with bound feet would walk an agonizing twenty *li* (about seven miles) carrying a sick child just to receive a simple medicine or an antiseptic dressing. The water supply invariably came from a well adjacent to a foul latrine. Children with diseases such as diphtheria or scarlet fever slept on the same *k'ang* with uninfected siblings.

With Grant's continuing counsel and support Ch'en developed a program in Ting Hsien that stands as a model even today. The key person in each com-

---

* Ibid.
† Ibid.
‡ Ibid.

munity was the village health worker, who was admitted to the training program after graduation from a people's school and on the recommendation of the village elder. The ten-day training course he underwent put the emphasis on practical essentials: registering births and deaths, smallpox vaccinations, and first aid. Since *paihua*, which was limited to everyday expressions, did not cover medical terminology it was necessary to fabricate names for diseases from the basic characters. Thus smallpox was termed "heavenly flowers"; tetanus neonatorum, "four-to-six-day wind"; and diphtheria, "white throat."

The badge of office for the village health worker was the first-aid box that he carried as triumphantly as a mace or as a medical student with his first stethoscope. The box contained simple medicines: tincture of iodine, zinc sulfate, castor oil, bandages, and smallpox vaccine. The box was purchased by the people's school alumni association of each village at a price of $3.00 (Mexican).

Above the village health worker in the organizational ladder stood the district health station, staffed by a doctor who was usually a graduate of a special medical school, and an auxiliary. Before assuming full responsibility for the station, the graduate of the special school was required to spend one year in a clerkship at a district health center. During the first six months there were assignments in vital statistics, epidemiology, school health, and sanitary engineering; the second half was spent in clinical practice. The doctor's primary responsibility at the health station was to train and supervise the village health workers and to handle problem medical cases. The health workers were required to report to him on their activities at weekly intervals. The program at the station also included health education, preventive immunizations against typhoid fever, diptheria, and cholera, daily clinics, and house calls.

The district health center stood at the top of the health ladder, with training programs for nurses and midwives. The staff included doctors from accredited medical schools, public health nurses, nurse-midwives from Marian Yang's North China School of Midwifery, and technicians. They were based in a fifty-bed district hospital that had a diagnostic laboratory for the examination of urine, stool, blood, and drinking water.

In his annual report for 1933 Ch'en made an interesting point on the impact of the successful work of the hospital and its staff on the peasants during a cholera epidemic.[38] There was the usual high mortality rate among patients who refused hospitalization, but among the forty-five patients who were admitted to the district hospital there was not a single death. Henceforth the doctors at the hospital were referred to by the peasants as "living Buddhas."[39]

Chou Mei-yu became director of the programs in nursing care and education at Ting Hsien. Her leadership and innovative contributions approached those of Ch'en Chih-ch'ien and marked the beginning of a brilliant career that brought her recognition as one of the leading nursing graduates of PUMC.

As advisor to Ch'en, Marian Yang brought to Ting Hsien the concepts that she had employed so successfully at the North China School of Midwifery. Yuan I-chin (PUMC 1927), the biostatistician in Grant's Department of Public Health, served as consultant on epidemiological surveys.

The educational program in public health at PUMC added a second innovative dimension in the spring of 1935: medical and nursing students, as well as graduates in medicine and nursing who were training in public health, were assigned to Ting Hsien for periods of one to four weeks.

As a result of a study by Ludwig Rajchman, medical director of the League of Nations, the league joined the attack on the rural miseries of China. From 1933 to 1936 the great Yugoslav public health leader, Andrija Stampar, known affectionately to his foreign colleagues as "the bull of the Balkans," was stationed in China as expert representative of the league. Working with J. Heng Liu, Yen, and Grant, Stampar developed plans for an integrated public health program under a National Economic Council, with land reform as its primary mission. Stampar's major recommendation on public health was the establishment of a network of health centers with programs in epidemic control, school health, and dispensary services.

Stampar was especially concerned with the neglect of the peasants by their landlords. He found little progress in the much heralded land reform programs, and he was deeply concerned that because of their constant economic and social grievances the peasants would regard public health programs as just another meaningless gesture by the government.

That the improvement of health should always be viewed as only one component of a total national and community development strategy was a concept that Grant stressed several decades before the philosophy of teamwork began to be adopted in programs aimed at assisting the "third world." In 1934 he described the role that a medical school, such as PUMC, and the Rockefeller Foundation might play in such programs: "The use of medical knowledge and the efficiency of health protection depend chiefly upon social organization. The lower economic levels are, the more does the use of medical knowledge depend upon organization."[40]

Grant proposed that the village health worker should be trained for a wide spectrum of tasks, especially health maintenance. He would be the key person in the Mass Education Movement because the shortage of doctors and of finances made it impossible for physicians to be available at the community level. In health maintenance the village worker's tasks should include first aid, smallpox vaccinations, and the gathering of vital statistics. But the village worker could only function effectively if supervised by a physician operating out of a district hospital with responsibility for perhaps ten villages. In Grant's view it was also essential to establish special provincial training centers to prepare physicians and other categories of medical personnel to function effectively in such an organized team approach. The usual educational programs in medicine and public health were not adequate for such responsibilities.

Grant saw PUMC as the pivotal institution

> at the apex of a medical system which reaches down and actually provides efficient health protection for the village inhabitant within the limitations of his present backward economic conditions. However, such a vertical medical system cannot stand by itself unless it is integrated with other vertical social activities in a joint horizontal attack upon the problem of social reconstruction.[41]

Grant then called for a nationally coordinated effort based on rural reconstruction centers and trained administrative personnel that would be located in every province in China. At the beginning, an integrated program might be most effectively developed through a prototype, comprehensive organization in a single province.

In the "oral history" he recorded with Saul Benison in 1960–61 John Grant recalled the summer of 1924 that he spent with W. W. Cort and Norman R. Stoll on the hookworm survey in north China.[42] Cort would only eat food that was steaming hot, and was horrified when Grant took his meals from the street vendors—doughnuts, watermelon, sugarcane, and pastries. But when Cort had the group checked for parasites at the end of the study, Grant was the only healthy member. "Cort and Stoll were infected with everything while I had nothing."[43] Grant concluded that his resistance to the parasites of China led Cort to undertake a study of immunity to parasites when he returned to Baltimore.

John Grant loved a good time. On one occasion in Peking he and an old friend, Borcic, of the League of Nations, spent a long evening that stretched into the morning hours discussing public health—and relaxing—in a hotel bar and, after it closed, in a nightclub. During the night Preston Maxwell was called out to see an obstetrical case with complications and was shocked to find a PUMC official vehicle parked in front of a notorious nightclub. He complained to Roger Greene who recommended to the International Health Board (IHB) that it should provide a car for Grant's use so that the reputation of PUMC would be unsullied.

In 1936 Grant left PUMC to devote his energies—and they were unbounded —to the work of the recently established North China Council for Rural Reconstruction, which was supported by the Rockefeller Foundation. It had been conceived by Selskar Gunn, vice president of the IHB, who proposed that the foundation should develop "something broader and deeper, [and more] firmly rooted in Chinese institutions than the existing programs led by PUMC."[44]

Firmly committed to comprehensive, peasant-oriented programs, Gunn felt that PUMC maintained standards that were too lofty, and that the college had too little relevance to Chinese culture: "Important as it is in its own sphere [it] has had a very limited effect nationally."[45] Several years later Gunn again expressed to the foundation his lack of enthusiasm for PUMC: "It is doubtful if the stereotyped medical education now being given at Peking Union Medical College is really meeting the medical and public health needs of China."[46]

In the meantime the Department of Public Health at PUMC had established a cooperative program with the Institute of Rural Administration of Yenching University based at the institute's rural demonstration area at Chingho. Gunn considered this to be a commendable development deserving special support from the foundation.

Gunn's criticisms of PUMC were understandable. He was totally committed to rural reconstruction as the primary need in China, and in his eyes the most direct solution to her problems. It was difficult for Gunn to accept the unswerving adherence to the policy that PUMC should emulate the best system in the West, and especially its insistence on small classes in the face of China's critical need for doctors and nurses for rural reconstruction.

Gunn was, however, unduly harsh in his criticisms, for Grant, with the full support of administration and faculty leaders, had established a trail-blazing, community-oriented program in public health. The finest testimonial to its impact on the students was the fact that almost 25 per cent of the graduates entered careers in public health, a contribution never equalled by any other medical or nursing school, before or since.

It was at this time that Grant, too, began to have increasing doubts about the educational policies of PUMC, for he shared Gunn's rural view. This led Grant to join Bobby Lim and J. Heng Liu in 1937 in proposing to Houghton and Dieuaide that there should be a re-examination of the mission of PUMC.

The programs to improve public health in China were of course dependent upon a nation at peace. The ascendancy of the Kuomintang in 1928 had given promise of a stable and unified country that would make a comprehensive, nationwide, public health program possible. But in 1937, before the efforts of Liu, Grant, Yen, Gunn, Stampar, and others began to produce substantial results, the full-scale war with Japan erupted.

Unfortunately, the Japanese unleashed some of their harshest aggressions against the institutions that were the base of the rural reconstruction movement. In his study of the Rockefeller Foundation's effort in the program, James C. Thomson, Jr., assistant professor of history at Harvard, concluded that the movement

> provided unique support for those who sought to change the conditions of life in village China. Yet gradualism required time; and time was the one element denied to the rural reconstructionists by external aggressor and internal rebel alike.[47]

In 1939 Grant moved to Calcutta as director of the All-India Institute of Hygiene and Public Health. Here he led the development of educational programs in public health for physicians, nurses, and allied health workers, and the establishment of India's first rural health training center in Singur, north of

Calcutta, which served as the field station for the All-India Institute. Many of his colleagues believe that Grant's contributions in India were at least equal to those in China. He was a chief architect of the Bhore Report, which charted in detail a long-range program in medical education and public health for the subcontinent after World War II. The men who worked with him in India hold an admiration for Grant equal to or surpassing that of his former associates in China.

At John Grant's death in 1962 the Medical Care Section of the American Public Health Association adopted a memorial that read:

> Throughout his long career, he has been a towering figure of vision, strength, statesmanship and leadership in the endless struggle to improve the welfare of mankind through the provision and modernization of health services—in China, India, Europe, the Americas—indeed, the whole world.[48]

Charles N. Leach, regional director of the International Health Division* for the Far East and China, came to Peking in 1934 as visiting professor of public health; he remained until 1938. In May 1939, Marshall C. Balfour, a graduate of Harvard Medical School who had been technical advisor to the Ministry of Health in Athens on assignment for IHD, succeeded Leach as regional director. The office was moved to the Philippines in 1940 and to India the following year.

Yuan I-chin succeeded Grant as leader of PUMC's program in public health. During his youth Yuan had evinced an interest in and aptitude for mathematics and had been awarded a scholarship for study at the University of Hong Kong. But influenced in part by Harry Taylor, a medical missionary in Anking, Yuan entered the Premedical School at PUMC in 1920.†

Yuan's first contact with John Grant came at the time of the dedication of the medical school, when he served as Grant's student-guide. On one occasion, after stripping his empty pockets, Grant, greatly embarrassed had to borrow ten cents from Yuan to pay his ricksha boy at the gate of the Imperial Palace.‡

Anxious to strengthen biostatistics in his department, in 1928 Grant selected Yuan for a CMB fellowship at the Johns Hopkins School of Hygiene and Public Health. Yuan's thesis for the diploma in public health was based on an analysis of the vital statistics of the family of Li T'ing-an (PUMC 1926) and the genealogy of the Li clan, which had been recorded systematically for several centuries.[49] Yuan expanded his thesis and in 1931 he was awarded a doctorate in science for his dissertation, *The Influence of Heredity upon the Duration of Life in Man, Based on a Chinese Genealogy from 1365 to 1914.*[50]

Returning to PUMC in 1932 Yuan placed the primary emphasis in public

---

* The International Health Board was renamed the International Health Division in 19:
† Yuan I-chin 1971: personal communication.
‡ Ibid.

health on epidemiology, whereas Grant had placed it on field work. After PUMC was closed by the Japanese, Yuan moved to Chungking in 1942 as director of the Epidemiological Section of the National Institute of Health. At the end of World War II he returned to Nanking as acting director of the institute. At the request of Y. T. Tsur, minister of health and former chairman of the Board of Trustees of PUMC, Yuan charted a national health program for China. But the mounting intensity of the civil war frustrated any efforts to implement national planning, and Tsur resigned with the rest of the cabinet on November 17, 1948. In the same year Yuan joined the regional office of WHO in Copenhagen; after three years he moved to UNICEF where he was chief medical advisor until his retirement at the end of 1959.

After Grant's departure, the number of graduates entering careers in public health declined. In addition to Ch'en Chih-ch'ien and Yuan I-chin, however, other men trained by Grant entered distinguished careers in public health. Fang I-chi became director of the Western Pacific Region of WHO; Li T'ing-an became commissioner of health in Shanghai; and Yen Ch'un-hui of the Department of Bacteriology became commissioner of health in Taiwan.

MEDICINE

Francis Dieuaide's contributions in the Department of Medicine were summarized by Harold Loucks, his opposite number in surgery: "PUMC owes more to Francis for scientific excellence than any other person. He was also our leader in medical education."* Although Dieuaide became increasingly involved with administrative problems, he filled the role of scientific and educational leader until his departure in 1938. He also continued to find time for clinical investigations, and in 1937 reported his studies on rheumatic fever in north China to the prestigious Association of American Physicians of which he was a member.

There had been a general impression in both China and the West that the incidence of rheumatic fever in China was rare, and that when it did occur the clinical course was mild. Dieuaide reported that while there probably was a lower incidence when compared with American cities of the same latitude (40°) as Peking, the incidence of the disease in north China appeared to be increasing, and its severity, as indicated by the frequency of cardiac involvement and of chorea, was the same as in the West.

G. Canby Robinson came to PUMC on a five-month appointment as visiting professor, beginning January 1, 1935, while Dieuaide was on leave. He had held posts of leadership in medical education at Washington University, Vanderbilt, and Cornell. In his autobiographical *Adventures in Medical Education*, Robinson paints a glowing picture of PUMC, the Department of Medicine, and Dieuaide. Before going on leave Dieuaide had spent a few weeks introducing

---

* Harold H. Loucks 1972: personal communication.

Robinson to the college and Robinson recalled his earlier appraisal of Dieuaide when he was at Hopkins:

> I admired at that time [1921–22] the high quality of work of this quiet, reticent young man, and was impressed by his mental ability. Although I had seldom seen him in the intervening years, I was not surprised to find that his department was excellent. He not only directed his large department very well, but was an intellectual leader in the college.[51]

Robinson made special note of the studies of Richard Sia in infectious disease; of C. U. Lee in kala-azar; of Chang Hsi-chun and Liu Shih-hao in metabolism; and of Wu Chao-Jen, who held a joint appointment in medicine and in public health.

In a letter to Alan Gregg shortly before his departure from Peking, Robinson gave a detailed report on the Department of Medicine:

> The routine ward service is excellent, both regarding the variety and interest presented by the patients and especially regarding the way the patients are studied. I have never seen them better studied anywhere. Practically all data that any case requires for diagnosis are speedily and accurately collected, and a high degree of intelligence is exercised in conducting the ward routine. . . .
>
> The various members of the staff who act in rotation as attending physicians impress me as being well trained and energetic. All members of the department, including the resident staff, are carrying on laboratory problems, and I have been much impressed not only with the variety of interests in the department, but with the good quality of their research.
>
> I feel justified in saying that the department is splendidly organized and staffed with a group of men who have had excellent training and show much interest. Dr. Cannon came to staff rounds a couple of weeks ago and told me he was astounded by the way the cases were worked up and presented. . . .
>
> It is excellent, too, the way the other departments, such as bacteriology and parasitology, cooperate in furnishing data on patients. To sum up, the medical clinic is as well organized as any I have seen, and I can only express enthusiasm for it. Dieuaide deserves great credit for the present status of the medical clinic.[52]

Research programs at PUMC continued to explore the diseases of China Liu Shiao-hao, director of the metabolic laboratory in the chemical division studied the effect of therapeutic doses of Vitamin D in rickets and in osteomalacia, and found a pronounced and prolonged response in both disorders In patients with osteomalacia, however, many months were required for complete recalcification of the bones; recalcification was more prompt in rickets.

After prolonged negotiations with the family, permission was granted for an autopsy on a patient who had died with osteomalacia. The histological picture of the skeleton was identical to that of rickets in infants and children; on histological basis, therefore, osteomalacia could be designated as "adult rickets. The global similarity of osteomalacia was stressed by the finding that the hyperplastic changes in the parathyroid glands of the Chinese patient were identical with those reported for patients dying from the disease in Eastern Europe.

Chu Hsien-i treated three cases of severe osteomalacia with ultraviolet irradiation from a mercury-vapor quartz lamp, and all showed marked clinical improvement. The effect on calcium-phosphorus metabolism was practically identical with that of Vitamin D. Chu suggested that a lack of sunlight was probably more important than dietary deficiency in both rickets and osteomalacia.

In 1938 Chung Huei-lan and Joseph H. M. Chang analyzed more than 400 cases of typhus fever that had been admitted to PUMC over a period of fifteen years. They found that the incidence of the disease rose sharply when there were extensive troop movements and when the soldiers were concentrated in camps. The cases were predominantly of the louse-borne variety.

While a high incidence of cerebral symptoms made differential diagnosis from meningitis difficult at the bedside, the fact that the Weil-Felix reaction became positive at the height of the disease in a high percentage of the cases was an important laboratory aid.

Studies were made of another common, louse-borne infection, relapsing fever, whose incidence was especially high in the spring when the poor removed their heavy winter clothing and their lice became active. The bodies and clothing of every patient admitted to PUMC were meticulously examined for lice. The incidence of relapsing fever was of such dimensions that a blood smear from every patient admitted with undiagnosed fever was studied in dark-field preparations for the causative spirochete, *Borrelia recurrentis*. If lice were found on the body or in clothing of a patient with fever the dark-field examination was repeated.

Secondary infection with *Salmonella enteriditis* in cases of relapsing fever at times reached almost epidemic proportions. Chung Heui-lan demonstrated the source of the *Salmonella* by culturing them from the same lice in which he identified the spirochetes of relapsing fever.

Chung and his associates showed that the disease could also be transmitted through intravenous heroin injections. The high frequency of advanced malnutrition among heroin addicts made the course of all febrile illnesses, such as relapsing fever, far more severe than for other patients.

Claude E. Forkner, who began his career in hematology with Florence Sabin at the Rockefeller Institute, was a member of the Department of Medicine from 1932 to 1936. He and Samuel Zia of the Department of Bacteriology were the first investigators to emphasize the occurrence of acute agranulocytosis in kala-azar; they found it in 8 per cent of their cases. With acute agranulocytosis the mortality was 20 per cent, compared with 5 per cent in other cases of kala-azar.

Forkner returned to the United States to become director of the CMB from 1943 to 1945. He later earned a reputation as a distinguished hematologist at the New York Hospital–Cornell University Medical Center.

One of Dieuaide's last house officers was Stephen Chang (PUMC 1935) the brilliant and charming son of a Christian bishop, who was the college organist and later a dormitory proctor. Of all its devoted alumni none surpassed Stephen Chang in love for PUMC; he richly deserved—and enjoyed—the accolade bestowed by his friends and classmates, "Mr. PUMC."*

Francis Dieuaide left Peking in 1938 to return to the United States after sixteen shining years at PUMC. While on leave in 1935, friends had sensed his uneasiness about the future of PUMC and had urged him to return to the United States. In 1937 he decided to leave because, as one of his friends, who wishes to remain anonymous, commented, "for Francis the light had failed." Dieuaide felt that with the Sino-Japanese War, and the budgetary strictures and administrative revisions at PUMC, it might be impossible to maintain the excellence to which he had been so unswervingly devoted. He knew, moreover, that he needed to get back to academic medicine in the United States where he could catch up with the rapid advances that were taking place in medical science.

Many medical schools can point to several men, or at times to one man, who were crucial to the development of the school. As Loucks so wisely commented, Dieuaide was by all odds *the man* who above all others was responsible for the stamp of excellence that adorned PUMC. He was the crucial man in the brilliant history of the college.

Dieuaide subsequently spent a few years at Harvard. During the war years he was in uniform as an expert on tropical medicine for the Army Medical Corps. He then became the leader of the newly founded Life Insurance Medical Research Fund through which he developed an excellent program to support research on cardiovascular disease.

Yu Ts'ai-fan (PUMC 1936), Dieuaide's last chief resident, was the first woman to hold that coveted appointment, and one of the stars in his crown—today she is a world authority on uric acid metabolism and gout at Mount Sinai Medical Center in New York City. A graduate of Ginling College in Nanking, where she completed the four-year premedical course in three years, Miss Yu was endowed with total dedication. There were always attractive opportunities at PUMC for qualified students to engage in research programs with the faculty, and during her sophomore year Miss Yu worked with Harry Van Dyke on neurohypophyseal hormones. When she was assistant resident in medicine Van Dyke offered her a fellowship, but she turned to metabolic research with Liu Shih-hao, and was continuing her studies on calcium metabolism and scurvy when she became chief resident. One of her most vivid memories of PUMC is the Sunday morning, February 12, 1938, when, while working in the laboratory she heard a strange voice with a heavy Dutch accent announce, "But I have

---

* Stephen Chang 1970: personal communication.

never had a woman as my resident."* The voice was that of Isidore Snapper, who had come to Peking as Dieuaide's successor from the Faculty of Medicine at Amsterdam, where he had reached the rank of professor of medicine and general pathology.

There could hardly have been a sharper contrast in personality and philosophy than Dieuaide and Snapper. Snapper epitomized the German system based on the *geheimrat* professor. (The literal meaning of *geheimrat* is secret counsellor to the throne.) Whereas Dieuaide was soft-spoken and reticent, Snapper was assertive and self-confident; while Dieuaide always presented controversial aspects of any medical question, Snapper's approach was authoritarian and positive; Dieuaide encouraged discussion, but Snapper preferred to lecture—and in the grand manner. The students preferred the more dogmatic Snapper approach: always a diagnosis; after presenting the several possibilities of a case, Dieuaide would leave questions unsettled.

Snapper had been studing problems in calcium-phosphorus metabolism since 1930, and the superb metabolic laboratories and clinical opportunities at PUMC gave him rich opportunities to continue and expand his research. His main collaborators were Liu Shih-hao, Yu Ts'ai-fan, and T. Chu, of the Department of Medicine, and Hu Cheng-hsiang, head of pathology.

A man of remarkable energy, soon after his arrival Snapper began to collect observations on the disease problems characteristic of China that he and his colleagues and predecessors at PUMC had made. In 1941, just three years after his arrival, he published this compilation as the first edition of *Chinese Lessons to Western Medicine*, a thorough and interesting documentation on medicine at PUMC—in his words, "geographic medicine."[53] The book linked his name inseparably with PUMC; for the general medical community, any reference to the college today immediately brings to mind the name of Isidore Snapper. Much of the information in Snapper's volume has already been cited in the present book; among his best descriptions are those of kala-azar, relapsing fever, and, not surprisingly, diseases relating to calcium-phosphorus metabolism. An interesting personal note is the description of his own illness in June and July 1940, contracted on a visit to Japan—either Japanese B encephalitis or poliomyelitis. Fortunately, his recovery was complete.

Although blood transfusions had come into wide use in the West, they continued to be a problem at PUMC because the Chinese were superstitious about both giving and receiving blood, even within the same family. The main sources of blood were the financially destitute, who were invariably malnourished and in poor health; others who might choose this means of obtaining quick cash were drug addicts whose blood was frequently infected with *Treponema pallidum*, malaria parasites, or the spirochetes of relapsing fever. Nevertheless the

---

* Yu Ts'ai-fan 1971: personal communication.

demands for blood by the staff, especially in the surgical fields, were greater than in the West because without it the patients were too anemic to tolerate major surgery. In Snapper's view, most of the patients admitted to the hospital needed blood even if no surgery was to be performed.

A touching photograph in Snapper's book shows the arrival at the outpatient clinic of the daily contingent of patients from the Peking municipal poorhouse. The women and children arrived in a handcart pushed by a coolie, with a policeman walking beside them, while the male patients walked behind—probably one of the few times in China when women were accorded such preferential treatment.

Snapper was especially distressed with the condition of another source of patients—the sweatshops: "In comparison a sweat shop in the West would be a Utopia."[54] The workers only recompense for dawn-to-midnight labor was an inadequate diet and a filthy mat; consequently they were prey to numerous and often fatal diseases.

The problems of human consumption of opium in China were historic. Addicts often began to smoke opium for the relief of pain, especially abdominal discomfort, which, with the high incidence of enteric infections, was a common occurrence. Opium smoking was also recommended for tuberculosis, the leading disease problem of China. Snapper believed that because opium addicts used a pipe, they did not show mental deterioration as toxic products were carried off in the smoke.

Acute opium poisoning after taking the drug by mouth was a continuing problem; between July 1938 and June 1940 Snapper supervised the care of 198 comatose patients. Seventy-five per cent were under thirty years of age; forty-one (21 per cent) died in twenty-four hours. Paralysis of the respiratory center was a frequent complication, and both Drinker respirators at the hospital were at times occupied by opium patients; the respiratory paralysis was usually associated with a secondary bronchopneumonia.

Some methods of suicide mentioned by Snapper were inhalation of coal gas, and ricin poisoning from castor-oil seeds obtained illegally from herbalists.

Snapper speculated that diets with a high ratio of polysaturated to saturated fatty acid, if begun immediately or shortly after the child is weaned, as is the custom in the Orient, might account for the low incidence of atherosclerosis among the Chinese. The Oriental diet, "devoid of cholesterol and rich in poly-saturated fatty acids, if taken from the cradle to the grave apparently prevents atherosis, i.e., the deposition of cholesterol in the arterial walls."[55]

Snapper shared the enthusiasm of so many other teachers at PUMC: "They were the best years of my life."* He found the program to be far ahead of most European and American schools, and he was especially impressed with the

---

* Isidore Snapper 1970: personal communication.

emphasis on practical work with the patient and the minimal time devoted to lectures in the clinical years—just one hour a day.

After a short period as a prisoner of the Japanese when they seized the college, Snapper came to New York in 1944 as clinical professor of medicine at Columbia University College of Physicians and Surgeons. He retired from P and S in 1952 and was appointed director of medicine and medical education at Beth-El Hospital in Brooklyn.

Pediatrics

Arthur P. Black, who put the emphasis on patient care and teaching, served as associate professor and head of the Division of Pediatrics from 1931 to 1936. L. K. Sweet of pediatrics and K'ang Hsi-jung (PUMC 1928) reported that in Vitamin A deficiency there was atrophy of the lacrimal glands and stenosis of the salivary glands. Meanwhile Chu Fu-t'ang (PUMC 1927) and Fan Ch'uan (PUMC 1931) were awarded CMB fellowships to study at the Children's Hospital in Boston, where Charles F. McKhann, one of their supervisors, recalls that they were "two of the keenest fellows that ever came to my laboratory."* Chu worked with McKhann on the preparation of an immune globulin from placental extracts to prevent measles.

In the winter of 1934–35, McKhann came to PUMC as a visiting professor and continued to be deeply impressed with the work of his two former fellows. As he and others had predicted, Chu Fu-t'ang soon moved into the position of leadership in the pediatrics program.

One of his studies was on the etiology of tetany in infants under six months of age. While European pediatricians held that tetany at such an early age could never be due to calcium deficiency, Chu and his associates had seen a sufficient number of infants with tetany, born to mothers with frank osteomalacia or subclinical deficiency, to lead him to challenge that tenet. Working with the metabolic unit in the Department of Medicine, Chu proved conclusively that tetany due to calcium deficiency could occur in infants under six months of age.

Irvine McQuarrie, head of pediatrics at the University of Minnesota School of Medicine, was visiting professor of pediatrics in 1939–40. McQuarrie had already established Minnesota as a leading center in academic pediatrics; in his era he was an acknowledged leader in training heads of pediatric departments. A man of infectious enthusiasm, he emphasized the scientific basis of pediatric diseases and the application of human biology to medicine; his philosophy was expressed in his description of metabolic and endocrine disorders as "experiments of nature."[56]

In Peking, McQuarrie continued his studied on the mechanism of insulin convulsions in adrenalectomized rats, and evaluated the effects of serum electrolytes and of oxygen-carbon dioxide tension in the respired air.

---

* Charles F. McKhann 1970: personal communication.

In one of his Porter lectures at the University of Kansas in 1944, McQuarrie presented his observations on some of the medical and social problems in China.[57] He compared statistics in Minnesota with those at the Special Health Station in Peking: the infant death rate was ten times as high in Peking, and maternal mortality was also comparably higher. In Peking, life expectancy was twenty-eight to thirty years compared with sixty-eight years in Minnesota; deaths under twelve years of age represented only 8 per cent of all deaths in Minnesota, but 75 per cent of all deaths in Peking.

The most frequent nutritional abnormalities were deficiencies of Vitamins A and D and of protein and calcium; subclinical ascorbic acid deficiency was described as "almost universal."[58] Among Chinese children typhus fever was mild, and in thirty cases seen at PUMC there had been no deaths, compared with an adult mortality of 10 per cent. The incidence of psychoneuroses, juvenile delinquency, and other behavioral problems of childhood were less frequent in China than in the West. Largely through the studies of the Kala-azar Unit, the mortality rate of treated cases of the disease at PUMC had dropped to 5 per cent; for untreated cases it continued to be as high as 95 per cent.

As a diversion, McQuarrie presented a rather detailed description of the orthopedic abnormalities that affected the many middle-aged and elderly women with bound feet whom he saw in Peking. The four small toes were bound under the plantar surface of the foot, and the great toe was compressed in extension. As a result, the heads of the metatarsal bones were drawn toward the os calcis and then wedged into an almost vertical position. Because of this deformity the posterior tip of the os calcis, the dorsal faces of the small toes, the head of the first metatarsal, and the ball of the great toe were the weight-bearing surfaces, and all four areas were frequently ulcerated. The bound foot was frequently no more than three or four inches in length and much more subject to tuberculous infection or gangrene than a normal foot. As a result of the crusades of the Natural Foot Society, established in 1885 by Western missionaries, and the programs of the Chinese Republic since its founding in 1911, the custom was eradicated in all but the most backward regions.

McQuarrie also included a note on drug addiction: opium smoking was regarded by Chinese civic and social leaders as a problem second in importance only to the war with the Japanese. On any late night in Peking one could see an addict stop at a closed door, roll up his sleeve, and pass money through a small aperture. He would then press his bared arm against the aperture to receive an injection of the opiate. The Japanese were fostering increased opium production, not only to control the people but as a money-making enterprise. At least two patients who had taken opium with suicidal intent were treated in the emergency clinic of PUMC each week; two-thirds of those in coma died, despite lavage, parenteral fluids, and the use of the Drinker respirator.

McQuarrie concluded with highest accolades for the students and staff at PUMC:

> Inspired by a faculty composed of well-trained, idealistic men, both Chinese and foreign, the Chinese students work incessantly to acquire every fact. . . . Consequently a "Visiting Professor" from the West finds teaching a pure joy for once in his academic life. Both as practical clinicians and as scientific investigators, modernly trained Chinese physicians have shown themselves to be exceptionally capable.[59]

He was impressed with the dedication of the staff at PUMC to the solution of the problems of China:

> They, like their fellow countrymen educated in other fields, are keenly aware of the plight of their people in matters of education and health. Under most discouraging conditions they are working courageously to improve the situation and fortunately their national government is doing its utmost to support them. When the present war has ended, a united China under such leadership can be expected to make strides in her health program which will amaze the outside world.[60]

Since her arrival at PUMC in 1924, Ruth Guy had been studying nutritional problems with Ernest S. C. Tso, and had been interested in the development of an easily available and inexpensive substitute for mother's milk. In 1938, with K. S. Yeh, she reported on her studies on the development of soybean "milk." She found that the yellow soybean, *Glycine soja*, "contains all amino acids needed for growth in good proportions, it easily makes a fine suspension, and it is cheap. The Vitamin B Complex is present in adequate amount. Phosphorus, potassium and iron seem to be sufficient. However, fat, carbohydrate, Vitamins A, D, and C, calcium and sodium chloride must be supplied from other sources."[61]

In their first efforts to prepare soybean milk as a base, they used *tou fu chiang*, a weak protein solution made from soybean that was sold in the lanes as a refreshment. Calcium lactate, sodium chloride, starch, and sugar, were added to the base. Vitamins A and D were supplied in cod liver oil, and Vitamin C in cabbage soup. They reported that "many infants take this preparation readily without upset, and when it is properly supplemented, grow and thrive."[62] But the problem of preparing *tou fu chiang* made its use impracticable, so as a base they used soybeans that had been dried, roasted, ground, and emulsified in water: a simpler and efficient process that produced equally good results.

Dermatology and Syphilology

When Chester Frazier arrived in Peking in 1922 there was little accurate information on the incidence of syphilis among the Chinese. Reports from John G. Kerr in Canton in 1862 and John Dudgeon in Peking in 1872 had stated that the Chinese seldom developed cardiovascular or central-nervous-system syphilis.

Frazier and Li Hung-chiung began a comparative study of the clinical picture of syphilis in Chinese, whites, and Negroes. The study was completed at the Johns Hopkins Hospital and the School of Hygiene and Public Health and published in 1948.[63]

The popular impression that syphilis was highly prevalent in China was disproven by the fact that of the first 26,300 patients discharged from PUMC, only 6.1 per cent had positive serologic tests for syphilis. Syphilis among PUMC patients was therefore no more prevalent than among the white patients in Baltimore who were admitted to the Johns Hopkins Hospital.

Frazier and Li found that "the higher incidence of latent disease in Chinese males and females indicated that they had a greater resistance to syphilis.[64] In the early stages the Chinese reacted more sharply in both neural (meningeal) and extraneural (skeletal) manifestations. Thus the Chinese male was fifteen times as often the subject of skeletal lesions, and twice as often of symptomatic meningeal lesions as white males. On the other hand, tertiary disease was far less severe in the Chinese than in white or Negro patients—it was primarily an extraneural disease, while in the white syphilitic the involvement was more often in the central nervous system.

As a generalization, syphilis was most severe in white patients and least severe in Chinese; Negroes were in an intermediate position. In all races syphilis was less severe in the female; syphilis in the Chinese was characterized as the "female" type.

Frazier speculated that the higher incidence of skeletal lesions among Chinese —1:5 compared with 2:100 for whites and 4:100 for Negroes—might be related to Vitamin C deficiency, which would lower periosteal resistance. He also found that Chinese with syphilitic paresis showed less deterioration of their mental processes than Caucasians.

Frazier, with Mu Jui-wu (PUMC 1925) and Hu Ch'uan-k'uei (PUMC 1927), both assistant professors of dermatology and syphilology, turned to the laboratory for further studies on sex as a factor in syphilis. They showed that resistance to syphilis in the male rabbit may be increased by administration of estrogens. Hu was able to lower resistance in the female rabbit by altering ovarian function.

Louise Pearce of the Rockefeller Institute was a visiting professor in syphilology in 1931–32. With Hu, she initiated a series of studies in which they compared the Chinese *Treponema pallidum* with the Nicholle and the Zinsser Hopkins strains isolated from patients in the United States. They demonstrated that in the laboratory animal, strains of *Treponema pallidum* recovered from Chinese patients differed little in their pathogenicity from strains isolated from Occidental patients in the United States. In separate studies, Pearce found that the Chinese strains evoked a more frequent reaction in ocular tissues than the Nicholle or the Zinsser-Hopkins strain. The significance of this finding was unclear.

Chester Frazier left PUMC at the outbreak of World War II. After earning a D.P.H. at Hopkins, he became head of dermatology at the University of Texas Medical School at Galveston. In 1948 he was appointed Edward Wigglesworth Professor of Dermatology at the Massachusetts General Hospital, where he served until his retirement in 1958.

SURGERY

Under the leadership of Harold S. Loucks, the Department of Surgery continued the standard of excellence established by Adrian Taylor. With his quiet manner, Loucks appeared to his students to be the antithesis of their traditional picture of the surgeon. He combined intelligence with a total dedication to scholarship and outstanding technical skill. Loucks's last resident, Morgan Liu (PUMC 1937), is today the leading thoracic surgeon in Hong Kong. In addition to the other admirable traits that we have cited, Liu recalls Loucks's "great sympathy for medical students and for junior staff."*

Loucks's principal interests were in gastrointestinal and thyroid surgery. In stressing abnormal physiology and surgical diagnosis as the tenets of his teaching program he was far ahead of most professors of surgery in the United States, who demanded that students memorize the technical steps in a long line of surgical procedures.

Looking back on his years as head of surgery, Loucks felt that one of the most important contributions from his department was the work of Wu Ying-k'ai on the surgical treatment of carcinoma of the esophagus. Wu, a graduate of Moukden Medical College, was described by his colleagues as Loucks's star pupil.†

Carcinoma of the esophagus had a very high frequency in China. In 1937 Kwan Sung-tao of the surgery department reported that it represented 51 per cent of all neoplasms of the alimentary tract and 10 per cent of all cancers admitted to the hospital. On the age scale, the highest incidence was in the fourth to sixth decades. In some hospitals esophageal cancer represented 25 per cent of all male cancers. The frequency was sixteen times greater in men than in women; in the United States it was only five times higher in men than in women.

Several theories were advanced for the high incidence of esophageal cancer in Chinese. One theory was that the disease was related to drinking hot tea, although tea-drinking in China was not as popular as in Japan where the incidence was not as great. *Pai kan*, a vodka-like distillate from *kao liang*, was another beverage that was suspect. With an alcohol content of 85 per cent, it

---

* Morgan Liu 1972: personal communication.
† Ibid.

also was drunk hot and was very popular among the farmers. A third reason suggested for the frequency of the disease was the ingestion of highly seasoned foods.

Adrian Taylor had considered the difficult problems of esophageal resection for cancer during his years at PUMC but turned to more fruitful efforts. Before Wu Ying-k'ai's studies there had been only two successful resections of lower-third lesions—one by Phemister and Adams at the University of Chicago and the other by Marshall in Boston.

A man of outstanding technical skills and creative talents, Wu perfected a transthoracic approach for carcinoma of the lower third of the esophagus. He was the first surgeon to demonstrate the practicability of direct esophago-gastric anastamosis in the thoracic cavity. In the *Chinese Medical Journal* of July 1941,[65] Wu and Loucks reported three patients on whom they had performed resections, at that time the largest study available. One of the patients died from tuberculous pneumonia seven months after surgery; one patient was alive and well; in the third patient, the anastamosis had broken down in the immediate postoperative period.

In 1941 Wu went to St. Louis on a CMB fellowship to spend one year with the great pioneer thoracic surgeon, Evarts A. Graham, who in 1933 had performed the first successful one-stage pneumonectomy for cancer of the lung. The outbreak of World War II prevented Wu's return to China and he did brilliant work in thoracic surgery in St. Louis until the end of hostilities.

Neurosurgery was led by Kwan Sung-tao, who had joined the staff in 1924 after graduating from Rush Medical College in Chicago. Kwan had served as a CMB fellow in neurosurgery with Charles H. Frazier, John Rhea Barton Professor of Surgery at the University of Pennsylvania School of Medicine. In 1932 Kwan reported that forty-six cases of trigeminal neuralgia seen at PUMC between 1921 and 1931 had been treated successfully with alcohol injections. With George Char in urology, Kwan developed the procedure of presacral neurectomy for the treatment of painful cystitis.

Kimm Hyen-taik (PUMC 1931), a Korean, worked in the tumor clinic with John W. Spies from 1931 to 1935. In 1932, with Ch'in Kuang-yu (PUMC 1930) of the Department of Pathology, Kimm collected ninety-seven cases of "lympho-epithelioma" from the records at PUMC. The tumor was seen frequently in north China, Indochina, and the Dutch East Indies; it usually appeared on a tonsil in childhood.

When A. M. Dunlap moved to Shanghai in 1930 to go into private practice, he was succeeded by Liu Jui-hua, the brother of J. Heng Liu.

Malignancy of the nasopharyngeal opening of the Eustachian tube and of the tube proper was seen with surprising frequency in the otolaryngology clinic at PUMC. An early sign was severe postnasal hemmorrhage, and in all such cases a meticulous and repeated examination was made for a tumor. If diagnosed at an early stage, treatment of the tumor with radium and with deep X-ray was usually successful.

Emile F. Holman, head of surgery at Stanford and a leading vascular surgeon, was visiting professor of surgery in 1930–31. In 1937 Max Cutler came from Chicago where he was director of cancer research at the Hines Veterans Administration Hospital, and with Sir George Cheatle, had written extensively on breast cancer.

OBSTETRICS AND GYNECOLOGY

J. Preston Maxwell returned to Britain in 1936 after seventeen years of total dedication to PUMC. During World War II he was drafted into the Emergency Medical Service and retired again, reluctantly, at the age of seventy-eight.

After spending five years at Hopkins, Nicholson J. Eastman came back to PUMC in 1933 as professor and head of obstetrics and gynecology. His rich clinical experience at PUMC had made a deep impression on his colleagues in Baltimore, and many years later Alan F. Guttmacher recalled his reactions:

> I was awed by the vast amount of blood and thunder obstetrics he had witnessed in China. For each ruptured uterus we operated, Nick had operated 10, and for each eclamptic we saw, he had seen 20.[66]

Throughout his career "Nick" Eastman frequently referred to his experiences in China. Discussing a paper on the controversial subject of natural childbirth, "Correlation of Physical and Emotional Phenomena of Natural Labor," Eastman emphasized the importance of fecundity to Chinese women:

> It is the fondest hope of every Chinese girl to have children and many of them; and conversely there exists no more abject and pitiful creature than the Chinese woman who is childless. Milleniums of a culture which has emphasized the family as its unit of civilization have placed childbearing on a pedestal and surrounded it with love and veneration,—the acme of happiness for every wife. As a consequence, Chinese women go through pregnancy with an exuberance and open pride quite rare in the Occident.[67]

Eastman had planned to study analgesia in labor at PUMC but soon realized that such a study was impossible in Chinese women:

> I quickly found, to my consternation, that these Chinese patients offered no material whatsoever for my proposed investigations because *they had virtually painless labors;* and looking back upon my experience there, which comprised several thousand labors in Chinese women, I can recall only two small groups of cases in which some form of pain-relief seemed called for: the patients with some mechanical obstruction to labor such as the osteomalacia group; and the hypersophisticated women of the upper classes, mostly graduates of American colleges, whose general background and attitudes were more Occidental than Chinese.[68]

A group of Russian mothers who had escaped across Siberia, and who had suffered indescribable hardships, contrasted sharply with the Chinese mothers: they were nervous wrecks.

> I shall never forget the screams of these poor creatures in their interminably long labors. Our Chinese house-staff scarcely knew what to make of the picture. In the course of their experience with Chinese patients it just hadn't been brought home to them that labor could be so painful.[69]

An ardent and pioneering proponent of the restoration of the midwife to a role in maternal and child health in the United States, Eastman had no use for the untrained midwives of China:

> Many years ago in Peking I used to number among my "friends" quite a few of these toothless, alcoholic old hags. To paraphrase the famous comment of Samuel Johnson on Lord Chesterfield, they have the morals of a whore but scarcely the manners of a dancing master. They think nothing of . . . boring through a complete placenta previa just to see what is the matter.[70]

In 1935 Eastman succeeded J. Whitridge "Bull" Williams, the father of academic obstetrics in the United States, as professor and head of the department at Johns Hopkins, and continued the high standards established by Williams, with special distinction as a teacher. In the words of Guttmacher, "Hopkins medical students were unanimous in the opinion that obstetrics was better taught than any other academic discipline."[71]

John L. McKelvey, a graduate of Queen's University Medical School in Ontario, who had then trained at Hopkins, was Eastman's successor. He was trained equally in obstetrics and gynecology but focused primarily on tissue pathology and the study of malignant tumors. The latter interests, combined with the availability of radium and a radon plant, established PUMC as the leading center in China for the study and treatment of gynecological malignancy.

McKelvey's most grateful patients were the women with deformed pelves caused by osteomalacia. Because they could not function sexually, their husbands had turned to other women or had dismissed them from their homes. Through extensive surgery McKelvey was able to restore their vaginas to sexual adequacy. Another group of women for whom restorative surgery was not possible were those who had used caustic soda as an abortifacient and had thus completely destroyed their vaginas.*

When Hans Zinsser came to Peking as a visiting professor in 1938, McKelvey learned from him the nine-day egg technique for culturing typhus organisms; he applied the technique successfully in culturing the causative virus from a granuloma that the Dutch in Indonesia had named "genito-anal syndrome."

Lim Kha-t'i was McKelvey's deputy; a third member of the department was Lin Sung, whose principal studies were on tuberculosis of the female generative tract.

Standardization of the iontoquantimeters for measuring radiation dosage in therapy of malignant disease was carried out in the nearest laboratory—the Na-

---

* John L. McKelvey 1971: personal communication.

tional Bureau of Standards in Washington, D. C. The meters were returned from Washington by mail and the physical bumping they received en route at times affected their adjustment. McKelvey directed the tumor therapy program in gynecology and, working with the radiation physicists in roentgenology, recalibrated the iontoquantimeters against known quantities of radium activity. Thus radiation dosage usually expressed as "roentgens," was expressed at PUMC as "Peking roentgens."*

The constant stream of cases of self-induced abortion were usually admitted with complicating infection and severe hemorrhage. In 1933 Amos Wong and his wife, D. H. Wong, reported that six cases of infection with *Clostridium Welchii* had been seen over a period of eighteen months, and noted that such infection was relatively frequent in China. The source of the infection was readily identified, for cultures of stool specimens showed that almost all gynecological patients had *C. Welchii* in their gastrointestinal tracts, although there were no significant clinical manifestations from the presence of the organisms.

McKelvey's fondest memories were of the students: "I was never associated with such students—they had a vision—they knew that they were working for China and they were out to do something of major importance." The burning desire of the house officers to uncover new knowledge was memorable: "We could not persuade them to leave the laboratories at night."†

In 1938 McKelvey left Peking and joined the University of Minnesota medical school as professor and head of obstetrics and gynecology, where he trained half a dozen men who were to become department heads elsewhere. On retirement, as had Paul Hodges and Harry Van Dyke, McKelvey returned to the Orient under the sponsorship of Harold Loucks and the CMB to spend a year as visiting professor at the Faculty of Medicine in Singapore.

Preston Maxwell, Nick Eastman, and Marian Yang had attacked the massive problem of neonatal tetanus through programs to train indigenous midwives; Lim Kha-t'i was probably the first physician in China to effectively prevent the disease by immunizing the mother against tetanus during pregnancy.

Placenta previa was the most common cause of hemorrhage in the third trimester of pregnancy. In 1938 Lim Kha-t'i reported a comparative study of ninety-three cases of placenta previa, and a group of cases of premature separation of the placenta (abruptio placenta). The incidence of placenta previa, one in fifty-six deliveries, was about double that in the United States; maternal morbidity was 34 per cent, and maternal mortality, 4.3 per cent. In premature separation of the placenta, on the other hand, the incidence was one in seventy deliveries, compared with one in 100 deliveries in the United States. For abruptio placenta, the maternal morbidity was 51 per cent, and the mortality 17 per cent. Lim stressed the frequency of opium addiction as a causative factor of abruptio

* Ibid.
† Ibid.

placenta in Chinese women. She attributed the high fetal mortality—39 per cent in placenta previa and 87.5 per cent in abruptio placenta—to prematurity and to maternal malnutrition.

Frank E. Whitacre, a graduate of the State University of Iowa School of Medicine, was the last head of obstetrics and gynecology before the outbreak of World War II. He arrived in Peking on February 12, 1939, from the Commonwealth Fund in New York, where he had spent the previous two years, on loan from the University of Chicago, organizing postgraduate courses in the state of Tennessee. Whitacre was interned at Santo Tomas in Manila from 1941 to 1943 and then repatriated to the United States. He served successively as head of obstetrics and gynecology at Tennessee, the Ochsner Clinic in New Orleans, and Vanderbilt.

OPHTHALMOLOGY

Arnold Pillat of Vienna succeeded Howard as head of ophthalmology in 1928. Pillat made an extensive study, comparing Chinese and Occidental eyes, based primarily on the physiologic content of pigment in the conjunctiva.

The strong ophthalmological ties with Vienna were continued in 1933 with the appointment of Peter Clemens Kronfeld as Pillat's successor. A graduate of Vienna in 1923, Kronfeld had then spent five years working with Fuchs in the Vienna Eye Institute. He came to the University of Chicago in 1928 as assistant professor of ophthalmology.

Kronfeld's studies were on the normal and abnormal physiology of the eye and the influences of the parasympathetic and sympathetic nervous systems. At PUMC Kronfeld also emphasized the importance of nutritional factors in diseases of the eye. He left Peking in 1939 to become head of ophthalmology at the University of Illinois.

Several investigators had studied the effects of sulfanilamide and related compounds in trachoma, but there was no unanimity in their reports. Luo Tsunghsien (PUMC 1932) and E. Chang (PUMC 1938) treated forty patients with sulfonamides and proved their efficacy: after three months of therapy 80 per cent were cured and 20 per cent had improved considerably. Toxic reactions were few and mild.

PSYCHIATRY

The establishment of a major program in psychiatry in 1932 came at a time when there was at best a handful of programs of academic status in the United States. For several years the Rockefeller Foundation had been evaluating the discipline for the possibility of a new major thrust, and Raymond B. Fosdick, president of the foundation, summarized their conclusions:

> . . . psychiatry was—and to a large extent still is today—the most backward, the most needed, and potentially the most fruitful field in medicine . . . teaching in psychiatry was poor, research was fragmentary, and application was feeble.[72]

It was not surprising then that there was essentially no academic psychiatry worthy of mention in China; Henry Houghton described the new program at PUMC as "the initial steps in promoting modern psychiatry in this country."[73]

Alan Gregg, who in 1930 had succeeded Richard Pearce as director of the foundation's Division of Medical Education, was a major influence in the development of psychiatry at PUMC. When Gregg made his first visit to the college in the fall of 1932 he had recently assumed the leadership of a new program in psychiatry and was deeply committed to its importance in academic medicine. Gregg gave a strong fillip to the program in psychiatry as well as to the program in public health, both through his visit to PUMC and through his active support on his return to New York.*

Richard S. Lyman, a graduate of Johns Hopkins, joined the faculty in 1932 as head of the Division of Neurology and Psychiatry. Lyman had trained in psychiatry and the neurological sciences at Johns Hopkins, at Queen's Square in London, and at Leningrad. His career in China had begun with a year as associate professor at the First National Medical School in Shanghai.

The limited inpatient and outpatient resources for psychiatry at PUMC were expanded and strengthened materially by an early affiliation with the Peking Municipal Psychopathic Hospital.

The educational program for medical students was similar to that in the handful of first-rate medical schools in the United States—and far ahead of the majority. In the second year, after a course in normal psychology, the students made intensive case studies based on a thorough evaluation of the backgrounds of selected psychiatric patients. The clerkship in internal medicine placed continuing emphasis on the psychosomatic aspects of disease. During the fourth year, three weeks were spent full-time in the outpatient department on the diagnosis and management of ambulatory psychiatric disorders. Three weeks at the Special Health Station included an assignment in psychiatry. Hsu Ying-k'uei (PUMC 1934), and Feng Ying-k'un (PUMC 1936) entered academic careers in psychiatry under Lyman's influence.

Research Programs in Psychiatry

Lyman and his colleagues at PUMC were the pioneers in psychiatric and psychological research in China.[75]

Addiction to opium, heroin, or morphine was a major cause of mental illness; Lyman estimated that there were 300,000 addicts in Peking. I. C. Fang, director of public health for the municipality of Peking, was developing an intensive program against drug addiction and turned to Lyman and his staff for an evaluation of various methods of treatment. They investigated electroshock and insulin

---

* Gregg's contact with PUMC actually went back to February 1919 when he applied to Wickliffe Rose for a post with the International Health Board. Rose mentioned several possibilities, commenting: "We are very anxious to get a man to start public health work at the school in Peking." Gregg chose instead to do research on hookworm and malaria in Brazil.[74]

shock therapy, both of which were becoming popular. With insulin therapy, they attributed any beneficial effects to the intense hunger caused by the high doses of insulin, which suggested that the craving for food might replace the craving for opium. But the procedure required hospitalization and intensive care by physicians and nurses to such a degree that the cost was prohibitive for general use.

There was a striking similarity in the relative frequency of psychiatric disorders in China and the West. Three-quarters of the patients seen in the neuropsychiatric clinic at PUMC had no demonstrable organic disease; 17.3 per cent were diagnosed as suffering from a psychoneurosis; and 8.1 per cent from a psychosis, epilepsy, or mental deficiency.

There was also a similarity in schizophrenia: "The differences between East and West in the clinical pictures are only superficial." Chinese schizophrenics exhibited "all of the characteristics of schizophrenia in the West."[76]

Lyman could not explain the relatively higher incidence of mental illness in the Manchus than in the Chinese. The singular faith that the Chinese held in the predictions of fortune tellers, and the widespread practice of hypnosis, were also noted.

W. H. Chao, a psychologist in the neuropsychiatric unit, made an interesting study of the interrelation between behavior and the construction of the characters in Chinese calligraphy—a comparative study based on the known effects of mental disorder on handwriting in the West. He found that striking patterns of abnormal behavior, such as occur in excitement or mental deterioration, especially in patients with syphilitic paresis, were clearly expressed in the way the patients drew the characters. The results were comparable to those found in the West, with interesting differences due to the technique of using the brush, and the complex structure of Chinese characters.

Lyman's studies on the use of shock therapy in schizophrenia gave the Communist government a potent propaganda tool when they launched a campaign to discredit the college. Lyman followed the common practice of taking movies of his shock-therapy patients when they were convulsing, and a copy of each film was filed in the records of PUMC. The movies were seized when the college was nationalized and stills from them were published in magazines as shocking evidence of American brutality and exploitation of the Chinese:

> Sometimes the patients broke their own bones, ground and broke their teeth, bit their tongues to pieces, or even stopped breathing altogether because of their extreme suffering. The cruel murderer published his "thesis" which was built on piles of skeletons of the Chinese working people.[77]

Lyman left Peking in 1937. After two years at Hopkins, and service in World War II, he joined the psychiatry department at Duke University medical school with the rank of professor.

Theron S. Hill, a 1925 graduate of the University of Michigan, succeeded Lyman and continued to lead the program in psychiatry until the college was occupied by the Japanese.

NOTES TO CHAPTER TEN

1. Theodore H. White and Annalee Jacoby, *Thunder out of China*, pp. 58–9.

2. *Ibid.*, pp. 59–60.

3. Hayes to Rockefeller, 11 April 1935, Arrival No. 2278, Archives of the London Missionary Society.

4. Theodore E. Hsiao, *The History of Modern Education in China*, pp. ix–x.

5. *Ibid.*, p. 28.

6. *Ibid.*, p. 129.

7. T'ao Lee, "Some Statistics on Medical Schools in China for 1932–33," p. 1027.

8. Aura E. Severinghaus, "The Miracle of ABMAC," Part I, p. 4.

9. *Ibid.*, p. 5.

10. George W. Corner, *A History of The Rockefeller Institute, 1901–1953*, p. 500.

11. Daisy Yen Wu, ed., *Hsien Wu, 1893–1959*, p. 41.

12. Walter B. Cannon, *The Way of an Investigator*, p. 182.

13. *Ibid.*, p. 183.

14. *Ibid.*, p. 182.

15. George E. Armstrong, "Robert Kho-seng Lim, Ph.D.," p. 2.

16. *Ibid.*, p. 2.

17. *Ibid.*, p. 3.

18. Barbara Tuchman, *Stillwell and the American Experience in China, 1911–45*, p. 265.

19. Theodore H. White and Annalee Jacoby, *Thunder out of China*, p. 138.

20. Aura E. Severinghaus, "The Miracle of ABMAC," Part I, p. 5.

21. Robert K. S. Lim, et al., *A Stereotaxic Atlas of the Dog's Brain*.

22. Harold Balme, *China and Modern Medicine*, p. 55.

23. Hans Zinsser, *As I Remember Him*, p. 405.

24. *Ibid.*, p. 406.

25. Chinese Society of Pathology and Microbiology, *Pathology, Microbiology, and Experimental Medicine*, Chinese Medical Journal Supplement 2 (March 1938).

26. K. Chimin Wong and Lien-teh Wu, *History of Chinese Medicine*, p. 78.

27. Bernard E. Read, "*Chinese Materia Medica: Animal Drugs*," p. 39.

28. J. L. Cranmer-Byng, ed., "Dr. Gillan's Observations on the State of Medicine, Surgery and Chemistry in China," p. 279.

29. Harry B. Van Dyke, "Studies in Neurohypophyseal Endocrinology," pp. ix–x.

30. Harry B. Van Dyke, *Physiology and Pharmacology of the Pituitary Body*, 2 vols. (Chicago: University of Chicago Press, 1936).

31. Harry B. Van Dyke, "Neurohypophyseal Endocrinology," p. xii.

32. *Ibid.*, p. xii.

33. Reinhard J. C. Hoeppli, *Parasites and Parasitic Infections in Early Medicine and Science* (Singapore: University of Malaya Press, 1959).

34. Reinhard J. C. Hoeppli, *Parasitic Diseases in Africa* and the Western Hemisphere: Early Documentation and Transmission by the Slave Trade (Basel: Friedrich Reinhardt, 1969).

35. Chinese Society of Pathology and Microbiology, *Pathology, Microbiology, and Experimental Medicine*, Chinese Medical Journal Supplement 3 (March 1940).

36. C. C. Ch'en, *Scientific Medicine as Applied in Ting Hsien*.

37. *Ibid.*, p. 3.

38. *Ibid.*, p. 27.

39. *Ibid.*, p. 27.

40. Conrad Seipp, ed., *Health Care for the Community*, p. 8.

41. *Ibid.*, p. 9.

42. Saul Benison, "The Reminiscences of Dr. John B. Grant."

43. *Ibid.*

44. James C. Thomson, Jr., *While China Faced West*, p. 126.

45. *Ibid.*, p. 131.

46. *Ibid.*, p. 136.

47. *Ibid.*, p. 150.

48. Conrad Seipp, ed., *Health Care*, p. vii.

49. I-chin Yuan, "Life Tables for a Southern Chinese Family from 1365–1849," *Human Biology* 3 (1930) no. 2: 157–73.

50. I-chin Yuan, "The Influence of Heredity Upon the Duration of Life in Man, Based on a Chinese Genealogy from 1365 to 1914" (Sc.D. Diss., Johns Hopkins University, 1931).

51. G. Canby Robinson, *Adventures in Medical Education*, p. 244.

52. *Ibid.*, p. 246.

53. Isidore Snapper, *Chinese Lessons to Western Medicine*, p. i.

54. *Ibid.*, p. 5.

55. *Ibid.*, p. 379.

56. Irvine McQuarrie, *The Experiments of Nature and Other Essays*, p. 2.

57. *Ibid.*, pp. 79–115.

58. *Ibid.*, p. 90.

59. *Ibid.*, p. 115.

60. *Ibid.*, p. 115.

61. R. A. Guy and K. S. Yeh, "Soybean 'Milk' as Food for Infants," p. 2.

62. R. A. Guy and K. S. Yeh, "Roasted Soybean in Infant Feeding," p. 1.

63. Chester N. Frazier and Hung-chiung Li, *Racial Variations in Immunity to Syphilis.*

64. *Ibid.*, p. 90.

65. Ying-k'ai Wu and Harold H. Loucks, "Surgical Treatment of Carcinoma of the Esophagus," p. 1–33.

66. Alan F. Guttmacher, "Some Not Too Sentimental Reminiscences," *Obstetrical and Gynecological Survey* 20 (June 1965) no. 3: 375.

67. Nicholson J. Eastman, *Obstetrical and Gynecological Survey*, p. 472.

68. *Ibid.*, pp. 472–3.

69. *Ibid.*, p. 473.

70. *Ibid.*, p. 506–7.

71. Alan F. Guttmacher, "Some Not Too Sentimental Reminiscences," p. 376.

72. Raymond B. Fosdick, *The Story of The Rockefeller Foundation*, p. 128–29.

73. Henry S. Houghton, Introduction to *Social and Psychological Studies in Neuropsychiatry in China*, edited by R. S. Lyman *et al.*, p. iii.

74. Wilder Penfield, *The Difficult Art of Giving*, p. 100.

75. R. S. Lyman *et al.*, eds., *Social and Psychological Studies in Neuropsychiatry in China.*

76. *Ibid.*, pp. 359–61.

77. "U.S. Imperialist Aggression Disguised as Friendship," p. 47.

CHAPTER ELEVEN

The School of Nursing

Peking Union Medical College established nursing as a respected profession for women in China, and in so doing it equalled or surpassed its leadership in the advancement of the profession of medicine. The School of Nursing trained an outstanding group of women who entered careers where they were most needed—in public health, maternal and child health, teaching, and administration.

The problems that arose in developing nursing were different—and more difficult—than those in medicine. Through the centuries, indigenous practitioners had established the importance of seeking medical care for an illness. In contrast, nursing was not recognized as a trade, much less a profession. Thus while there was a surfeit of bright students in China for the study of medicine, nursing was starting from scratch. The thought that their daughter should contact the body of a man drew bitter opposition from parents, especially when efforts were made to enroll nursing students from families with status in a community.

For many centuries the care of the sick in China rested with the family, assisted at times by an *amah* if the patient were female. Male patients were cared for exclusively by men who, after the advent of Western missionaries, received apprenticeship training in the missionary hospitals, where nursing care was the responsibility of missionary nurses from the West. In the missionary hospitals for women, Chinese girls were given short periods of training to serve as aides to the nurses.

Before PUMC was founded there had been earlier but limited efforts to train Chinese women for nursing. The medical pioneer, William Lockhart, in 1884 opened what was probably the first such program at his Chinese Hospital in Shanghai. A few other such efforts were made in the ensuing years. H. W.

Boone, director of the medical department at St. John's University in Shanghai, established a training program for nurses in 1887; of the two students in the first class, one was a woman. At the turn of the century several other programs were established: in Shanghai in 1901, and in Canton, Hankow, and Chungking in 1902. The Union School of Nurses, which opened in October 1906 as part of the Union Medical College, accepted only male students into a three-year training program.

An important program for training both male and female nurses was opened at the Canton Hospital in 1914. The hospital's report for that year noted that the Chinese nursing staff consisted of one male and two female graduate nurses. There were eleven students in the first-year class—seven men and four women.

From his position as director of the Red Cross Hospital in Shanghai, Henry S. Houghton became a pioneer spokesman in promoting nursing as a respected profession for well-educated young women from good families. Accordingly, in October 1914 he opened a program at the Red Cross Hospital with four young women students in a three-year curriculum.

Another nursing program to train men and women was opened in Hsiang-ya in 1913 by Edward H. Hume. The curriculum was four years in duration. By 1921, however, only twenty students had successfully completed their studies.

In all of these male-dominated programs the aim was to train nurses for service in the hospital sponsoring the training school. In this they followed the pattern of hospitals in the United States and Britain.

The Nurses' Association of China (NAC), a missionary organization whose first president was Carolina Maddock, was founded in 1909. The registration of nursing schools began five years later, and certifying examinations for graduates were held in 1915.

The opportunity for PUMC to establish a school of nursing was noted by the First China Medical Commission when it reported that "high grade nurses are as much needed as physicians."[1] At the first meeting of the China Medical Board on December 11, 1914, five scholarships were made available for Chinese women to come to the United States to be trained as nurses, and a small grant was made to the NAC to support the translation of nursing texts. The Second China Medical Commission recommended that a training school for male and female nurses should be an essential part of the new program at Peking. On July 1, 1915, when the CMB took over the UMC, there were two classes enrolled in a three-year course for nurses, but admission was still restricted to male students.

The plans developed by Franklin McLean, Houghton, and Roger Greene in the fall of 1916 called for a program in nursing education at a standard of excellence comparable to that envisaged for the medical college. In aiming at such standard, however, they had few if any models in the United States to guide them. A drive to improve educational standards had been launched at the end of the nineteenth century but it was firmly opposed by hospitals, which saw their training schools as sources of free services by student nurses.

The first preparatory course in the United States was developed at the Johns Hopkins Hospital School of Nursing in 1901. It was described as a

> well-balanced 6 months' program of theory and practice, which gave priority to the learning needs of students and compared favorably with most collegiate programs in the level of its teaching, attention to serious study, and well-organized laboratory and ward practice.[3]

The first school of nursing in a university was established at Minnesota in 1909 with a three-year basic program. It was not until 1916, however, that a five-year degree program was introduced that placed equal emphasis on general and nursing education.

STAFFING THE SCHOOL

Once plans for the school at PUMC were underway, the next step was the appointment of a superintendent of nurses, and the choice turned to Johns Hopkins and Anna Dryden Wolf. Miss Wolf had unique qualifications for the post through her origins in a Lutheran missionary family in Guntur, Madras Presidency, India, where her father was head of the American Evangelical Lutheran Mission College. After graduating from Hopkins in 1912, she earned a master's degree at Columbia University Teachers College, and was then appointed assistant superintendent of nurses and instructor in nursing at Johns Hopkins.

In the summer of 1918 Anna Wolf was a member of the faculty of the Vassar College Training Camp for Nurses, a war recruitment measure opened on June 24, 1918, which brought into nursing more than 400 graduates from over 100 colleges. An intensive summer program, emphasizing the theory of nursing, it was limited to female graduates who wished to become hospital nurses.

Having accepted the offer of the post at Peking on June 1, 1919, Miss Wolf arrived at PUMC in August with twelve American nurses for the nursing school and hospital services whom she had recruited in just one month. Such was the lure of China!

During the interval between their arrival and the opening of the school, Miss Wolf's new staff studied Chinese at the North China Union Language School and worked on the nursing services at the old Hsin Kai Lu Hospital of the UMC. One of the group was Katharine Caulfield, also from Hopkins, who remained at PUMC for five years. She was the first trained operating room supervisor to teach in China, and she established a program to train male and female operating room assistants. Faye Whiteside was associate supervisor of nurses from 1920 to 1926.

While a majority of the nurses' training schools in the United States continued to be operated by their hospitals solely for nursing services, in Peking Miss Wolf was directed to place the emphasis on nursing education. The nursing school, with classes of no more than twenty-five students, would not be a service pool for the hospital; the first responsibility of the student nurses would be to learn, not to assist in patient care. Thus the program represented a unique opportunity for the new superintendent, as well as for the students.

The training school opened on September 28, 1920, with three students, two of whom were subsequently dropped for academic deficiencies. In addition to Miss Wolf there were five instructors on the faculty, one of whom was Chinese. The medical faculty participated by teaching aspects of the basic and clinical sciences.

In 1924 the "Training School of Nurses" became the "School of Nursing," as a more appropriate university-level designation, and the leader of the program was designated as "dean" as well as "superintendent of nurses."

STUDENTS

The caliber of the nursing students matched that of the medical students: "excellent, conscientious, hard working—so very bright."[*] The graduates held a similar respect for the faculty, especially for their emphasis on developing in the students a sense of personal responsibility for learning, instead of the traditional Chinese pattern of relying exclusively on their teachers and on rote memory. Self-discipline, strength of character, and total devotion to the call of nursing were other qualities inculcated in the students. The mutual admiration and respect generated between teachers and students, the excellence of the educational program, as well as the stimulating ambience of PUMC, made the nursing alumnae as devoted to the college as were the graduates in medicine.

EDUCATIONAL PROGRAMS

There were two educational programs: Course I was three years in duration and led to a diploma in nursing; a five-year program, Course II, leading to a bachelor of science degree from Yenching University, in addition to the diploma in nursing, was established in 1922. The requirements for admission to Course I included six years of middle school and the successful completion of a one-year prenursing course in the College of Natural Sciences of Yenching. Admission to Yenching was based on entrance examinations in English, Chinese, mathematics, Chinese and Western history and geography, and one of the natural sciences. The School of Nursing received candidates from this course without further examination.

After an introduction to the basic medical sciences, the students in the diploma program, Course I, learned the practice of nursing in carefully supervised programs on the medical wards.

In Course II the first two academic years were spent at Yenching in general education and selected courses in the physical and social sciences. In the third and fourth years the student nurses studied the basic sciences and clinical nursing at PUMC. Clinical nursing was divided into six major areas of study: nursing techniques and the tools of nursing; medicine; surgery, including operating room procedures; obstetrics; pediatrics; and public health. The fifth and final year was divided between the wards of PUMC, the Special Health Station and electives. There was usually a significant attrition rate due not only to academic failure but to loss of interest and family pressures.

---

[*] Gertrude E. Hodgman 1971: personal communication.

Subsequently, joint programs leading to the bachelor of science degree and the nursing diploma were established with Ginling College in Nanking, Lingnan University in Canton, and Soochow University, as well as with Yenching. After 1932, hospitals in Peking and Tientsin affiliated with the School of Nursing so that their nurses could receive special training in operating room techniques, pediatrics, obstetrics, surgical nursing, and public health. The school also offered fellowships for advanced study to nurses from other hospitals in China with the stipulation that they would return to their institutions upon completion of their training.

In 1934 the school established postgraduate courses in institutional nursing and in public health nursing. Candidates for admission were required to have graduated from a school approved by the NAC and to be members of that association. In the institutional courses preference was given to applicants who had completed junior middle school. One institutional course of eight months' duration prepared nurses for careers as teachers, and applicants were required to have had previous experience in either teaching or hospital administration. A second, five-month course prepared them for supervisory positions in nursing services (Table 1).

In the public health course, preference was given to senior middle school graduates (Table 2).

When the Sino-Japanese War erupted on a national scale in 1937 the CMB created a fellowship program for refugee nurses coming to Peking. Programs were designed to meet individual needs and to prepare the refugees for new positions of responsibility in nursing schools and on nursing services. Special courses were offered in Mandarin.

Occasionally there were opportunities to render nursing services outside of PUMC on humanitarian programs, and these brought singular satisfaction to both students and faculty. At the battle at Nanyuan in December 1925

> there was a special opportunity of working among wounded soldiers in the camp hospital, which gave us the type of nursing experience which ordinary hospital experience does not provide.[4]

On another occasion floods in Hankow that made thousands homeless were soon followed by a cholera epidemic. Through John Grant's efforts, the government's petition for assistance was answered when student nurses were sent to Hankow to assist in the care of the sick and to apply sanitary precautions in controlling the spread of disease.

But the most interesting and rewarding experience for most of the students was the twelve-week assignment to the Special Health Station.

THE SPECIAL HEALTH STATION

The opening of the Special Health Station in September 1925 was of at least equal importance for the educational program in nursing as it was for that in medicine. It created a generation of public health nurses whose services to their

TABLE 1. CURRICULUM IN INSTITUTIONAL NURSING AT PUMC*

Descriptive Title	Class Hours	Practice Hours	Total
†Principles of Hospital Administration............	30		30+
Ward Management 12			
Hospital Economics...................... 10			
‡Hospital Administration.................. 8		(Hours to be	
Observation and Practice in Supervision......		arranged)	
†Problems of Nursing Education.................	38		38+
A Practical Course in the Principles of			
Teaching 14			
Ward Teaching, Including Case Study			
Method............................... 14			
‡Nursing School Administration, Including			
Curriculum Planning.................... 10		(Hours to be	
Observation and Practice Teaching........		arranged)	
†The Teaching of Nursing Principles			
and Methods...............................	25	25	50
Introductory Nursing...................... 25			
Demonstrations........................... 25			
†Nursing Survey..............................	22	34	56
History of Nursing........................ 12			
Professional Problems..................... 10			
Excursions............................... 34			
Methods of Health Teaching, Including			
Personal Hygiene...........................	16	8	24
†Nutrition and Dietetics........................	30	20	50
Normal Nutrition ⎫ 45			
Diet in Disease ⎭			
Home Economics......................... 5			
†Sociology....................................	20	6	26
Elementary Psychology.......................	15		15
Mental Hygiene	12		12
Bacteriology.................................	16	16	32
Elective in Nursing	10		10+
Theory 10			
Practice			
		(Hours to be	
General Nursing Practice......................		arranged)	
Total Hours	234	109+	343+

* Reprinted from *Peiping Union Medical College Annual* Announcement 1934–36. (Peking: July 1, 1934) p. 4
† Required for those taking the five-month course, with a total of 209 hours in theory.
‡ Elective course.

TABLE 2.   CURRICULUM IN PUBLIC HEALTH NURSING

Descriptive Title	Class Hours	Labora-tory Hours	Field Hours	Total
Principles of Public Health Nursing, Including				
Evolution of Public Health Nursing..........	36	20	594	650
Introduction to Public Health Nursing, Including				
Administration, Sanitation and Vital Statistics..	33	14		47
Special Fields in Public Health Nursing.........	40	70		110
Maternity and Child Health, Including				
Eugenics and Birth Control............ 16				
Communicable Disease Control, Including				
Tuberculosis and Venereal Diseases..... 12				
School and Factory.................... 12				
Applied Sociology	40			40
Applied Psychology..........................	30			30
Home Economics and Nutrition..............	30	15		45
Methods of Health Teaching, Including				
Personal and Oral Hygiene.................	30	24		54
Public Health Nursing Problems	20			20
Case Work and Conferences.................	12	8		20
Excursions.................................			42	42
Electives..................................	6		148	154
Total	277	151	784	1212

* Reprinted from *Peiping Union Medical College Annual* Announcement 1934–36. (Peking: July 1, 1934) p. 52.

country were comparable to those of the PUMC medical graduates who entered careers in public health.

At the Special Health Station the student nurse divided her time between programs in industrial health, the district visiting-nurse service, maternal and child health, mental health, school health, and nutrition. Nursing students came to the station in groups of no more than six, which made possible an emphasis on individual instruction and practical training.

The program in industrial health was limited by the fact that there were only a few factories in the area. But each factory had one room designated as a clinic, with a nurse on duty, and the health of the workers and their families was carefully monitored.

The largest program was in school health, with at least one nurse assigned to each school in the district. It began with examinations, immunizations, and medical care for kindergarteners, and continued through primary and middle school. In the lower grades there were daily health inspections, monthly checks on weight, and constant dietary supervision.

The maternal-health program included prepartum and intrapartum care, supervised by a nurse-midwife who shared the responsibility for postpartum care with the visiting nurse.

Anne McCabe, who was head of nursing at the health station, described the change in the attitude of Chinese families toward their nurses:

> When two nurses started out together, in their uniforms, to go from house to house in the community to explain what it was all about, some of the people listened with interest, some paid very little attention, and others screamed at them to get off the premises calling them "foreign devils."

> Today, in the Demonstration Area, the "King Kung Wei Sheng Chuan Tao Yuan" (as they are called) is looked upon as a real friend and most families watch and anxiously await her arrival, for she knows *what* to do when the baby is sick; *where* to send any one when they have a stomach or tooth ache; *where* and *how* to find a trained midwife for delivery; *what* to have ready in the home when the midwife or doctor arrives; *where* to send the children when mother goes to the hospital; *where* to go for food and clothing when they are hungry and cold; *why* every one should be vaccinated; *why* the food should be covered and the windows screened; *why* they should be careful where they get their water; and *why* it should be boiled before drinking. The health teacher knows, teaches, and demonstrates, and like the native trumpeter on a tiger hunt who paves the way for the hunter, the "Chuan Tao Yuan" in Peking has paved the way for all other health workers who may join the ranks.[5]

The mental health–child guidance program at the health station was limited in scope until a full-fledged academic program in psychiatry was established in 1932. In the early years the staff consisted of a psychologist, a nurse-supervisor, and a staff nurse. A main problem was the attitude held by families that children and adults with mental disorders or significant behavioral deviations were blots on the family's reputation. Psychiatric patients were hidden in the home under physical restraints; their existence was not acknowledged publicly.

The annual "Health Education Week" was one of the most interesting and rewarding events for the student nurses, who showed the children how to draw colorful posters with simple couplets or doggerel to emphasize the importance of good health.

In 1924 Anna Wolf accepted Franklin McLean's offer of the post as director and associate professor of nursing in the clinics of the University of Chicago. Later she directed the nursing school at the New York Hospital Cornell University Medical Center, returning to Hopkins in 1940 as director of nursing.

It was primarily her outstanding work at PUMC that drew for Anna Wolf a high accolade on her return to Hopkins: "A rich background of education, general and professional, and a record of educational organization and administration, international in scope and internationally recognized."[6] She was one of Johns Hopkins's most distinguished graduates in nursing.

Ruth Ingram, who succeeded Miss Wolf as dean, was the daughter of James H. Ingram of the American Board of Congregational Missions, a highly respected medical missionary stalwart in China and a key figure in the relations between PUMC and the missionary groups. An ophthalmologist, Ingram had served briefly on the staff of the UMC and had translated Herbert A. Hare's *Textbook of Practical Therapeutics* into Chinese.[7]

Born in China, Ruth Ingram graduated from the nursing school of the University of Pennsylvania and returned to China in 1918 to become assistant supervisor of nurses at PUMC under Anna Wolf. In addition to her excellent training and executive ability, she brought the added asset of a rich background in Chinese culture and the ability to speak fluent Mandarin. John Grant described Ruth Ingram as "the most colorful member of the nursing faculty."[8] She placed special emphasis on training in public health and maternal and child health. In 1928 Miss Ingram moved to Barnes Hospital in St. Louis as director of nursing, and then to the Touro Infirmary in New Orleans. She later returned to China and Southeast Asia under the public health nursing programs of UNRRA and WHO.

Gertrude E. Hodgman succeeded Ruth Ingram as dean in the fall of 1930. With her excellent background in public health nursing and her personal qualities, Miss Hodgman was an ideal leader for the PUMC School of Nursing. After graduating from Vassar she studied at the Johns Hopkins Hospital School of Nursing, and then joined the Vassar Unit. As World War I approached its end, she went to France and to Lebanon to work in public health programs.

On her return to the United States, Miss Hodgman served under Lillian Wald as assistant supervisor and later educational supervisor of the nursing service at the Henry Street Settlement in Manhattan, the headquarters of the first nursing service and the first mental health service in the country. That remarkable leader of nursing education, Annie B. Goodrich, had promised women who served in the Army School of Nursing that they would receive four months of public health practice training at the settlement. Despite the pressures of her responsibilities as supervisor of educational programs and an overload of students, Miss Hodgman was able to earn a master's degree at Columbia University Teachers College.

She was then appointed educational secretary of the National Organization for Public Health Nursing and was a founding member of the Committee on Grading of Nursing Schools. In the latter capacity she visited and accredited university nursing schools, applying the same high educational standards that characterized her brilliant career: "A lot of people hated me. They were afraid when they saw me coming!"*

From 1926 to 1929 Miss Hodgman served as assistant professor of public health nursing and assistant supervisor of nursing at the New Haven Hospital under Annie Goodrich, now dean of nursing at Yale. Wishing to have a hospital of her own, Miss Hodgman then moved to Toledo, but within a year she was visited by Annie Goodrich and Mary Beard, director of the Rockefeller Foundation's program in nursing. They had returned from PUMC and, at

---

* Gertrude E. Hodgman 1972: personal communication.

Roger Greene's request, had agreed to find a dean for the nursing school. Gertrude Hodgman was their first and obvious choice, but she was hesitant to leave Toledo. She never regretted her decision to go to PUMC, however: "They were unforgettable years."* A highly intelligent woman with strong qualities of leadership, Dean Hodgman was uncompromising in her conviction that the education of nurses at PUMC must always hold to the highest standards.

Faye Whiteside, who had left PUMC in 1926 to serve as head surgical nurse at Chicago, rejoined the staff at PUMC with Miss Hodgman in 1930 and was responsible for graduate courses in nursing administration. When Miss Hodgman withdrew from the post as superintendent of nurses in 1938 to concentrate on her role as dean, Miss Whiteside succeeded her.

In 1932 Dean Hodgman prepared an extensive report on the School of Nursing for the Rockefeller Foundation's series of publications on "Methods and Problems of Medical Education." The number of graduates had increased slowly: from a single graduate in the first class of 1924 to a high of nine graduates in 1930. As of July 1, 1932, a total of thirty-nine nurses had graduated in eight classes. Of the thirty-five alumnae in active nursing careers, eleven had educational or nursing service appointments at PUMC. Of special significance: half of those in active careers were in public health or midwifery.

Dean Hodgman energetically continued the campaign initiated by Anna Wolf and Ruth Ingram to alter the Chinese concept of nursing as an impossible profession for women; she recalls it as her "greatest challenge."† One of her approaches was to visit the leading middle schools in north China to discuss with students and their families the opportunities for relieving human suffering and preventing disease through careers in nursing. She found of course that the students were far more easily persuaded than their parents.

A talk that Dean Hodgman presented at Chengtu was so persuasive that one young lady arrived at the Registrar's Office at PUMC before the dean had returned from her recruiting tour. Since her qualifications were excellent, she was admitted immediately—but without the consent of her parents, whose approval was a crucial factor; there could be no assurance of her continuing her training without it. It took six weeks for her letter, informing her parents of her new plans, to reach Chengtu, and she had completed three months of training before their reply reached her. While she was strictly forbidden to continue the study of nursing, in a surprising twist they urged her to enter the medical school instead. She dutifully transferred, but her heart was set on nursing, and Dean Hodgman and her associates took it to be their special responsibility to persuade the parents to let their daughter return to the nursing school. They were finally won over.‡

---

* Ibid.
† Ibid.
‡ Ibid.

Nieh Yu-chan (Vera) (PUMC 1927) had completed postgraduate studies at Columbia Teachers College and at the University of Toronto before returning to Peking. A woman of great ability—and great determination—she sought the post as head of nursing at the Special Health Station and in 1932 was appointed successor to Anne McCabe.

When Robert K. S. Lim, J. Heng Liu, and Grant recommended that the nursing school as well as the medical school might place more emphasis on quantity and less on quality in order to increase the graduate output, Dean Hodgman and the faculty of the School of Nursing joined Francis Dieuaide and Harold Loucks in firmly opposing the proposal.

On January 14, 1937, the Ministry of Education ordered that the School of Nursing should be reorganized as a special (*chuan shou*) school, which would have lowered it to the same level as the average diploma school and allowed a major increase in enrollment. The nurses, however, felt that the primary aim of their school should continue to be the development of teachers and leaders capable of holding positions of leadership in nursing schools and on nursing services, especially in public health; the school could not produce leaders of this caliber if educational requirements were lowered. The issue was settled by the Japanese when they conquered north China; thenceforth the Ministry of Education in distant Chungking had no voice in the affairs at PUMC.

At the same time a concerted effort was made to replace nursing school staff members from the West with Chinese, especially graduates of PUMC. This was achieved progressively and satisfactorily: in 1933 there were nineteen officers of instruction, none of whom were Chinese; eight years later, in 1941, of the twenty-two members of the staff, eighteen were Chinese.

THE WAR ERUPTS

The eruption of the full-scale war with Japan in the summer of 1937 saw alumni of the nursing school move into positions of national leadership in the armed forces.

Yu Tao-chen, a graduate of the combined Yenching-PUMC program in the class of 1937, enlisted in the Red Cross program under Robert Lim in January 1938, and was assigned to the unit at Changsha where she was "thrilled and surprised to find many PUMC alumni."[*] Miss Yu joined the retreat to western China where she nursed many cases of smallpox, scarlet fever, cholera, dipheria, and typhoid fever. Today she is dean of the School of Nursing at the National Taiwan University.

Hsu Ai-chu (PUMC 1930) was described by Dean Hodgman as "particularly outstanding, and a very strong person."[†] Miss Hsu taught public health nursing at the Special Health Station with Anne McCabe and later with Vera Nieh. In

---

[*] Yu Tao-chen 1969: personal communication.
[†] Gertrude E. Hodgman 1972: personal communication.

1935 she left the college to become head of nursing in the National Health Administration in Nanking. She joined the retreat to Chungking in 1938, where she served as head of nursing services in the National Institute of Health. Miss Hsu later served as chief nursing officer for the National Health Administration on Taiwan. Wang Hsiu-ying (PUMC 1936), who Dean Hodgman recalls as "very tactful and charming,"* succeeded Miss Hsu at the Special Health Station. Today Miss Wang is teaching nursing at the Capital Hospital in Peking—formerly known as PUMC.

Sun Ching-feng (PUMC 1930), who taught ward nursing, was described by Miss Hodgman as "a backbone of the school."† Miss Sun's mother was the *amah* for Ida Pruitt, chief of social services at PUMC from 1921 to 1939, and Miss Pruitt "adopted" Miss Sun as her daughter. It was a tragic loss to the nursing school when Sun Ching-feng died of typhus fever in 1936.

Any conversation with PUMC nursing alumnae turns to "the General," Chou Mei-yu (PUMC 1929), considered by many to be the most outstanding, and certainly the highest ranking of all the graduates of the nursing school. When Miss Chou wished to join Jimmy Yen's program at Ting Hsien in 1931, she first sought Dean Hodgman's approval. Faced with the continual conflict of whether to try to keep the graduates at PUMC or allow them to leave the school, Dean Hodgman urged Miss Chou to stay on for six more months, which she agreed to do; at the end of that period she moved to Ting Hsien.

When the Japanese came, Miss Chou fled from Ting Hsien on her beloved bicycle, but as the Japanese scouts approached she was forced to abandon it, with the greatest reluctance—and a few tears—when it fell into a mire.

At Wuhan, Chou Mei-yu founded the Army Nursing School at a time when nurses were still not awarded commissions in the armed forces. At the end of World War II she moved the school to Shanghai. After the fall of the Kuomintang in 1949 she, her staff, and her students went on to Taiwan where she established the school as a component of the National Defense Medical Center and, following the educational models at PUMC, developed both a degree course and a diploma course. Her promotion to brigadier general made her the first woman in China to hold that rank. When Dean Hodgman asked her how this near-miracle had been accomplished, Miss Chou replied: "Well, I recited to my superiors my many achievements for the army. I could see no reason why they should not promote me to the rank of general—and I told them so!"‡

Vera Nieh was appointed assistant dean of the nursing school in 1938, in the same year that Dean Hodgman decided that a Chinese nurse should be dean. Dean Hodgman left PUMC in 1940, having guided the school through ten difficult years to new heights of excellence. Two assignments at the Russell

---

* Ibid.
† Ibid.
‡ Ibid.

Sage College were interspersed with positions in other programs in public health nursing, one in Brazil with the *Servicio Public de Salud.*

Miss Nieh was appointed dean in October 1941. It was a proud moment not only for the Chinese students and alumnae but for the foreign staff who saw their long-range goal of Chinese leadership accomplished. Miss Nieh had little idea of the war-torn years that lay ahead, or of tests of character and fortitude that would fall upon her just two months later.

1,000 MILES TO CLASS

On the morning of December 8, 1941, when Japanese soldiers occupied PUMC, the class of 1942 was so preoccupied with examinations that they failed to recognize the significance of the event. They had become familiar with the passage of Japanese soldiers through the compound, and it was not until the three-day examination period was completed that the true nature of developments became known to them. They soon learned that all nursing students must be out of their quarters by January 31.

After a hurried consultation between Houghton, Loucks, and Dean Nieh, it was decided that nursing school and medical school seniors should be awarded their degrees immediately. It was a far cry from the splendor of the earlier ceremonies, as medical and nursing students came to the administrative offices to be handed their makeshift diplomas.

Dean Nieh, a woman of singular poise and self-confidence, conducted herself with admirable calm and efficiency. She made arrangements for the first- and second-year student nurses to be transferred to the nurses' training school of the Presbyterian Douw Hospital in Peking, and for the junior students to continue their training in other schools in Peking and Tientsin. For the medical students, the school's principal effort was devoted to returning them to their homes. Some Chinese members of the medical faculty moved to other hospitals, principally in north China, while others gravitated to Chungking.

Dean Nieh and about ten nursing faculty members, however, decided that free China's need for nurses was too great for them to remain inactive in Peking during the war years that lay ahead. They determined to take the hazardous, and, to some of their colleagues, ridiculous, step of moving westward: their target was Chengtu, the site of West China Union University.

A small group of nursing students was enlisted, and faculty and students started out, traveling singly and in groups of two and three, having discarded their starched uniforms for tattered peasants' clothing. They rode burros or carts or trucks—any conveyance they were fortunate enough to find—but mainly they travelled on foot, just as others had moved westward in 1937. Their necessarily circuitous trek to avoid Japanese forces was later estimated to have stretched for 1,000 miles—they were described as "the students who walked 1,000 miles to class!"* The "walk" to the classroom lasted for more than seven

---

* Stephen Chang 1970: personal communication.

weeks, with little food, little rest, and constant fear of seizure by the Japanese whose inhuman treatment of Chinese women had been well established at Nanking.

Day by day they slipped into Chengtu, and although in poor physical condition they had joyous reunions, regaling each other with harrowing tales and making great plans for the future. Within a few weeks they were settled in a wing of the hospital of West China Union—the nursing school of Peking Union Medical College was restored to service.

Despite their hospitable reception, conditions in Chengtu and West China Union University under wartime measures were not to be compared with those at PUMC. The dormitory furnishings were limited and crude; there was no electricity, and medicines had to be measured by the flickering flame of a candle; the only water came from open wells and had to be boiled.

But both students and faculty were in high spirits, filled with patriotic fervor. Thirty years later one of the nurses looked back on the years in Chengtu as a grand adventure:

> It was all such a new experience. If we could work under those conditions we knew that we could work anywhere. Nothing could faze us!*

As the refugees and soldiers, the sick and wounded, streamed into the area, the demands for nursing services became so pressing that the PUMC staff and students worked night and day, seven days a week. Yet Vera Nieh insisted that the educational programs be continued at the same high standard as at Peking.

On the other hand, the few off-duty hours brought a social life that was more pleasant than in Peking. Four other institutions of higher education had sought safety in the area: the University of Nanking, Ginling College, Shantung (Cheeloo) Christian University, and Yenching. There was a surfeit of students, predominantly male. "We had lots of fun," one of the nurses recalled, "Far more than in Peking."† So they worked hard and they played hard; several met their future spouses in Chengtu.

Other alumnae of the nursing school joined Dean Nieh in Chengtu after long and perilous journeys. Gertrude Pao (PUMC 1929) had gone to Nanking Central Hospital in 1936 to work on the nursing services, but when the Japanese began systematic bombing in August 1937 the supervisor of nursing services and the principal of the nursing school left the city hurriedly.‡ Miss Pao was persuaded by J. Heng Liu, against her better judgment, to take over the leadership of both programs in nursing, and soon after she led the evacuation of 150 student nurses and nursing staff from Nanking to Hangchow. After a period of military service in that city, Miss Pao and her band of nurses moved on to Changsha where they joined a contingent of refugee nurses from St. John's

---

* Jane Long 1971: personal communication.
† Gertrude Ai-ching Pao Sing 1971: personal communication.
‡ Ibid.

University in Shanghai. Here again they set up a nursing service, but after eight months they moved southwest to Kweiyang where, after the example of John Dudgeon and John Grant, they converted an old temple into a hospital and a nursing school. At least four of Miss Pao's nurses were killed by Japanese bombs. Some of their equipment came from the Red Cross, some was makeshift, and some was hardware that they had transported in a wreck of an ambulance. Soon Miss Pao and her temple-based hospital were joined by a public health unit and a mobile army hospital that were connected with Bobby Lim's program. Their final move was to a wartime hospital in Chungking.

In 1941 an American medical commission came to Chungking to inspect hospitals and medical care programs, and Miss Pao was asked to join it as the nursing representative on the wracking trip to inspect clinics that were being constructed along the Burma Road. Since it was impassable to automobiles, the male members of the commission rode horseback while Miss Pao enjoyed the "luxury" of a bamboo chair.*

Miss Pao then went on to Chengtu where she spent six months as a superintendent of nurses with Miss Nieh and the other refugees from PUMC. In 1944 she came to the United States with UNRRA, returned briefly to China, and settled permanently in the United States in 1950.

THE SCHOOL REOPENS

When the Executive Committee of the trustees of PUMC met in New York on February 26, 1946, to plan the future of the college, they decided that the nursing school should be reopened as soon as possible after the faculty and students returned from Chengtu, which they hoped could be arranged between April 15 and June 1.

On April 24, after more than two years in Chengtu, Vera Nieh led a group of fifty staff and students out of the campus of West China Union University on the return journey to Peking. The country was still in a state of turmoil and confusion; a few unscheduled trains were operating but they were in poor condition and there were as many passengers on the roof as inside the cars. Travelling by truck, by car, by bus, and by train, but mostly by foot, the group reached Peking two months later, in mid-June, 1946. The only difference from the trip to Chengtu, two-and-a-half years earlier, was that they had been able to travel openly; otherwise it was equally as gruelling in terms of transport, food, personal safety, and lodgings.

What a thrill it was when at long last Dean Nieh led the nurses, who had walked 1,000 miles to class, down Hatamen Boulevard and through the gate of PUMC! They were soon surrounded by nurses and doctors, welcoming the returning heroines, and asking countless questions. For many days and many

---

* On one occasion when no bamboo chair was available Miss Pao insisted on riding a horse, but after two falls in rapid succession she was persuaded to await the arrival of a chair.

nights they described their saga—it will always stand as one of the proudest achievements in the history of PUMC.

The nursing school reopened in September 1946 with an enrollment of sixty-two students. The sixteen in the first-year class studied anatomy, physiology, and biochemistry at National Peking University, while the second- and third-year students did their clinical work at several Peking hospitals—Chung Ho, Hopkins Memorial, and the Children's Hospital.

The first graduate program was reopened in 1947 with eleven students enrolled in courses in public health. Three groups of graduate students who had returned from Chengtu were assigned to the Douw Hospital in Peking, the McKenzie Memorial Hospital in Tientsin, and the Army Hospital in Shanghai. Their expenses were carried by the Commission on Medical Education of the Ministry of Education.

We cannot leave the story of the nursing school without repeating a question that we have been asked: Why did not the staff of the medical school move to the Chungking area during the war and re-establish the program in medicine? Instead they dispersed to a number of hospitals, primarily in north China. There were certainly comparable opportunities for the nurses to remain in north China instead of making the rugged march to Chengtu. The medical staff was as patriotic and held an equal pride in the reputation of the college. Some of the possible answers that have been suggested are: that the nurses were a more cohesive group; that Chinese women have an unusually strong character and strong will; and that there was no Vera Nieh to lead the medical faculty. Probably all three factors contributed to the brilliant performance of the School of Nursing during World War II.

NOTES TO CHAPTER ELEVEN

1. China Medical Commission of The Rockefeller Foundation, *Medicine in China*, p. 37.

2. Mary E. Ferguson, *China Medical Board and Peking Union Medical College*, p. 23.

3. Isabel Maitland Stewart and Anne L. Austin, *A History of Nursing*, p. 207.

4. Peking Union Medical College, *The Unison*, vol. II (*1927*): p. 97.

5. Anne McCabe, "Maternity and Child Health Work of the First Health Station, Peiping," pp. 14–15.

6. Ethel Johns and Blanche Pfefferkorn, *The Johns Hopkins School of Nursing, 1889–1949*, p. 246.

7. Hobart A. Hare, *A Textbook of Practical Therapeutics* (Philadelphia: Sea Bros., 1890).

8. Saul Benison, "The Reminiscences of Dr. John B. Grant."

CHAPTER TWELVE

Leadership in a New China

On September 4, 1945, a few weeks after the end of the war, T. V. Soong, president of the Executive Yuan of the National Government of the Republic of China, addressed a letter to Raymond B. Fosdick, president of the Rockefeller Foundation, requesting that all programs at Peking Union Medical College be re-established as soon as possible. Fosdick posed two questions concerning the future of PUMC to the Joint Planning Committee representing the Rockefeller Foundation and the China Medical Board: (1) What shall we do? and (2) How shall we do it?

Fosdick's unswerving devotion to PUMC was mirrored in a letter that he addressed to John D. Rockefeller, Jr. on November 26, 1945:

> The work of the PUMC is among the bright jewels in our crown, and I think we have the strongest kind of obligation to continue our support of modern medicine in China.[1]

The foundation thereupon appointed a commission to go to China and make a broad study of the situation; it was composed of Alan Gregg, director of the Division of Medical Sciences of the foundation, as chairman, Sidney C. Burwell, dean of the Harvard Medical School, and Harold H. Loucks, now a member of the staff of the CMB. They stayed in China from May 13 to July 22, 1946.

The major recommendation of the commission was that the foundation, through the CMB, should direct its principal effort toward re-establishing PUMC at its former level of excellence, with an emphasis on teacher training, preventive medicine, and public health. The commission also recommended that funds should be given to other medical institutions in China. Thus on January 16, 1947, the foundation, with Rockefeller's firm support, gave a terminal grant of $10 million to the CMB, bringing its total endowment to $22 million.

Meanwhile, PUMC was serving as headquarters for General George Catlett Marshall, who had been asked by President Truman to mediate peace and seek a united government for China. As the forces of Mao Tse-tung gained victory after victory, however, the aspirations of the Marshall mission faded, and on January 7, 1947 he was recalled to become Secretary of State. The mission moved out of PUMC the following month.

Steps were then taken toward reopening the college, and Lee Chung-en (C.U.) who had served in the Department of Medicine from 1923 to 1937, was appointed director. Hu Shih, chairman of the trustees of PUMC, offered the post of vice director first to Alan Gregg and then to A. Baird Hastings. Because of his commitments to the foundation, however, Gregg declined.[*]

Hastings had kept in close touch with PUMC through graduates who came to Harvard on fellowships and through his deep personal commitment to the advancement of medicine in China. He discussed Hu Shih's offer with President Conant of Harvard, but tied by the restrictions at the university, which limited sabbatical leave to a single year, Hastings decided that he could not resign his professorship on the faculty.[†] The post of vice director was therefore left unfilled.

Entrance examinations were held in Peking and Shanghai in September 1947, and twenty-two students began the study of medicine the following month. Among the twenty-one former members of the PUMC faculty who returned to the staff were twelve graduates of the college. The alumni group included Lim Kha-t'i in obstetrics and gynecology; Liu Shih-hao and Chu Hsieni-i in medicine, Chu Fu-t'ang in pediatrics; Li Hung-chiung in dermatology. Hsieh Chih-kuang in radiology; Hu Cheng-hsiang in pathology; Wu Ying-k'ai in surgery; and Samuel H. Zia in bacteriology also resumed their positions on the faculty. Harold Loucks returned as director of the CMB and professor of surgery. William H. Adolph, who had taught chemistry at Yenching, and had studied the nutritive value of the sweet potato, was appointed professor of biochemistry.

The rehabilitation of the physical plant moved ahead slowly, handicapped by the depredations of the Japanese, and there were shortages of supplies, equipment, and fuel. Fortunately, the library had been preserved intact under the watchful eyes of Lieutenant Matsuhashi of the Japanese Medical Corps who had used it frequently before Pearl Harbor. The first units of the hospital were opened on May 1, 1948, and by the following autumn the physical plant was essentially restored to full service.

As the school was reopening in October 1948, however, Mao Tse-tung's Eighth Route Army was approaching Peking and the situation in the city was

---

[*] Alan Gregg 1952: personal communication.
[†] A. Baird Hastings 1971: personal communication.

deteriorating steadily. On Christmas Eve ten students who had originally been in the class of 1943, and who had completed their studies at other medical schools, received PUMC diplomas in a ceremony that Mary Ferguson described as "an all-College party in the Auditorium, ending with carols around the Christmas tree!"[2]

Peking fell to Mao's forces on February 3, 1949. The final, increasingly frustrating months under the new regime, exacerbated by the invasion of South Korea on June 25, 1950, and the intervention of the United States two days later, have been described by Mary Ferguson.[3] She, Loucks, and all other Americans on the staff were recalled to New York. A cablegram from C. U. Lee announced that the college had been nationalized on January 20, 1951. It had been a noble but abortive effort to re-establish the programs—for a second and final time PUMC was a victim of war.

PUMC IN THE PEOPLE'S REPUBLIC

In the same month that PUMC was nationalized, it was renamed the Union Medical College of China (Chung-kuo hsieh-ho yi-hsueh-yuan). The faculty now included Chang Hsiao-ch'ien, head of medicine; Chang Hsi-chun, head of physiology; Ch'iu Tsu-yuan in public health; Chu Fu-t'ang, head of pediatrics; Hu Cheng-hsiang, head of pathology; Lim Kha-t'i, head of obstetrics and gynecology; Liu Shih-hao in medicine; Tseng Hsien-chiu, Wu Ying-k'ai, and Yu Sung-t'ing in surgery; and Samuel H. Zia in bacteriology. Reinhard J. C. Hoeppli continued as head of parasitology until he moved to Singapore in 1952.

At the end of 1957 the Union Medical College of China was made a division of the Chinese Academy of Sciences (Chung-kuo hsieh-ho ke-hsueh-yuan). The hospital was established as a separate institution and designated the Peking Union Hospital (Pei-ching hsieh-ho yi-yuan). In 1968 the name of the hospital was changed again, this time to the Peking Anti-Imperialist Hospital (Pei-ching fan-ti yi-yuan).

Sir Theodore Fox, distinguished editor of *The Lancet*, was a member of a team of British physicians that visited China in August 1957. A perceptive scholar, with a worldwide knowledge of medical education, Fox fortunately included a detailed statement and analysis of medical education and PUMC in his report of the mission.[4] He found that the former PUMC

> . . . despite vicissitudes retains its position as the Johns Hopkins of China. . . . Though times have changed, and the international staff has long since gone, the PUMC retains much of its excellence, and could hold a key position in medical China.[5]

Fox went on to note the Russian influence in medical education:

> In China as in Russia, the Communist policy was to produce more doctors quickly. Before Liberation, medical training, except in certain Army schools,

lasted at least six years; but the new government reduced it to five years, and followed the Soviet plan by which some of the students, halfway through the course, begin to specialize in pediatrics or public health.[6]

In Peking, students were admitted at the age of nineteen after six years' primary and six years' secondary education. They were required to have passed a state examination in biology, chemistry, physics, Chinese literature, and political science. Forty-four per cent of the students were women.

With classes of almost 600 students it was necessary to allocate one-half of the total curriculum of 5,000 hours to lectures. Two-and-one-half years were devoted to the basic sciences, the next one-and-one-half to clinical instruction, and the fifth to an internship. Two-hundred-and-seventy hours were assigned to political studies. All teaching was in Chinese; as an aftermath of the Korean War and as a result of Soviet assistance, Russian had become the second language.

Fox concluded that standards had been downgraded to an unfortunate degree by shortening the curriculum and by an overexpansion of the student body. He suggested that it would be more desirable to train Russian-style feldshers than second-rate doctors.

After graduation the young doctors who were selected for hospital careers were usually required to spend four years in specialty training—three years for pediatrics or ophthalmology. Other graduates spent shorter periods in specialty training.

Peking and Hankow were the two centers for postgraduate training; the program at Peking was designed to prepare the graduates to teach in other colleges:

> The teaching there is at present on a smallish scale. Courses lasting two to four months are given from time to time in special subjects (e.g., medical entomology, histology, haematology). There are also refresher courses, chiefly clinical. But, from the standpoint of science, perhaps the PUMC's chief service could be the training of research fellows (38 at present) who come, at the expense of their own colleges, to work for a "candidate's" degree course. Whether, in view of the training these young people have already had, it is really necessary that their course should be so much concerned with materialist dialectics and the history of the Revolution is no doubt a matter of opinion. So also is the question whether it includes too much theory and too little practice of research. The ultimate pattern, we were told, will emerge with experience; and for my part, as one who is now eager to see Chinese medical science develop, I frankly hope that this pattern will prove to be rather more functional and rather less imitatively Russian than the present one.[7]

When Edgar Snow visited China in 1960 he reported that:

> The PUMC is still an important hospital. . . . The former PUMC, now Peking Hospital [sic], is not a college any more but a large polyclinic combined with an institute of gynecology and pediatrics. New buildings have doubled the number of beds (560).[8]

The Institute of Gynecology was directed by Lin Chiao-chih (Lim Kha-t'i) and the Institute of Pediatrics by Chu Fu-t'ang. Other section chiefs listed by Snow were: Cheng Ch'ao-chien (Chang Hsiao-ch'ien), medicine; Tou Tsung-shen (Luo Tsung-hsien), ophthalmology; Chang Tsing-tsun (Chang Ch'ing-sung), otorhinolaryngology; and Tseng Hsien-chiu (Tseng Hsien-chu), surgery. Snow noted that women comprised half of the staff.

Another report was published by the distinguished Canadian neurosurgeon, Wilder Penfield, who visited China in the autumn of 1962 as the guest of the Chinese Medical Association. In outlining the official position in medical education, the vice minister of health, Tsui Yi-tien, told Penfield that:

> One college calls for a curriculum of 8 years—the Chinese Medical College in Peking.* It is planned to train teachers and research workers. Each physician should have mastered two foreign languages before graduation from this college. Of the other medical colleges, one-third now provide a 6-year curriculum, and less than two-thirds, a 5-year curriculum. A very few schools have a 3-year course, which is intended to prepare men for the practical needs of factories, mines and farms.[9]

The director of the college, Huang Chia-ssu, (PUMC 1933) was a thoracic surgeon who had trained at Ann Arbor. The Chinese Academy of Medical Sciences was located in the former PUMC, and a new hospital facility was nearing completion.

In his article, Penfield summarized developments in neurosurgery in China since 1940, beginning with an interesting comment: "No help from the traditional doctors can be expected in neurosurgery (in their literature there is not even a word for brain tumor!)."[10]

One of Penfield's former fellows, Chao Yi-ch'eng (PUMC 1934) had returned to PUMC in 1940 after two years at the Montreal Neurological Institute and had joined the surgery staff. After Liberation, Chao moved to the medical school in Tientsin where he joined an outstanding group of PUMC graduates led by Chu Hsien-i (PUMC 1930), now professor of medicine and dean of the Tientsin Medical College, and Lin Sung (PUMC 1932), professor of obstetrics and gynecology. Their excellence drew the accolade, "little PUMC," for Tientsin.†

In 1954, at the height of the Sino-Soviet involvement, A. I. Arutyunov, director of the Neurological Institute in Kiev, had come to China to advise on the development of neurosurgery. He soon recognized Chao's outstanding talents and his recommendation that Chao be brought back to Peking to lead a new neurological institute was accepted. Thus a PUMC graduate today holds the leading post in neurosurgery in China.

Penfield's general assessment of medicine in China was that clinical medicine was "first class;" while "basic medical science and new approaches to research

---

* The former PUMC was usually referred to by this name.
† Brown Chang 1972: personal communication.

lag behind, waiting, no doubt, for scholarly scientists to appear who can be freed from the full weight of medical practice."[11]

In the meantime, anti-Western propagandists had selected prewar PUMC as their prime target and the college was being flailed mercilessly in the press. It was portrayed as a den in which sadistic American doctors used the Chinese people as human guinea pigs. One article bore the headline, "Crimes Committed toward Children by American Doctors."[12] Based on documents claimed to be case histories from the hospital, the article announced that in August 1921, as part of a research project an ophthalmologist named Howard (Harvey J. Howard) deliberately introduced trachoma virus into the eyes of a healthy patient. Other inhuman procedures were dramatized with hair-raising examples that included the wanton destruction of the scalp and brain by irradiation, and the placing of boxes of fleas on the bodies of children in order to study the life cycle of the flea in a human environment.

PUMC—THE WHIPPING POST

With the explosion of the Cultural Revolution in 1966, "evil PUMC" continued as a favorite whipping post for the years of Western influence in China. In 1967 we find an article linking the college with the hated Liu Shao-chi, now described as "China's Krushchov."[13] Liu is accused of having revived "the collapsed citadel of U. S. cultural agression by founding the China Medical College on the basis of the old PUMC." In this restored PUMC, the faculty

> used a heavy school programme to squeeze out proletarian politics. The students, in fact, had no time even for reading newspapers, let alone participating in political activities."[14]

In November 1968 "the old PUMC" was in the headlines again with the accusation that the college had been "established on Chinese soil but it was in fact a colony of U. S. imperialism."[15] John D. Rockefeller, Sr., described as the "King of Oil," was castigated severely for having chosen medicine for his major program in China. According to the article there were absolutely no humanitarian instincts at work; instead the United States imperialists "thought the nature of their vicious spiritual aggression against the Chinese people could more easily be disguised as medical work."[16] Peking was selected as the site for the college because it

> offers opportunities for influencing the educational as well as the administrative officers of the government to an extent that cannot be equalled anywhere else in China. What venomous aims the U.S. imperialists had![17]

Virtually every program was interpreted as an effort to brainwash the Chinese

> The U.S. imperialists also set up in the college religious organizations, Y.M.C.A. and Y.W.C.A. branches, to preach bourgeois "humanism," "equality," "freedom" and "love." Through the activities of "Christian fellowships" they encourage the students to spend one evening a week at the homes of the professors to ea

drink, read the Bible, and play cards. The dormitories were furnished with modern facilities. Students, one or two to a room, were waited upon by staff specially hired for this purpose. These decadent bourgeois ideas and living style were all intended to corrupt the thinking of students."[18]

PUMC was described as a "living hell" in which an untold number of Chinese people became victims:

> To obtain human organs, or to try out a medicine or to conduct some other experiments, the U.S. imperialists used living Chinese working people as if they were mice and rabbits. There are no statistics to tell how many innocent people were slaughtered in this way. Leafing through "case histories" of the old P.U.M.C. Hospital, we were unable to restrain our fury against these monsters who murdered our people but left no bloodstains."[19]

While the faculty had taken pride in the fact that 25 per cent of the graduates entered careers in governmental health services, this too was denounced by the Communists because the graduates had served and were serving the Kuomintang.

In the same article there is a photograph of the courtyard of PUMC in November 1968, jammed with students in white coats; a crowd outside the gate is carrying an enormous portrait of Mao Tse-tung and everyone is clutching the national flag. The caption reads: "Red Guards put up the sign 'Peking Anti-Imperialists Hospital' after they had destroyed the old one which was a symbol of U. S. imperialist aggression."[20]

As they stood in the courtyard the revolutionary students chanted:

"These eight years in the old Chinese Medical College—/The havoc they wrought./ In three years, no medicine did we glean;/ In five years, no patients we've seen;/ A full eight years, and no contact with workers and peasants brought."[21]

THE CAPITAL HOSPITAL

With the subsidence of the Cultural Revolution and the positive efforts toward an accommodation with the United States, the attacks on old PUMC abated. A significant step came on January 1, 1972, when the Anti-Imperialist Hospital became the Capital Hospital.

PUMC is today the leading medical center in China and the principal members of the staff continue to be former PUMC faculty. For foreign visitors, medical and nonmedical, PUMC is always included in the itinerary as a showplace of China's accomplishments in medicine.

PUMC graduates are among the authoritative voices in medicine and public health and several hold high positions in the party. Chu Fu-t'ang, China's leading pediatrician, disdained any political interests when he was Ashley Weech's most promising resident—today he is a deputy to the People's Congress. On International Children's Day, May 31, 1972, he was quoted by the New China News Agency as stating that kala-azar had been virtually eliminated, as had smallpox, plague, and cholera. Chu attributed this in large measure to a vast national health and sanitation program:

> Refuse accumulated over 400 or 500 years from the Ming and Ching dynasties was finally cleared away. The sewerage system was renovated and improved. Knowledge of environmental hygiene was spread far and wide.[22]

Chu Hsien-i, also a deputy, was described in the newspaper, *Ta Kung Pao*, in 1971 as a famous doctor in Tientsin and director of the medical school in that city. He was designated to serve as physician for Prince Sihanouk when the latter accepted exile in Peking after fleeing from his throne in Cambodia.

Lim Kha-t'i is one of the three most respected women in China today and the leading obstetrician-gynecologist. She has answered the call to work in the rural areas on several occasions. Once a devout Christian, she is now a leader of the party; she has stood with Mao Tse-tung and Chou En-lai on the Gate of Heavenly Peace in the May Day celebrations, and has been elected repeatedly to serve as a deputy in the People's Congress. In her public statements she looks back on her days at PUMC with mixed feelings.

Wu Ying-k'ai, who with Harold Loucks had developed the techniques for esophageal resection, is now director of a chest institute at the former PUMC, and Loucks estimates that he has probably compiled the world's largest series of successful resections for esophageal cancer.*

SUMMARY

We can summarize the story of PUMC as beginning with an American phase that extended from the founding of the college until 1941—the period that is essentially the story in this book. A casualty of World War II, there was a brief effort to re-establish the college between 1947 and 1949. With the nationalization of the college on January 20, 1951, PUMC became an instrumentality of the People's Republic of China.

For over two decades, PUMC and Tsinghua University were the principal intellectual bridges between China and the United States; of the two we believe that PUMC was the most important. The intelligent, at times brilliant, and invariably personable PUMC graduates who came to the United States on CMB fellowships were the most important bridgeheads.

The American physicians who returned from Peking to become leaders of academic medicine in the United States were continuing purveyors to their university colleagues and the public of a wide range of information on China—a country to which they and their wives held a singular devotion. The visiting professors returned with a comparable dedication to serving as messengers of the richness of China.

An unanticipated dividend from PUMC was its role as the training ground for leaders in academic medicine in the United States: Franklin McLean, Paul

---

* Harold H. Loucks 1972: personal communication.

Hodges, Oswald Robertson, Chester Keefer, Harry Van Dyke, Ashley Weech, Nicholson Eastman, John McKelvey, Carl Schmidt, Frank and Henry Meleney, Aura Severinghaus, and Jerome P. Webster. The School of Nursing produced leaders of equal importance: Anna Wolf, Gertrude Hodgman, and Ruth Ingram. These individuals, and many others, made PUMC by all odds the most successful international program in medical education.

The scientific contributions of the research programs at PUMC between 1919 and 1941 were outstanding, especially for their attacks on health problems of China such as communicable diseases and parasitology and nutritional deficiencies. The introduction of ephedrine stands as the greatest contribution to modern medicine from the materia medica of an indigenous system of medicine. The studies on Peking man that were centered at PUMC were epochal.

In its relatively brief lifespan, PUMC soon became the leading medical center in Asia, its influence extending throughout that vast region. As Carrington Goodrich expressed it: "It held up the highest standards in science and the human approach to medicine and this affected all institutions of higher learning from Tokyo to Bombay."*

The emphasis on excellence through small classes of carefully selected students was a reflection of the philosophy that the founders of the school—Welch, the Flexners, Pearce, and Eliot—were applying in the United States. We were closing medical schools in the wake of the Flexner Report, and we were insisting on quality and discarding quantity. With the closing of one-third of the nation's medical schools, there was a sharp fall in the number of new doctors: from 5,700 graduates in 1900 to 2,300 in 1919. It was only natural that the leaders of American medicine should apply this philosophy in Peking; and in our opinion it was the correct philosophy.

Two criticisms have been leveled at the graduates of PUMC; one is that they were proud of their educational lineage and that they were clannish—they were. A second is that they would not leave PUMC and move out to other institutions where they were more urgently needed. The records show that this accusation is groundless. Beginning with the first class, there was a steady flow of graduates moving out to other institutions to establish and maintain the high standards that had been inculcated in them at PUMC.

Thus the PUMC Announcement for 1937–38 stated that only 21 per cent of the fifty-six graduates of the first six classes had remained at PUMC. Members of the class of 1928 were serving as chiefs of services in hospitals in Shanghai, Changsha, Paoting, Nanking, and Weihsien. Others held leading posts in public health: as commissioner of public health for Greater Shanghai, as medical officer in the Chinese Maritime Customs in Shanghai, and as staff member with the Manchurian Plague Prevention Service in Harbin. And when the United States decided to build up Taiwan as the stronghold for the Kuomintang,

---

* L. Carrington Goodrich 1972: personal communication.

graduates of PUMC became the leaders there in medicine, public health, and nursing.

That PUMC was strikingly successful in training the leaders of medicine for China is attested by the fact that when it closed in December 1941, fewer than ten of its graduates were in private practice. Virtually all of the alumni were teaching medicine, leading hospital medical services, or in governmental positions in public health. A survey shortly before the nationalization of the school showed that six of the national medical schools of China were under the leadership of PUMC graduates, and that six others were headed by individuals who had received part of their training at PUMC.[23]

Medicine in China today represents a curious blend of Western medicine and traditional medicine. But Western medicine is firmly implanted in China and PUMC was its principal vehicle. And, as its founders had hoped, the institution that was PUMC is sponsored and supported exclusively by the Chinese government, its leaders are graduates of PUMC, and as the Capital Hospital it is the leading medical center in China.

NOTES TO CHAPTER TWELVE

1. Mary E. Ferguson, *China Medical Board and Peking Union Medical College*, p. 196.

2. *Ibid.*, p. 209.

3. *Ibid.*, pp. 210–26.

4. Sir Theodore Fox, "The New China," pp. 935–9, 995–9, 1053–7.

5. *Ibid.*, p. 939.

6. *Ibid.*, p. 937.

7. *Ibid.*, p. 939.

8. Edgar Snow, *The Other Side of the River*, p. 307.

9. Wilder Penfield, "Oriental Renaissance in Education and Medicine," p. 1154.

10. *Ibid.*, p. 1157.

11. *Ibid.*, p. 1158.

12. "Crimes Committed toward Children by American Doctors."

13. "China's Krushchov Resurrected to Advance Revisionist Line in Education," pp. 890–2.

14. *Ibid.*, p. 891.

15. "U.S. Imperialist Cultural Aggression Disguised as Friendship," p. 48.

16. *Ibid.*, p. 44.

17. *Ibid.*, p. 44.

18. *Ibid.*, p. 46.

19. *Ibid.*, p. 47.

20. *Ibid.*, p. 45.

21. "Thoroughly Criticize and Repudiate the Eight Year Medical Education Program Pushed by China's Krushchov," p. 165.

22. "Chinese Have Virtually Wiped Out Killer Disease."

23. Raymond B. Fosdick, *The Story of The Rockefeller Foundation*, pp. 90–1.

Bibliography

Andrews, Roy Chapman. *Meet Your Ancestors: A Biography of Primitive Man.* New York: Viking Press, 1945.

Armstrong, George E. "Robert Kho-seng Lim, Ph.D.: Doctor, Soldier, Patriot." *The ABMAC Bulletin* 30, nos. 7, 8 (July, August 1969): 1–4.

Aub, Joseph C., and Hapgood, Ruth K. *Pioneer in Modern Medicine: David Linn Edsall of Harvard.* Cambridge: Harvard Medical Alumni Association, 1970.

Balme, Harold. *China and Modern Medicine: A Study in Medical Missionary Development.* London: United Council for Missionary Education, 1921.

Balme, Harold, and Stauffer, Milton T. "An Inquiry into the Scientific Efficiency of Mission Hospitals in China." Paper read at the Annual Conference of the China Medical Missionary Association, February 21–27, 1920, Peking, China.

Barlow, C. H. "Experimental Ingestion of Ova of Fasciolopsis Buski; Also the Ingestion of Adult Fasciolopsis Buski for the Purpose of Artificial Infestation." *Journal of Parasitology* 8 (1921): 40–4.

———. *The Life Cycle of the Human Intestinal Fluke, Fasciolopsis Buski (Lankester),* American Journal of Hygiene Monographic Series No. 4. Baltimore: Johns Hopkins Press, 1925.

Barlow, Claude H., and Meleney, Henry E. "A Voluntary Infection with *Schistosoma Haematobium.*" *American Journal of Tropical Medicine* 29 (1949): 79–87.

Benison, Saul. "The Reminiscences of Dr. John B. Grant," vol. 1, 1960–69, Living History Series No. 398. Department of Oral History, Columbia University, New York City.

Bowers, John Z. "Chung-I: Chinese Traditional Medicine." *Asia* 5 (1966): 62–9.

———. "The Founding of Peking Union Medical College: Policies and Personalities." *Bulletin of the History of Medicine* 45, no. 4 (July–August 1971): 305–21, and no. 5 (September–October): 409–29.

Burton, Ernest DeWitt, and Chamberlin, Thomas Crowder. Report of the Oriental Education Commission of the University of Chicago, December, 1909.

Cadbury, W. W., and Jones, M. H. *At the Point of a Lancet, One Hundred Years of the Canton Hospital, 1835–1935.* Shanghai: Kelly and Walsh, 1935.

Cahell, J. M. Keen, ed. *Medical Research and Education, by Richard M. Pearce and Twenty-one Other Authors.* New York: Sharrison, 1913.

Cajdos, Stephan, and Chang, Joseph. *Studies on Typhus Fever in China: Contributions from the Microbiology Laboratory.* Peking: The Catholic University Press, The Catholic University of Peking Science Publications, January 1933.

Cannon, Walter B. *The Way of an Investigator: A Scientist's Experience in Medical Research*. New York: W. W. Norton, 1945.

Cash, J. R. "Kala-azar: Demonstration of Leishmania Donovani in the Skin and Subcutaneous Tissue of Patients: Possible Relation to the Transfer of Disease." *Journal of the American Medical Association* 89 (1927): 1576–7.

Chang, Stephen. "Foot Prints on the Sands of Time." Mimeographed. Undated paper read at Queen Mary Hospital, Hong Kong.

————. Report on PUMC to Claude E. Forkner. Archives of The Rockefeller Foundation, New York City.

Chen, K. K., and Schmidt, Carl. "The Action of Ephedrine, the Active Principle of the Chinese Drug *Ma Huang*." *Journal of Pharmacology and Experimental Therapeutics* (1924): 339–57.

Chen, M. P.; Ch'eng, Y. L.; and Lyman, R. S. "Insulin Treatment of Drug Addiction." *Journal of Nervous and Mental Diseases* 83 (March 1936): 281–8.

Chen, S. M.; Van Gorder, G. W.; and Yuan, Y. K. "Amoebic Liver Abscess." *National Medical Journal of China* 17, no. 4 (1931): 393–409.

Ch'en, C. C. *Scientific Medicine as Applied in Ting Hsien*. Annual Report, January 1933.

Ch'en, Shou-yi. "Hu-Shih (1891–1962)" in *The American Philosophical Society Year Book 1962*, pp. 135–43. Philadelphia: George H. Buchanan, 1963.

Cheng, Tien-hsi. "Schistosomiasis in Mainland China: A Review of Research and Control Programs in 1941." *American Journal of Tropical Medicine and Hygiene* 20 (1971): 26–53.

China Medical Commission of The Rockefeller Foundation. *Medicine in China*. Chicago and New York: University of Chicago Press, 1914.

"China's Kruschov Resurrected to Advance Revisionist Line in Education." *China's Medicine* 12 (December 1967): 890–2.

"Chinese Have Virtually Wiped Out Killer Disease." *South China Morning Post*, 2 June 1972.

Christie, Dugald. *Thirty Years in Moukden, 1883–1913: Being the Experiences and Recollections of Dugald Christie, C.M.G.: Edited by His Wife*. London: Constable & Company, 1914.

Chung, Huei-lan, and Chang, Joseph H. M. "Studies on the Etiology of Typhus Fever in North China." *Chinese Medical Journal* 53 (June 1938): 513–38.

Churchill, A., and Churchill, J. *A Collection of Voyages and Travels, Some Now First Printed from Original Manuscripts, Others Now First Published In English, In Six Volumes, With a General Preface, Giving an Account of the Progress of Navigation, from Its First Beginning*, 3rd ed., vol. 1, London: 1774.

Cochrane, Thomas. *Survey of the Missionary Occupation of China*. Shanghai: Christian Literary Society for China, 1913.

Corner, George W. *A History of The Rockefeller Institute, 1901–1953: Origins and Growth*. New York: Rockefeller Institute Press, 1964.

Cort, W. W.; Grant, J. B.; and Stoll, N. R. *Researches on Hookworm in China*, American Journal of Hygiene Monographic Series No. 7. Baltimore: Johns Hopkins Press, October 1926.

Cowdry, E. V. "Anatomy in China." *Anatomical Record* 20 (1920–21): 32–60.

Cranmer-Byng, J. L., ed. "Dr. Gillan's Observations on the State of Medicine, Surgery and Chemistry in China," in *An Embassy to China, Being the Journal Kept by Lord Macartney . . . 1793–1794*, pp. 279–91. London: Longmans, 1962.

"Crimes Committed toward Children by American Doctors." *Peking Daily*, 22 May 1964.

Curran, Jean A. "The Harvard Medical School of China." *Harvard Medical Alumni Bulletin* 38, no. 2 (Christmas 1963): 12–9.

Dewey, John, and Dewey, Alice Chipman. *Letters from China and Japan*. New York: Dutton, 1920.

Dickie, Walter M. "Plague in California 1900–1925." *Proceedings of the Conference of State and Provincial Health Authorities of North America* (1926): 30–2.

Dieuaide, Francis R. "Observations on Rheumatic Fever: With Special Reference to Epidemiological Considerations Based on a Series of Cases in China." *Transactions of the Association of American Physicians* 52 (1937): 379–88.

Director's Minute Book, 1914–1915. Archives of the London Missionary Society.

Duffus, Robert Luther, and Holt, Luther Emmett, Jr. *L. Emmett Holt, Pioneer of a Children's Century*. New York and London: D. Appleton-Century, 1940.

Eastman, Nicholson J. "The Blood Sedimentation Test in the Puerperium." *China Medical Journal* 41 (1927): 517–25.

———. ed. *Obstetrical and Gynecological Survey: Dr. Nicholson J. Eastman: A Special Issue* 20, no. 3. Baltimore: Williams and Wilkins, June 1965.

Eliot, Charles W. *Some Roads towards Peace: A Report to the Trustees of the Endowment*. Washington, D. C.: Carnegie Endowment for International Peace Publication No. 1, 1914.

Fang, I-chi, and Li, Ting-an. "School Health in the Peiping Special Health Area." *China Medical Journal* 43 (1929): 697–706.

Faust, E. C. "Notes on Larval Flukes from China." *Parasitology* 14 (1922): 248–67.

———. "The Distribution and Differentiation of Human Helminths in China and Adjacent Territories: A Syllabus for the Clinicians of China." *China Medical Journal Supplement* (February 1923): 1–43.

———. "Studies on Some Larval Flukes from the Central and South Coast Provinces of China." *American Journal of Hygiene* 4, no. 4 (July 1924): 241–301.

———. "Parasitic Infections and Human Disease in China." *Archives of Pathology and Laboratory Medicine* 2 (August 1926): 223–40.

Faust, E. C.; Khaw, Oo-kek; Yao, Ke-fang; and Chao, Yung-an. *Studies on Clonorchis Sinensis (Cobbold)*, American Journal of Hygiene Monographic Series No. 8. Baltimore: Johns Hopkins Press, March 1927.

Faust, E. C., and Meleney, H. E. *Studies on Schistosomiasis Japonica, With a Supplement on the Molluscan Hosts of the Human Blood Fluke in China and Japan, and Species Liable to Be Confused with Them, by Nelson Annandale*, American Journal of Hygiene Monographic Series No. 3. Baltimore: Johns Hopkins Press, 1924.

Ferguson, Mary E. *China Medical Board and Peking Union Medical College: A Chronicle of Fruitful Collaboration: 1914–1951.* New York: China Medical Board of New York, 1970.

Flexner, Abraham. *I Remember: The Autobiography of Abraham Flexner.* New York: Simon and Schuster, 1940.

Flexner, Simon. "Report of the Second China Medical Commission." Mimeographed. Papers of Simon Flexner, Archives of the American Philosophical Society, Philadelphia, Pennsylvania.

Flexner, Simon, and Flexner, James T. *William Henry Welch and the Heroic Age of American Medicine.* New York: Viking Press, 1941.

Fosdick, Raymond B. *The Story of The Rockefeller Foundation.* New York: Harper & Brothers, 1952.

Fox, Theodore F. "The New China: Some Medical Impressions." *The Lancet,* no. 7002 (9 November 1957): 935–9; no. 7003 (16 November 1957): 995–99; and no. 7004 (23 November 1957): 1053–7.

Frazier, C. N., and Li, Hung-chiung. *Racial Variations in Immunity to Syphilis: A Study of the Disease in the Chinese, White and Negro Races.* Chicago: University of Chicago Press, 1948.

Frazier, C. N., Mu, J. W., and Hu, C. K. "Influence of Estrogenic Substance upon Experimental Syphilis of the Adult Male Rabbit." *Proceedings of the Society of Experimental Biology and Medicine* 33 (1935): 65.

French, Francesca. *Thomas Cochrane: Pioneer and Missionary Statesman.* London: Hodder and Stoughton, 1956.

Fuchs, Adelbert. *Wie Ein Augenarzt Die Welt Sah, Selbstbiographe und Tagebuchblatter.* Vienna: Urban and Schwarzenberg, 1946.

Goodman, Louis S., and Gilman, Alfred. *The Pharmacological Basis of Therapeutics,* 2nd ed. New York: Macmillan Company, 1955.

Gordon, C. A., comp. *An Epitome of the Reports of the Medical Officers of the Chinese Imperial Maritime Customs Service from 1871–1882.* London: Balliere, Tindall, and Cox, 1884.

Guy, R. A., and Yeh, K. S. "Soybean 'Milk' as Food for Infants." *Chinese Medical Journal* 54, no. 1 (July 1938): 1–30.

———. "Roasted Soybean in Infant Feeding." *Chinese Medical Journal* 54, no. 2 (August 1938): 101–10.

Harvard Medical School of China, Inc. Second Annual Report of the Executive Committee, Cambridge, Massachusetts, November 4, 1912.

———. Third Annual Report of the Executive Committee, Cambridge, Massachusetts, November 3, 1913.

———. Fourth Annual Report of the Executive Committee, Cambridge, Massachusetts, November 3, 1914.

———. Fifth Annual Report of the Executive Committee, Cambridge, Massachusetts, November 8, 1915.

———. Regular Report of the Executive Committee, Cambridge, Massachusetts, November 1917.

Heiser, Victor G. *An American Doctor's Odyssey: Adventures in Forty-five Countries.* New York: W. W. Norton, 1936.

Hodges, Paul C. "A Comparison of the Teleoroentgenogram with the Orthodiagram." *American Journal of Roentgenology and Radium Therapy* 11 (1924): 486–94.

———. "The Development of Western Medicine in China." Paper read at the University of Florida College of Medicine, 28 May 1970.

Hodgman, Gertrude E. "School of Nursing, Peiping Union Medical College." *Methods and Problems of Medical Education*, Twenty-first Series. New York: The Rockefeller Foundation, 1932.

Hood, Dora. *Davidson Black: A Biography.* Toronto: University of Toronto Press, 1964.

Howard, Harvey J. *Ten Weeks with Chinese Bandits.* New York: Dodd, Mead, 1926.

———. "My Bandit Clinic." *Journal of the American Medical Association* 88 (21 May 1927): 1669–70.

Hsiao, Theodore E. *The History of Modern Education in China.* Shanghai: The Commercial Press, 1935.

Hu, C. K. "Lowered Resistance to Syphilitic Infection in Ovariectomized Rabbits." *American Journal of Syphilis, Gonorrhea and Venereal Disease* 23 (1939): 446.

Huc, Evariste Regis. *Christianity in China, Tartary and Thibet*, vol. 3. London: Longman, Brown, Green, Longmans, and Roberts, 1857.

Hume, Edward H. *The Chinese Way in Medicine.* Baltimore: Johns Hopkins Press, 1940.

———. *Doctors East, Doctors West: An American Physician's Life in China.* New York: W. W. Norton, 1946.

James, Henry. *Charles W. Eliot, President of Harvard University, 1869–1909*, Boston: Houghton Mifflin, 1930.

Johns, Ethel, and Pfefferkorn, Blanche. *The Johns Hopkins School of Nursing, 1889–1949.* Baltimore: Johns Hopkins Press, 1954.

Keefer, C. S. "The Treatment of Secondary Anemia: A Study of the Results in One Hundred and Twenty-six Cases." *Archives of Internal Medicine* 48 (October 1931): 537–68.

Keefer, C. S.; Berglund, Hilding; and Yang, Chi-shih. "Deficiency Anemia in Chinese, Responding to Cod Liver Oil." *Proceedings of the Society of Experimental Biology and Medicine*, no. 26 (March 1929): 418–21.

King, Gordon. "Eclampsia in Chinese Patients: A Clinical Study Based on 33 Cases." *National Medical Journal of China* 16 (December 1930): 653–72.

———. "The Place of Spinal Anesthesia in Obstetrics and Gynecology." *National Medical Journal of China* 16 (December 1930): 711–22.

Korns, J. "The Incidence of Tuberculous Infection in China." *Chinese Medical Journal* 39 (January 1925): 10–19.

Latourette, K. S. *A History of Christian Missions in China.* London: Society for Promoting Christian Knowledge, 1929.

League of Nations Health Committee. *The Report on Medical Schools in China*, by Knud Faber, Professor of Medicine at Copenhagen University (League of Nations Publications Series 3, Health, Official No. C. H. 961), 30 June 1931.

Lee, T'ao. "Some Statistics on Medical Schools in China for 1932–33." *Chinese Medical Journal* 47 (1933): 1029–39.

Lim, R. K. S.; Liu, Chan-nao; and Moffitt, Robert L. *A Stereotaxic Atlas of the Dog's Brain*. Springfield, Illinois: C. C. Thomas, 1960.

Lin, Evelyn S. "Background and Early History of the School of Nursing of the Peiping Union Medical College: An Historical Study." Submitted in Partial Fulfillment of the Course in Problems and Field Studies in Nursing Education, January 1943.

Loucks, Harold H. "Hydatid Cyst, a Review and Report of Cases from North China." *National Medical Journal of China* 16 (August 1930): 402–96.

Lyman, R. S.; Maeker, V., and Liang, P., eds. *Social and Psychological Studies in Neuropsychiatry in China*. Peking: Henry Vetch, 1939.

Ma, Wen-chao. "The Relation of Mitochondria and Other Cytoplasmic Constituents to the Formation of Secretion Granules." *American Journal of Anatomy* 41 (1928): 51–61.

Manual for the Medical Services of the Peking Union Medical College Hospital, 4th ed., revised by the Staff of the Department of Medicine. Peiping: Peking Union Medical College Press, 1933.

Manson-Bahr, Sir Philip H., ed. *Manson's Tropical Diseases: A Manual of the Diseases of Warm Climates*, 15th ed. London: Cassell, 1960.

Maxwell, J. Preston. "Osteomalacia in China." *China Medical Journal* 37, no. 8 (August 1923): 625–42.

———. "On Puerperal Mortality and Morbidity." *National Medical Journal of China* 16 (December 1930): 684–703.

———. "Osteomalacia and Foetal Rickets." *British Journal of Radiology* 3 (August 1930): 375–8.

McCabe, Anne. "Maternity and Child Health Work of the First Health Station, Peiping." *Nursing Journal of China* 12, no. 4 (October 1931): 14–5.

McLean, Franklin C. "Adventures in Medical Education." *Bulletin of the Alumni Association, School of Medicine University of Chicago* 17, no. 1 (1960): 9–12.

McQuarrie, Irvine. *The Experiments of Nature and Other Essays*, The Porter Lecture Series No. 12. Lawrence: University of Kansas Press, 1944.

Meleney, Henry Edmund. "The Histopathology of Kala-azar in the Hamster, Monkey and Man." *American Journal of Pathology* 1, no. 2 (March 1925): 147–68.

Miles, Lee Monroe, and Feng, Chih-tung. "Calcium and Phosphorous Metabolism in Osteomalacia." *Journal of Experimental Medicine* 41 (1925): 137–57.

Morse, William R. *Chinese Medicine*. New York: Hoeber, 1934.

Nathan, Carl F. *Plague Prevention and Politics in Manchuria, 1910–1931*. Cambridge: Harvard East Asia Monographs, 1967.

Needham, Joseph. *Science and Civilisation in China: History of Scientific Thought*, vol. 2. Cambridge: Cambridge University Press, 1956.

Needham, Joseph, and Lu, Gwei-djen. "Chinese Medicine," in *Medicine and Culture*, edited by F. N. L. Poynter. London: Wellcome Institute of the History of Medicine, 1969.

Opie, Eugene L. "Tuberculosis of First Infection and of Reinfection; Their Frequency in Chinese People of Peking." *Chinese Medical Journal* 56, no. 3 (1939): 197–215.
———. "Tuberculosis of First Infection in Adults from Rural Districts of China." *Chinese Medical Journal* 56, no. 3 (1939): 216–24.

Parker, Peter. *Journal of an Expedition from Singapore to Japan, With a Visit to Loo-Choo*. Revised by the Rev. Andrew Reed, D.D. London: Smith-Elder & Co., 1838.
Peabody, F. G. *Francis Weld Peabody, 1881–1927: A Memoir*. Cambridge: Riverside Press, 1933.
Peabody, Francis W. "The Department of Medicine at the Peking Union Medical College." *Science* 56, no. 1447 (1922): 317–20.
Phillips, Clifton Jackson. *Protestant America and the Pagan World: The First Half Century of the American Board of Commissioners for Foreign Missions, 1810–1860*. Cambridge: East Asian Research Center, 1969.
Peiping Union Medical College. *Annual Announcement, 1929–30*. Peiping: Peiping Union Medical College Press, 1 July 1929.
Peking Union Medical College. *Addresses & Papers, Dedication Ceremonies and Medical Conference, Peking Union Medical College, September 15–22, 1921*. Concord, New Hampshire: Rumford Press, 1922.
———. The Unison, vol. I (1924).
———. The Unison, vol. II (1927).
———. The Unison, vol. III (1931–32).
Penfield, Wilder. "Oriental Renaissance in Education and Medicine." *Science* 141, no. 3586 (20 September 1963): 1153–61.
———. *The Difficult Art of Giving: The Epic of Alan Gregg*. Boston: Little, Brown, 1967.
PUMC Weekly Calendar.
PUMC Weekly Newsletter.

Read, Bernard E. "Metabolism Studies with Chaulmoogra Oil: I. Influence of Chaulmoogra Oil on Calcium Metabolism." *Journal of Biological Chemistry* 62, no. 2 (December 1924): 515–40.
———. "Metabolism Studies with Chaulmoogra Oil: II. The Influence of Hydnocarpates upon Urinary Nitrogen Partition in the Dog." *Journal of Biological Chemistry* 62, no. 2 (December 1924): 541–50.
———. "Chinese Materia Medica: Animal Drugs: From the *Pen Ts'ao Kang Mu* by Li Shih-chen." *Peking National History Bulletin* 5 (1931), Part 4: 37–80, and 6 (1931), Part 1: 1–102.
Records of the Examination Committee, 1915. Archives of the London Missionary Society.

Reeves, William, Jr. "Sino-American Cooperation in Medicine: The Origins of Hsiang-Ya (1902–1914)," in Liu Kwang-ching, ed., *American Missionaries in China.* Harvard East Asian Monographs No. 21, pp. 129–82. Cambridge: East Asian Research Center, 1966.

Robinson, G. Canby. *Adventures in Medical Education: A Personal Narrative of the Great Advance of American Medicine.* Cambridge: Harvard University Press, The Commonwealth Fund, 1957.

Russell, Bertrand. *The Problem of China.* New York: Century, 1922.

———. *The Autobiography of Bertrand Russell, 1914–1944.* Boston and Toronto: Little, Brown; Atlantic Monthly Press Book; 1951.

Schmidt, Carl F. "Some Experiences with Chinese Drugs." *Transactions and Studies of the College of Physicians of Philadelphia,* Series 4, vol. 30, no. 2 (October 1962): 66–72.

———. "Ephedrine after 40 Years." President's Address at the Opening of the Second International Pharmacological Meetings, Prague, Czechoslovakia, July 1963.

———. "New Challenges for Clinical Pharmacology." *Journal of Clinical Pharmacology and Journal of New Drugs* 9, no. 5 (September–October 1969): 269–81.

Seipp, Conrad, ed. *Health Care for the Community: Selected Papers of Dr. John B. Grant,* American Journal of Hygiene Monographic Series No. 21. Baltimore: Johns Hopkins Press, 1963.

Severinghaus, Aura E. "The Miracle of ABMAC." *The ABMAC Bulletin* 32, Part 1, nos. 1, 2 (January, February 1971), and Part 2, nos. 3, 4 (March, April 1971).

Snapper, Isidore. *Chinese Lessons to Western Medicine: A Treatise in Geographic Medicine.* New York: Interscience Publishers, 1941.

Snow, Edgar. *The Other Side of the River.* New York: Random House, 1961.

Snyder, Charles. "7 Green Pea Street: The Canton Ophthalmic Hospital and Its Founder." *Archives of Ophthalmology* 75 (June 1966): 887–91.

Spence, Jonathan. "Peter Parker, Bodies or Souls" in *To Change China: Western Advisors in China: 1620–1960.* Boston and Toronto: Little, Brown, 1969.

Stevens, George B. *The Life, Letters and Journals of the Rev. and Hon. Peter Parker, M.D., Missionary, Physician, Diplomatist: The Father of Medical Missions and Founder of the Ophthalmic Hospital in Canton.* Boston and Chicago: Congregational Sunday School and Publishing Society, 1896.

Stewart, Isabel Maitland, and Austin, Anne L. *A History of Nursing.* New York: Putnam, 1962.

Stock, Francis E. "Medical Education and Practice in Hong Kong." *The Lancet* 2 (1962): 714–6.

Stuart, John Leighton. *Fifty Years in China: The Memoirs of John Leighton Stuart: Missionary and Ambassador.* New York: Random House, 1954.

Sweet, L. K., and K'ang, H. J. "Clinical and Anatomic Study of Avitaminosis A Among the Chinese." *American Journal of Diseases of Children* 50 (September 1935): 699–734.

Thomson, James C., Jr. *While China Faced West.* Cambridge: Harvard University Press, 1969.

"Thoroughly Criticize and Repudiate the Eight Year Medical Education Program Pushed by China's Kruschov." *China's Medicine* 3 (March 1968): 164–9.

Todd, Frank Morton. *Eradicating Plague from San Francisco*, Report of the Citizens Health Committee, p. 54. San Francisco: C. A. Murdock, 31 March 1909.

Tsurumi, M. "Public Hygiene in Manchuria and Mongolia." *Light of Manchuria*, the Monthly Organ of the Manchuria Enlightening Society, no. 6 (1 February 1921): 1.

Tuchman, Barbara. *Stillwell and the American Experience in China, 1911–45*. New York: Macmillan Company, 1970.

Urist, Marshall R. "The McLean Campaign for Full-time Academic Medicine." *Clinical Orthopaedics* no. 17 (1960): 15–33.

"U. S. Imperialist Cultural Aggression Disguised as Friendship." *China Reconstructs* (November 1968): 44–8.

Van Dyke, Harry B. *Physiology and Pharmacology of the Pituitary Body*. 3 vols. Chicago: University of Chicago Press, 1936.

———. "Studies in Neurohypophyseal Endocrinology, the Sir Henry Dale Lecture for 1970." *Journal of Endocrinology* 47 (1970): ix–x.

Van Slyke, Donald B.; Wu, Hsien; and McLean, Franklin C. "Studies of Gas and Electrolyte Equilibria in the Blood. V. Factors Controlling the Electrolyte and Water Distribution in the Blood." *Journal of Biological Chemistry* 56, no. 3 (July 1923): 765–849.

Wald, Lillian D. *The House on Henry Street*. New York: Dover Publications, 1971.

Wallnofer, H., and von Rottauscher, A. *Chinese Folk Medicine*. New York: Crown Publications, 1965.

Watson, Robert Briggs. "Patterns and Effectiveness of Past and Present Overseas Programs of Cooperation in Medical Education, and a Forecast of the Future" in *Manpower for the World's Health—Part 2*, Journal of Medical Education Monograph, Chapter 6. Washington, D. C.: Association of American Medical Colleges, 1966.

Weech, A. Ashley. "Association of Keratomalacia with Other Deficiency Diseases." *American Journal of Diseases of Children* 39 (June 1930): 1153–66.

———. "Scarlet Fever in China; Some Impressions Concerning the Value of Serum Treatment in a Malignant Form of the Disease." *New England Journal of Medicine* 204 (May 1931): 968–74.

Weech, A. Ashley, and Chu, F. T. "Pulmonary Tuberculosis of the Epituberculous Type." *National Medical Journal of China* 16 (1930): 1–27.

Welch, William Henry. *Papers and Addresses by William Henry Welch*, vol. 3. Baltimore: Johns Hopkins Press, 1920.

White, Theodore H., and Jacoby, Annalee. *Thunder Out of China*. New York: William Sloane Associates, 1946.

Williams, S. Wells. *The Middle Kingdom: A Survey of the Geography, Government, Literature, Social Life, Arts, and History of the Chinese Empire and Its Inhabitants*. 2 vols. New York: Charles Scribner's Sons, 1895.

Wong, A., and Wong, D. H. "*Bacillus Welchii* Infection in Cases of Abortion." *Chinese Medical Journal* 37 (1933): 877–87.

Wong, K. Chimin. *Lancet and Cross: Biographical Sketches of Fifty Pioneer Medical Missionaries in China*. London: Council on Christian Medical Work, 1950.

Wong, K. Chimin, and Wu, Lien-teh. *History of Chinese Medicine: Being a Chronicle of Medical Happenings in China From Ancient Times to the Present Period*. Tientsin: Tientsin Press, 1932.

Wu, Daisy Yen. *Hsien Wu, 1893–1959: In Loving Memory*. Boston: publisher unknown, 1960.

Wu, Hsien. *A Guide to Scientific Living: How Man Can Apply Science to Achieve Optimum Living*. Taipei: Academia Sinica, 1963.

Wu, Lien-teh. *Plague Fighter: Autobiography of a Chinese Physician*. Cambridge, England: W. Heffer & Sons, 1959.

Wu, Ying-k'ai, and Loucks, Harold H. "Surgical Treatment of Carcinoma of the Esophagus." *Chinese Medical Journal* 60, no. 1 (July 1941): 1–33.

Yen, F. C. "An Example of Cooperation with the Chinese in Medical Education." *Journal of the American Medical Association* 44, no. 17 (April 24, 1915): 1385–7.

Young, C. W. "Kala-azar in China." *China Medical Journal* 37, no. 10 (October 1923): 797–822.

Zinsser, Hans. *Rats, Lice and History*. Boston: Little, Brown; Atlantic Monthly Press Book, 1935.

———. *As I Remember Him*. Boston: Little, Brown, 1940.

Index of Individuals

Subject Index